P9-APQ-377

Theory of Mechanical Vibration

JOHN WILEY
& SONS, INC.

NEW YORK
LONDON

Theory of Mechanical Vibration

KIN N. TONG Professor of Mechanical Engineering
Syracuse University

SECOND PRINTING, JUNE, 1963

Library of Congress Catalog Card Number: 60-6460

Printed in the United States of America

To the memory of my father

Preface

This book is the outgrowth of lecture notes for a course given to beginning graduate students and qualified seniors. Because of this origin, it is primarily a textbook, although some utility as a reference volume is also intended.

A course in mechanical vibrations can be organized in one of two ways, which may be described as problem-centered and theory-centered. This book is written for a theory-centered course, which develops the basic principles in a logical order, with engineering applications inserted as illustrations. No attempt is thus made to cover all problems of technological importance or to restrict the discussion only to topics having immediate applications. It is felt that a theory-centered course has its place in an engineering mechanics curriculum, since the analytical aspects of the theory have pedagogical values beside their utility in solving vibration problems.

The book is divided into four chapters. Chapter 1 treats systems having a single degree of freedom. All the basic concepts pertaining to mechanical vibrations are presented, with the exception of vibration modes. Chapter 2 introduces the concept of vibration modes in a multidegree-freedom system, using a system with two degrees of freedom as a simple model. The discussion is kept as close as possible to physical aspects of the problem. By means of matrix algebra and generalized coordinates, Chapter 3 extends the results previously obtained. In this way this chapter also lays the foundation for the solution of vibration problems on digital computers and provides a heuristic picture of what is to follow. Chapter 4 discusses the vibration of continuous media. Because only a limited amount of student knowledge in elasticity can be assumed, the systems selected for illustration in this chapter are relatively simple, yet the theory presented is quite general.

The layout of this book is somewhat different from the usual. In the beginning of each chapter fundamental principles are presented in a connected series of articles. Articles dealing with examples, applications, and specialized topics, which are more or less independent of one another, are placed at the ends of the chapters. (In the first three chapters these articles are grouped into two sections, A and B. The same grouping is not indicated in the fourth chapter, since there the demarcation is not so clear.) The purpose of this arrangement is twofold. It emphasizes the structural coherence of the theory, and it affords flexibility in classroom assignments. The instructor can plan his lectures by following the main development of the theory. At intervals appropriate to the level and the interest of a particular class, he may discuss, or assign as home reading, examples, applications, and methods selected from this book or from other sources. A number of exercises is given at the end of each chapter. Many of these exercises supplement the material in the text.

The students are assumed to have the usual preparation, including a course in differential equations, in undergraduate mechanics and mathematics. Certain fundamental theorems in advanced calculus and in vector analysis are referred to in a few isolated passages; these can be omitted, if necessary, without disrupting the continuity of presentation. An appendix on the basic ideas of matrix algebra is given. The scope of this appendix is limited, but it contains all that is needed for studying Chapter 3. In short, little prior knowledge is required to understand this book, although some degree of maturity is indispensable.

To keep the scope of the book within the limits of a two-semester course and to preserve the unity of the entire presentation, certain topics are omitted. These include nonlinear vibrations and the solution of transient problems by operational calculus. However, seeding ideas pertaining to these topics are planted in Arts. 1.4, 1.10, 1.11, 1.13, 1.14, 2.8 and 3.8, but their complete development is left to other standard courses generally available to advanced students.

Many persons helped to prepare this book. I wish especially to thank Professor Harold Lurie for a thorough reading of the manuscript and for offering valuable suggestions. Thanks are due to Mrs. Patricia Fisch and Mrs. Marilyn Levine for typing the manuscript and to Mr. C. Y. Chia and Mr. K. Ruei for assisting in various other ways.

KIN N. TONG

Syracuse, New York
October 1959

Contents

Introductory Remarks

Vibratory motions in machines and structures are of frequent concern in engineering practice. Such motion is usually objectionable; it may sometimes be desirable; and frequently its presence reveals to us the inner workings of complex machinery in operation. Whether our object is to minimize vibrations, to enhance them, or to utilize them for "diagnostic" purposes, it is essential that the physical laws which govern such motions be studied.

Vibratory motions are essentially periodic in character. Theory of vibration is therefore a special topic in analytical dynamics dealing principally with periodic motions of mechanical systems. In recent times, however, we have come to appreciate that the susceptibility of a mechanical system to vibrations describes certain intrinsic properties of the system, from which its general dynamic behavior can often be deduced even when periodic motion is not involved. Thus in a subtle way the principles governing the vibratory behavior of a system may often be advantageously used to supplement or even to replace the differential equations of motions in analyzing a number of problems in dynamics.

Theory of vibration also claims kinship in varying degrees of removedness with such studies as acoustics, alternating current circuits, and electromagnetic waves. All these studies concern themselves in part with periodically changing phenomena which are governed by more or less unified principles; and the analytical results obtained in these disciplines often have interchangeable applicabilities. Furthermore, if we examine some of the analytical tools used in theory of vibration, we will also find that they resemble those used in a still larger class of physical and mathematical problems. These include problems in elastic instability, periodic structures and linear transformations.

For the various reasons stated it then becomes justified to lift the study of vibratory motions from its parent body, analytical dynamics, and to place it on a pedestal of its own. In developing this subject, we have therefore not confined our attention strictly to the utility of the theory in solving vibration problems but have cast occasional glances upon many of its neighboring domains, into which we are likely to excurse in our future studies. Consequently, certain terms and concepts are introduced, not because of any immediate bearing they have upon the subject on hand but because of the desirability of acquainting ourselves with the many bridges that connect seemingly unrelated fields.

CHAPTER 1

Systems with a Single Degree of Freedom

SECTION A. THEORY AND PRINCIPLES

1.0 Introduction

Our study begins with the discussion of vibrations of a system having only a single degree of freedom. We shall, however, refrain from defining at this moment precisely what is meant by such terms as "vibrations," "systems," and "degree of freedom." Instead, we shall try to build up our theory by analyzing some simple and readily visualized physical systems and leave the precise definitions of these terms to more opportune moments. In the meantime, terminologies not specifically defined are to be interpreted according to their accepted meanings in mechanics, in mathematics, and in the English language.

1.1 Simple Harmonic Motion

The simplest form of vibratory motion is a simple harmonic motion, which is defined in kinematics as a rectilinear motion of a point whose acceleration at any time t is proportional and opposite to its displacement x. The mathematical description of this motion is therefore the differential equation

$$\frac{d^2x}{dt^2} = -\omega^2 x$$

or[1]

$$\ddot{x} + \omega^2 x = 0 \tag{1}$$

[1] The symbols $\dot{x}$ and $\ddot{x}$ stand for the first and second time derivatives of the function $x(t)$, respectively. This notation, employed originally by Newton, is used throughout this book, except when ambiguity may arise.

in which ω is a real number, hence the constant of proportionality, $-\omega^2$, is always negative. A simple example of a motion described by (1) is that of the mass particle in the system shown in Fig. 1. This system consists of a linear coil spring having a spring constant k and a mass particle of mass m, which is attached to the spring and constrained to move along the axis of the spring. Let 0 be the position occupied by *m when all the external forces acting on m are in equilibrium*, and let x be the displacement of m from 0 at time t. If the displacement x causes a change only in the force exerted by the spring *while all the other forces on m remain constant*,[2] then according

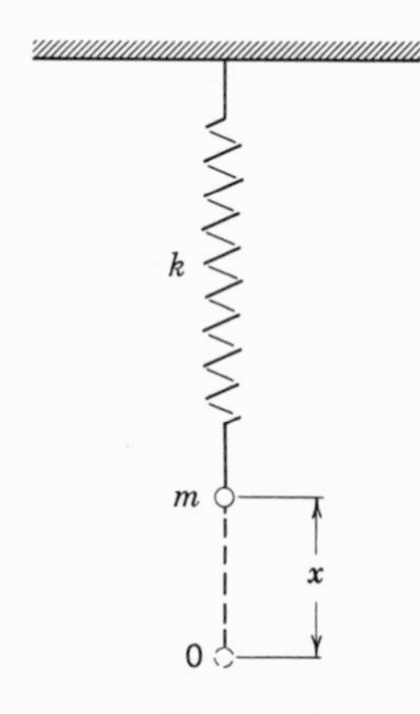

Figure 1

to Hooke's law of elasticity and Newton's law of motion the acceleration of m due to its departure from its equilibrium position is given by

$$m\ddot{x} = -kx$$

or

$$m\ddot{x} + kx = 0 \tag{2}$$

If we let

$$\omega^2 = \frac{k}{m} \tag{3}$$

we reduce (2) into the form of (1).

The solution of the differential equation (1), that is, the relationship of x versus t which obeys (1), is known to be expressible in the general form

$$x(t) = A \cos \omega t + B \sin \omega t \tag{4}$$

---

[2] According to the way we formulate this problem, the question whether or not there is a gravity force is irrelevant.

This expression has two constants of integration, A and B, which are not contained in the original differential equation and are therefore not determined by it. In other words, the physical constants of the system alone do not specify the motion uniquely without some other information concerning the actual motion itself. This information may be furnished by the *initial condition*,[3] that is, the displacement x_0 and the velocity $\dot{x}_0$ at the instant $t = 0$. Substituting this condition in (4), and in the equation obtained by differentiating (4), we have

$$x_0 = A \qquad \dot{x}_0 = B\omega \tag{5}$$

It is sometimes more convenient to express the solution in the form

$$x(t) = C \cos (\omega t - \alpha) \tag{6}$$

where

$$C \cos \alpha = A \qquad C \sin \alpha = B$$

or

$$C^2 = A^2 + B^2 \qquad \alpha = \tan^{-1} \frac{B}{A} \tag{7}$$

In a simple harmonic motion the displacement is therefore a sinusoidal function of time, and the motion is a periodic oscillation characterized by the quantities ω, C, and α. The quantity ω, which is determined by the properties of the system, is called the *circular frequency*. It is related to the *frequency* f and the *period* T by

$$\omega = 2\pi f \qquad T = \frac{1}{f} = \frac{2\pi}{\omega} \qquad (8)^4$$

The quantity C, which is the maximum displacement in the oscillatory motion, is called the *amplitude*. Ordinarily, frequency and amplitude taken together are enough to give a complete description of a harmonic oscillation, just as pitch and intensity are enough to describe a pure musical tone. The need here for a third quantity α, which is called the *time-phase angle*, therefore deserves further explanation. We see from (6) that α is an angle whose cosine gives the ratio of the displacement at $t = 0$ to the amplitude of vibration. Hence the value of α depends on the designation of an instant corresponding to $t = 0$. For a truly periodic phenomenon, which,

---

[3] Although the term "initial condition" has the connotation of the condition at the beginning of the motion, the condition at any specific instant can be used for this purpose, and no generality is lost in setting $t = 0$ for the instant in question.

[4] The difference between ω and f is merely a matter of units. The conversion factor is the constant 2π radians per cycle. Hence, whenever this difference is immaterial to our discussion, we use the term frequency for ω also.

as described by (1) and (6), has no beginning and no end, this designation is an arbitrary act, and the value of α has very little physical significance. If, however, the relations (1) and (6) come into effect only at the instant $t = 0$, when a sudden change of external conditions affecting the system takes place, then the time-phase angle α contributes toward the description of this initial condition. For instance, if the spring-mass system is set into motion at $t = 0$ by external means acting momentarily to give the mass a displacement x_0 and velocity $\dot{x}_0$, these quantities are then related to α through the equation

$$\tan \alpha = \frac{B}{A} = \frac{\dot{x}_0}{x_0 \omega} \tag{9}$$

When two periodic phenomena of the same frequency are studied together, the difference between their time-phase angles is called the *phase difference*. The phase difference measures how far these two periodic phenomena are out of step with each other. In many problems this phase difference rather than the absolute value of the time-phase angle has physical meaning.

1.2 Complex Number and Graphical Representation of a Sinusoidal Function

It is known in algebra that trigonometric functions are related to exponential function by Euler's formula:

$$e^{i\theta} = \cos \theta + i \sin \theta$$

For real values of θ the real part of the complex number $e^{i\theta}$ is $\cos \theta$. If we use the symbol "Re" to mean "the real part of," we may write (6) as

$$\begin{aligned} x &= C \operatorname{Re} (e^{i(\omega t - \alpha)}) = \operatorname{Re} (Ce^{-i\alpha} e^{i\omega t}) \\ &= \operatorname{Re} (\lambda e^{i\omega t}) \end{aligned} \tag{10}$$

where

$$\lambda = Ce^{-i\alpha} = C \cos \alpha - iC \sin \alpha = A - iB \tag{11}$$

This quantity λ is called the *complex amplitude* of the sinusoidal function $x(t)$.

At this point it seems unnecessarily complicated and highly artificial to represent a cosine function by the real part of a complex exponential function. Certain advantages of this representation will, however, reveal themselves in time.

A complex number

$$a + ib = re^{i\theta}$$

can be represented by a vector in the so-called *Argand's diagram*, as shown in Fig. 2. The length of the vector r is called the *absolute value* (or *modulus*) and the angle θ, the *argument* (or *amplitude*)[5] of the complex number in question. Hence the absolute value of λ is the amplitude of $x(t)$, and the argument of λ is the time-phase angle of $x(t)$. In this way λ gives a complete description of the integration constants, whereas the parameter of the original differential equation, viz., ω, is contained in the factor $e^{i\omega t}$. In (10) we may say that $e^{i\omega t}$ represents the differential equation (or the system) and λ represents a particular solution of the equation (or a particular motion of the system).

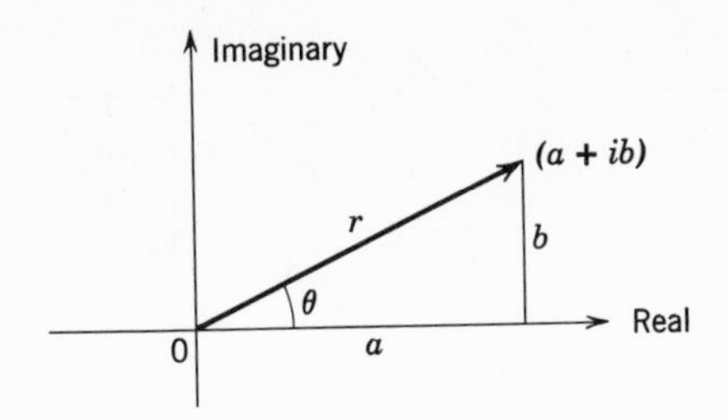

Figure 2

In Argand's diagram representation the complex amplitude λ is shown as OL in Fig. 3. The complex number whose real part represents x at time t is represented by rotating OL through an angle ωt to OX. The value of x is then equal to the projection of OX on the real axis as it rotates around O with uniform angular velocity ω. The vector OX is called a rotating vector.[6] When two or more rotating vectors with the same ω are involved in a problem, it is only their relative positions that are usually of importance. Hence their positions may be "frozen" at a chosen instant, say $t = 0$, when their relation is studied. For instance, if $x(t)$ is a sinusoidal function having the frequency ω and is represented by a rotating vector $\lambda e^{i\omega t}$, then $\dot{x}$ and $\ddot{x}$ are represented by rotating vectors 90 and 180° "ahead" of $\lambda e^{i\omega t}$, respectively. The relative positions of these rotating vectors do

[5] It is unfortunate that the word "amplitude" is used both in the description of a complex number and in that of an oscillatory phenomenon. It becomes doubly unfortunate that the amplitude of one does not correspond to that of the other when a complex function is used to describe an oscillatory phenomenon. For this reason we use the word "amplitude" only in describing an oscillation and the word "argument" in describing a complex number.

Those who are interested in the vagary of meaning of the word "amplitude" should also look up its definition in astronomy.

[6] It is also called a phasor or a sinor.

not change as they rotate en masse with the same angular velocity ω. The position of a rotating vector at $t = 0$ is, of course, the vector representing the complex amplitude; therefore we often use the complex amplitude alone to represent a sinusoidal function of time if the frequency ω is known to be constant and is of little consequence in the discussion.

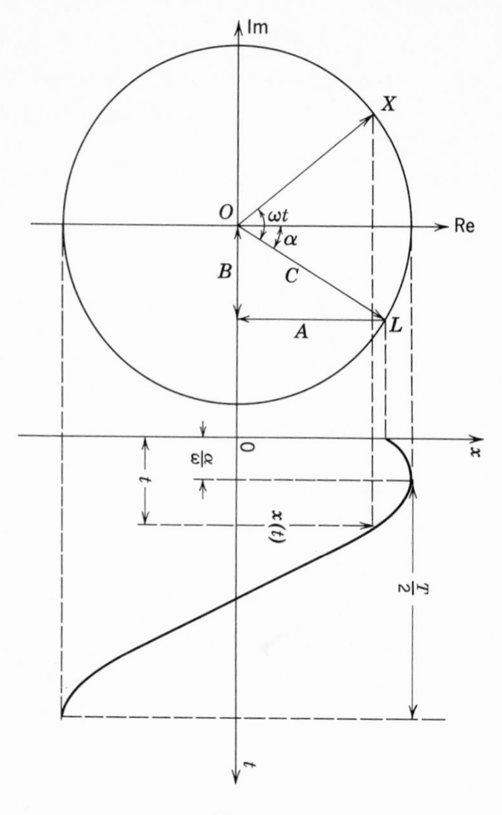

Figure 3

It can easily be verified that the sum of two complex numbers is represented in Argand's diagram by a vector that is the vectorial sum of the two vectors representing the two numbers. Furthermore, a little analysis (see Exercise 1.5) will show that superposition of two sinusoidal functions of time having the same frequency yields another sinusoidal function of the same frequency, whose complex amplitude is the sum of those for the original functions. Hence parallelogram theorem in Argand's diagram represents the rule for the superposition of sinuosidal functions of the same frequency. Rotating vectors of the same circular frequency therefore have the properties of vectors insofar as addition law is concerned. However, they do not possess all of the properties of vectors in the usual sense.

1.3 Harmonic Oscillation of Systems with a Single Degree of Freedom—General Discussion

The discussion so far is essentially a study of the solution (and of its representations) of a differential equation. The spring-mass system shown in Fig. 1 is merely an illustration of a physical system whose motion is described by the differential equation. Needless to say, the results obtained in this study, being mathematical in nature, are applicable to the motions of all other systems in which the same mathematical formulation is valid.[7] We now discuss this class of systems in general.

The spring-mass system illustrated is said to have a single degree of freedom because only a single variable is needed to specify the configuration of the system. By *configuration* we mean the location of all mass particles of the system in space.[8] A system generally consists of many, or infinitely many, mass particles. But in a system with a single degree of freedom the spatial coordinates of these mass particles are interrelated to one another and restricted to vary in such a way that only a single (but not unique) quantity is required to specify their locations. This restriction in their movements is supplied by what we call the *constraints* of the system. In the spring-mass system studied we have tacitly assumed that (*a*) the mass m is a rigid body, (*b*) external things, such as guides, restrict the motion of m to a translation, (*c*) the spring is weightless.[9] Under these assumptions, the configuration of this system at any instant can be represented by a single function of time, $x(t)$, called the coordinate of the system, for which we chose the displacement of m from its equilibrium position. Other choices can be made to serve our purpose equally well; but, whatever the particular choice may be, physical reasoning leads to the conclusion that it must be a periodic function of time having the identical

---

[7] This observation may sound trite but upon it rests the most imposing edifice of mathematical physics.

[8] This means that in this definition we are concerned only with the geometrical state of the system, not with its general dynamic state, which involves also the velocities or the momentum of the mass particles, discussed in Art. 1.4.

[9] If you do not like the idea of weightless things, we can compromise the situation in the following manner. We assume that the mass of the spring is relatively small so that its deformation is largely produced by the forces acting at its two ends without any measurable contribution from the inertia force of the spring itself. In that case the displacement of each particle of the spring is determined by its total elongation and the laws of elastic deformation. (See also Art. 4.0.)

frequency. In other words, *the frequency of a vibratory system is a physical property independent of the choice of the coordinate.*

A number of vibratory systems with a single degree of freedom are illustrated in Arts. 1.12 and 1.13. However, for our present exposition we may continue to use the spring-mass system as a model without the loss of generality.

1.4 Energy Relation, Rayleigh's Principle, and Phase Trajectory

The systems being studied are called *conservative systems* because they contain no mechanism for the dissipation of mechanical energy. Therefore, once such a system is set into vibration, it contains a fixed amount of mechanical energy. This amount is divided between the potential and the kinetic energy. The vibration of the system can be considered as a periodic transferring back and forth of the energy from one form to the other. At the instant the system assumes its equilibrium configuration, its potential energy is a minimum,[10] or zero, and its kinetic energy, a maximum. When the system is momentarily at rest, the reverse is true. The maximum potential energy and the maximum kinetic energy occurring at these two extreme configurations obviously must be equal.

Using T and V as symbols of kinetic energy and potential energy, respectively, we have for a simple spring-mass system

$$T = \tfrac{1}{2}m\dot{x}^2 \qquad V = \tfrac{1}{2}kx^2$$

Since the motion is a harmonic oscillation and the maximum kinetic energy T_m and the maximum potential energy V_m are equal, we have

$$T_m = \tfrac{1}{2}m\omega^2C^2$$

$$V_m = \tfrac{1}{2}kC^2$$

and

$$T_m = V_m \qquad \text{or} \qquad \omega = \sqrt{k/m} \tag{12}$$

In many problems in which ω is to be determined it is easier to express the energies in terms of the amplitude C than to write the equation of motion, especially when approximations are involved. This method of determining the natural frequency of a system in harmonic oscillation is called *Rayleigh's method.* Its application to vibration problems is illustrated in Art. 1.13 The reader is advised to study these illustrative problems before proceeding further.

---

[10] Recall the theorem in mechanics which states that the necessary condition for a system in stable equilibrium is that its potential energy is at a minimum.

In a more general discussion both m and k in the energy expressions must be considered as functions of the coordinates x. Hence[11]

$$T = \tfrac{1}{2}m(x)\dot{x}^2 \qquad V = \tfrac{1}{2}k(x)x^2$$

For conservative systems the conservation of energy demands that

$$T + V = \text{constant}$$

or

$$\tfrac{1}{2}m(x)\dot{x}^2 + \tfrac{1}{2}k(x)x^2 = \tfrac{1}{2}h^2$$

$$\frac{\dot{x}^2}{h^2/m} + \frac{x^2}{h^2/k} = 1 \tag{13}$$

in which h is a constant.

Consider a coordinate system in which the coordinate axes are the displacement x and velocity $\dot{x}$. A generic point P in this coordinate plane, which is called the *phase plane* of motion, represents a *dynamic state* of the system, specified by the displacement and velocity taken together. The motion of the physical system is represented by the motion of P in the phase plane. The locus traced by P is called the *phase trajectory*, and the velocity of P in the phase plane along the phase trajectory is the *phase velocity*. Much about the motion of a system can be revealed by studying the topological structure of its phase trajectory in the phase plane.

The phase trajectories of a given system are described by (13), in which m and k are determined by the system and h is a parameter determined by the initial condition (or energy content) of the system. For conservative systems in oscillation the phase trajectory must be a closed curve. The totality of all possible oscillations for a given system is represented by a one-parametric family of such curves.

According to (13), the phase trajectory of the motion of a spring-mass system in which m and k are constants is an ellipse, shown in Fig. 4. The ratio of the two axes of the ellipse is the circular frequency of the system, and their absolute lengths are determined by the total energy content of the system in motion. Therefore, one may say that the constants of the system determine the shape of the ellipse, and the initial conditions, the size.[12] For a given system, through each point in the phase plan except

---

[11] How x and $\dot{x}$ enter into these expressions is discussed more fully in Chapter 3 and is of no importance to our present discussion. See also Art. 1.13 and Exercise 1.26.

[12] It is an important property of a linear system that its natural frequency is independent of its amplitude. The definition of the term "linear system" is discussed more thoroughly in Art. 1.10.

the origin, there passes a unique phase trajectory (ellipse). By giving the system an initial condition or dynamic state corresponding to this point, the resulting motion is depicted by the ellipse passing through this point.

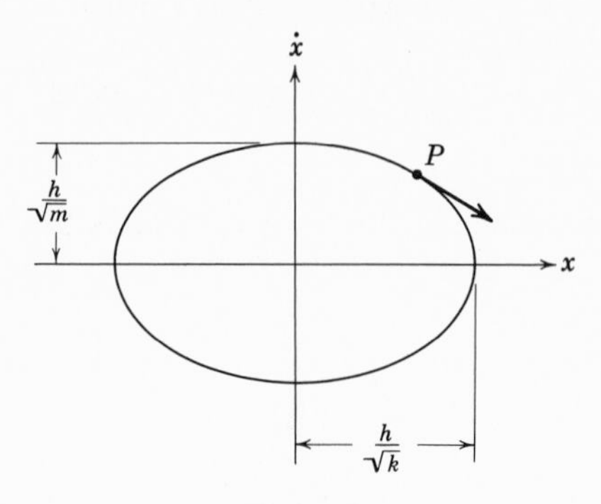

Figure 4

1.5 Damped Vibration with Viscous or Linear Damping

A *viscous damper* is a device that offers a resistance to motion proportional to the time rate of its deformation. If such a device is incorporated

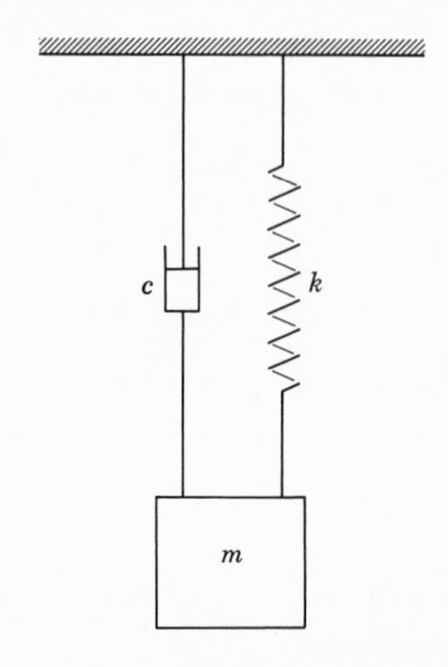

Figure 5

into the spring-mass system studied, as shown in Fig. 5, the resulting equation of motion is

$$m\ddot{x} = -kx - c\dot{x}$$

or (14)

$$m\ddot{x} + c\dot{x} + kx = 0$$

The constant of proportionality c is called the *damping constant*, or simply *damping*. The general solution of (14) is given by

$$x(t) = C_1 e^{s_1 t} + C_2 e^{s_2 t} \tag{15}$$

where

$$\left.\begin{matrix} s_1 \\ s_2 \end{matrix}\right\} = \frac{-c \pm \sqrt{c^2 - 4mk}}{2m} \tag{16}$$

and C_1 and C_2 are constants of integration to be determined by the initial condition. There are three possible cases of the resulting motion.

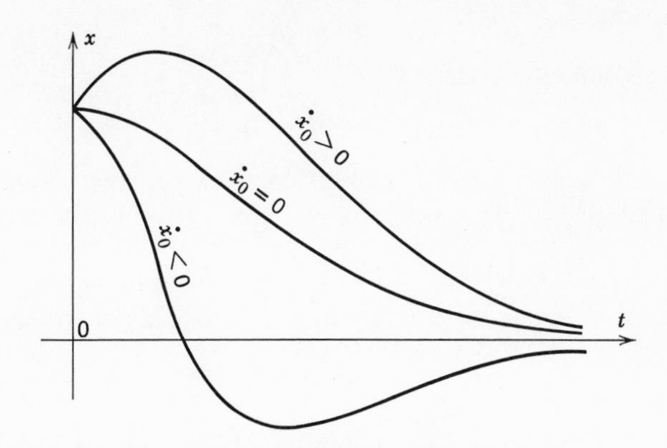

Figure 6

Case 1. OVER-DAMPED SYSTEMS

$$c^2 - 4mk > 0$$

In this case s_1 and s_2 are both real and negative. For the motion with the initial condition

$$x = x_0 \qquad \dot{x} = \dot{x}_0 \qquad \text{at} \qquad t = 0$$

the constants are

$$C_1 = \frac{-s_2 x_0 + \dot{x}_0}{s_1 - s_2} \qquad C_2 = \frac{-s_1 x_0 + \dot{x}_0}{s_2 - s_1} \tag{17}$$

The resulting motion may be one of the types represented in Fig. 6. Depending upon the relative magnitudes of x_0 and $\dot{x}_0$, the curve may cross the t-axis at most once. (See Exercise 1.20.) At any rate, no oscillation may take place; and x and $\dot{x}$ approach zero asymptotically. The motion is said to be *aperiodic*.

Case 2. CRITICALLY DAMPED SYSTEM

$$c^2 - 4mk = 0 \qquad c = c_c = 2\sqrt{mk}$$

For this particular value of damping, c_c, called the *critical damping* of the system, we have

$$s_1 = s_2 = -\omega$$

and the solution of (14) becomes

$$x(t) = C_1 e^{-\omega t} + C_2 t e^{-\omega t} \tag{18}$$

with

$$C_1 = x_0 \qquad C_2 = \dot{x}_0 + \omega x_0$$

The motion does not differ from that of Case 1 in its essential character. It is also aperiodic.

Case 3. UNDER-DAMPED SYSTEM

$$c^2 - 4mk < 0$$

In this case s_1 and s_2 are a pair of complex conjugate numbers with negative real parts. The solution is more conveniently expressed as

$$x(t) = e^{(-c/2m)t}(A \cos \omega_c t + B \sin \omega_c t) \tag{19}$$

or

$$x(t) = Ce^{(-c/2m)t} \cos (\omega_c t - \alpha) \tag{19a}$$

where

$$\omega_c = \frac{\sqrt{4mk - c^2}}{2m} = \omega \sqrt{\left(1 - \frac{c^2}{c_c^{\,2}}\right)} \tag{20}$$

and the relationships among A, B, C, and α are the same as in (7). The motion is therefore oscillatory in nature and is often called a *damped oscillation*. It can also be conveniently thought of as a sinusoidal motion with diminishing amplitude.[13]

In complex number representation (19) and (19a) may also be written

$$x = \text{Re}\,(\lambda e^{i\sigma t}) \tag{21}$$

where

$$\lambda = Ce^{-i\alpha} = A - iB$$

and

$$\sigma = \omega_c + i\frac{c}{2m} = \omega_c + i\frac{c}{c_c}\omega \tag{22}$$

The quantities λ and σ are called the *complex amplitude* and the *complex frequency* of a damped vibration. From (22) it is seen that σ is a property of the system, whereas λ describes the initial condition.

---

[13] To say that this description is mathematically unacceptable, since a sinusoidal motion must have a constant amplitude, is "justified quibbling."

For

$$x = x_0 \qquad \dot{x} = \dot{x}_0 \qquad \text{at} \qquad t = 0$$

$$x_0 = \text{Re}\,(\lambda) = A$$

$$\dot{x}_0 = \text{Re}\,(i\sigma\lambda)$$

Hence

$$\lambda = A - iB = x_0 - i\,\frac{c_c\dot{x}_0 + c\omega x_0}{\omega_c c_c} \tag{23}$$

Returning to (19), we see that the ratio of two displacements at any two instants a period, $T = 2\pi/\omega_c$, apart is a constant.

$$\frac{x(t)}{x(t+T)} = e^{(c/2m)T} \tag{24}$$

In other words, at regular time intervals of $2\pi/\omega_c$ the displacement decreases in a *geometric progression.* The natural logarithm of this ratio is called the *logarithmic decrement*, denoted by the symbol Δ.

$$\log\frac{x(t)}{x(t+T)} = \frac{c}{2m}\frac{2\pi}{\omega_c} = \Delta \tag{25}$$

The value of Δ is a measure of the amount of damping the system possesses. In many actual systems the damping force is not so localized that the damping constant c can be directly measured. If such a system is set into vibration, one can observe Δ and deduce an *equivalent damping constant* for the system by the following relationships:

$$\Delta = \frac{c}{2m}\frac{2\pi}{\omega_c} = 2\pi\frac{c}{c_c}\frac{\omega}{\omega_c}$$

Electrical engineers, for good reasons, generally prefer to use a quantity called *quality factor* Q to describe the damping property of a circuit. The quantity Q can be defined by

$$Q = \frac{\pi}{\Delta}$$

From (20) we also have

$$\left(\frac{\omega_c}{\omega}\right)^2 + \left(\frac{c}{c_c}\right)^2 = 1 \tag{26}$$

Thus the three ratios ω_c/ω, c/c_c, and $\Delta/2\pi$ can be expressed as three trigonometric functions of a single angle δ, as shown in Fig. 7.

$$\sin \delta = \frac{c}{c_c} \qquad \cos \delta = \frac{\omega_c}{\omega} \qquad \tan \delta = \frac{\Delta}{2\pi} \tag{27}$$

and

$$\sigma = \omega e^{i\delta}$$

Theoretically, the equivalent damping constant can also be obtained from measuring ω_c, but practically this cannot be done with accuracy when the amount of damping is small. For example, it can be seen in

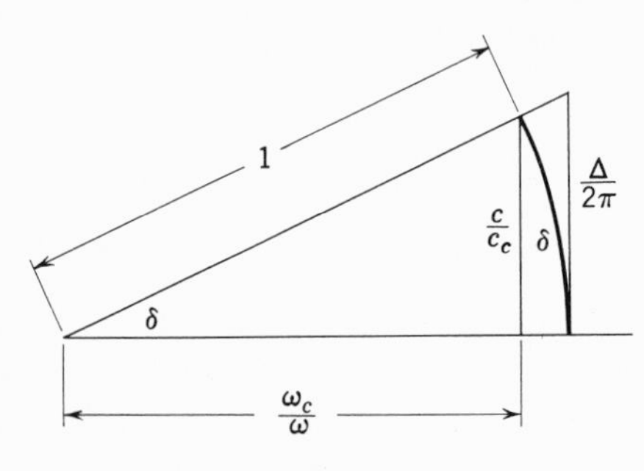

Figure 7

(26) that with a damping of 20 per cent of the critical value there is only less than 2 per cent difference between ω and ω_c. This also shows that the introduction of a moderate amount of damping changes the frequency of a vibratory system only slightly. Furthermore if the damping is small,

$$\frac{c}{c_c} \doteq \delta \doteq \frac{\Delta}{2\pi} \tag{28}$$

A graphical representation of the motion can now be constructed, as shown in Figs. 8 and 9. We see from (21) that the displacement x is represented by the projection on the real axis of the vector in Argand's diagram representing the complex number $\lambda e^{i\sigma t}$. This vector rotates with angular velocity ω_c and decreases in length exponentially. The end of the vector describes a *logarithm spiral*,[14] which has the geometric property that the angle between its radius vector and its normal is constant. Let it be an exercise (Exercise 1.12) to prove that this angle is the angle δ defined in (27). (Work Exercise 1.11 also.)

[14] A logarithm spiral has many other interesting geometric properties. It fascinated the famous mathematician Jakob Bernoulli (1654–1705) so much that he willed it to be inscribed on his tombstone. Unfortunately, the execution of his will was not done with mathematical care and the inscription appeared to resemble an Archimedian spiral.

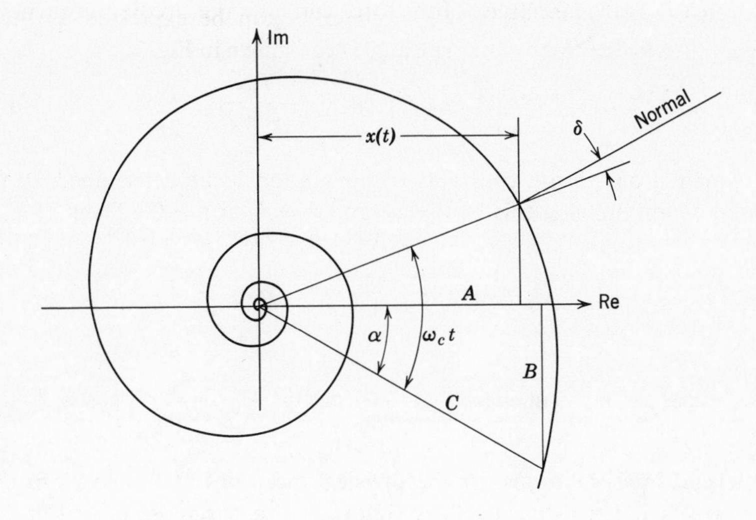

Figure 8

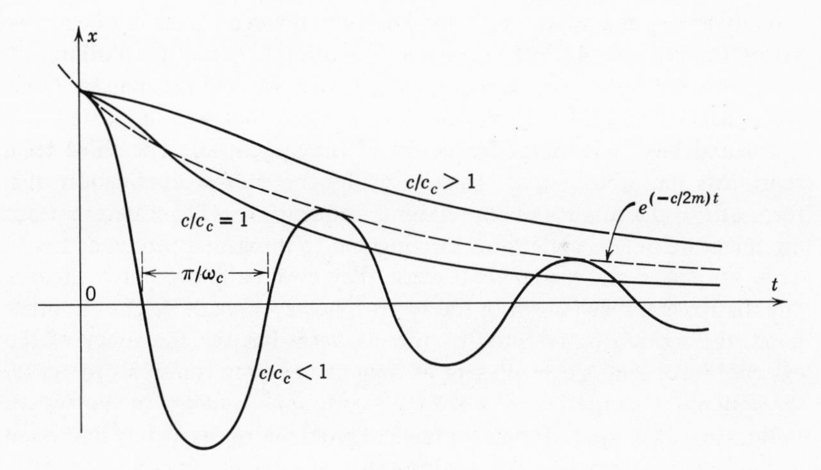

Figure 9

1.6 Forced Vibration under a Harmonic Force

(A) UNDAMPED SYSTEM

Let an external *harmonic force*, that is, a force which is a sinusoidal function of time, be acting on the spring-mass system shown in Fig. 1. The differential equation of motion may be written

$$m\ddot{x} + kx = F_0 \cos \omega_f t \tag{29}$$

in which F_0 is the amplitude of the force and ω_f is the circular frequency.[15] The solution of (29) is

$$x = A \cos \omega t + B \sin \omega t + \frac{F_0}{k - m\omega_f^2} \cos \omega_f t \tag{30}$$

in which A and B are constants of integration to be determined by the initial condition. Let this be $x = x_0$ and $\dot{x} = \dot{x}_0$ at $t = 0$. Then

$$A = x_0 - \frac{F_0}{k - m\omega_f^2} \qquad B = \frac{\dot{x}_0}{\omega} \tag{31}$$

and

$$x = x_0 \cos \omega t + \frac{\dot{x}_0}{\omega} \sin \omega t - \frac{F_0}{k - m\omega_f^2} \cos \omega t + \frac{F_0}{k - m\omega_f^2} \cos \omega_f t \tag{32}$$

Several interpretations for the physical meanings of the terms in (32) are possible. Let us consider the following one. Suppose prior to $t = 0$ the system is in free vibration, and at $t = 0$, when its displacement and velocity are x_0 and $\dot{x}_0$, respectively, an external force $F_0 \cos \omega_f t$ begins to act on the system. Both the equation of motion (29) and its solution (32) are then valid for $t \geq 0$. Comparing (32) with (4) and (5), one sees that the first two terms of (32) represent the motion that was in existence at $t = 0$ and has the natural frequency of the system ω. The third term represents the motion that is produced by the sudden application of a force at $t = 0$ and also has the natural frequency ω. These two motions are therefore due to conditions existing and to things happening at $t = 0$. They are called the *transients* because they eventually die out if there is any dissipation mechanism in the system, however small.[16] On the other hand, the motion represented by the last term has the frequency of the external force and is ever present as long as the force continues to act on the system. This motion is called the *steady-state response* of the system to the force $F_0 \cos \omega_f t$. In many practical problems one is merely interested in motions that persist. An analysis that ignores the transient terms is called a *steady-state analysis*.

---

[15] The physical meanings of the words "amplitude" and "frequency" when applied to a harmonic force should be obvious.

[16] The decay of these transient terms is analogous to that of (19) if there is any damping force. Physical reasoning also shows that unless a system is completely free from disturbances or is unstable its condition at time $t = 0$, which determines the magnitude of the first three terms in (32), must have decreasingly small influence on its condition at subsequent instants. Note also that the quantity F_0 in (31) is better interpreted as the value of the force at $t = 0$ than the amplitude of the harmonic force.

The steady-state response of the system being analyzed is thus

$$\frac{F_0}{k - m\omega_f^2} \cos \omega_f t = \frac{\delta_{st}}{1 - (\omega_f/\omega)^2} \cos \omega_f t = |\lambda| \cos \omega_f t \qquad (33)$$

where $\delta_{st} = F_0/k$ is called the *static deflection*, which is the deflection of the spring under a static force equal to the amplitude of the external harmonic force.[17]

The nondimensional ratio $|\lambda|/\delta_{st}$, called the *magnification factor*,[18] versus the *frequency ratio* ω_f/ω is plotted in Fig. 10. It is seen that for

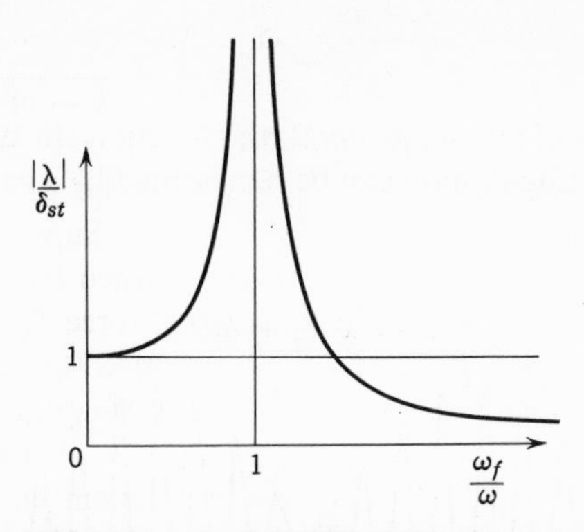

Figure 10

forcing frequency ω_f below the natural frequency ω, $|\lambda|$ and F_0 have the same sign, and the displacement is in phase with the force. As ω_f increases toward ω, $|\lambda|/\delta_{st}$ increases from unity to larger values.

According to (33), for ω_f larger than ω, F_0 and $|\lambda|$ have opposite signs. This is to be interpreted that the displacement is 180° out of phase with the force. The amplitude decreases with increasing ω_f and approaches zero as a limit. At $\omega_f = \omega$ the amplitude is indeterminate, and a condition called *resonance* exists.

To study what takes place at resonance, let us consider first the case in which ω_f is nearly equal to but slightly smaller than ω, or

$$\omega - \omega_f = 2\Delta\omega$$

---

[17] Note carefully the definition of δ_{st}. Although it may have other physical meanings in other special cases, the definition given here is a more general one.

[18] Further discussions on "magnification factor" are contained in this article and in Art. 1.11.

Assuming in (32) that the system is at rest at $t = 0$, that is, $x_0 = \dot{x}_0 = 0$, we have

$$x = \frac{F_0}{k - m\omega_f^2}(\cos \omega_f t - \cos \omega t)$$

$$= \frac{\delta_{st}}{1 - (\omega_f/\omega)^2} 2 \sin \frac{(\omega_f + \omega)t}{2} \sin \Delta\omega\, t$$

$$= \frac{\omega^2 \delta_{st}}{\Delta\omega\,(\omega + \omega_f)} \sin \Delta\omega\, t \sin \frac{(\omega_f + \omega)t}{2} \tag{34}$$

Since

$$\frac{\omega_f + \omega}{2} \doteq \omega \gg \Delta\omega$$

within a few cycles of $\sin (\omega_f + \omega)t/2$, the function $\sin \Delta\omega\, t$ changes only slightly. The resulting motion can be represented by a series of sine waves

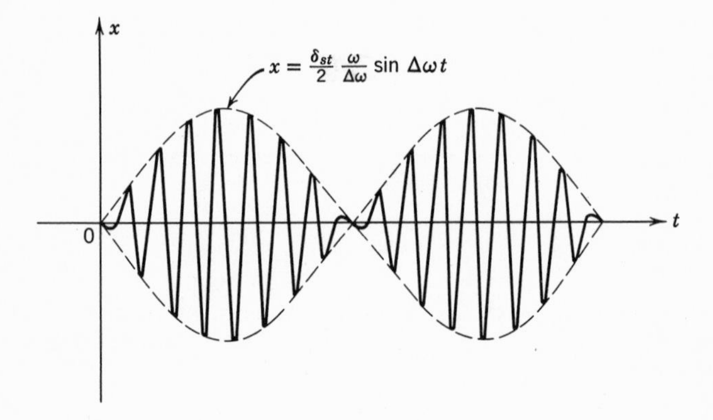

Figure 11

whose amplitudes change slowly within envelopes which are two sine waves of frequency $2\Delta\omega$,[19] shown in Fig. 11.

Returning to (34), we now let $\Delta\omega \to 0$; then

$$\sin \Delta\omega\, t \to \Delta\omega\, t$$

$$\lim_{\Delta\omega \to 0} x(t) = \delta_{st}(\omega t/2) \sin \omega t \tag{35}$$

[19] Since $\sin \Delta\omega\, t$ enters as a part of the amplitude only, its absolute value alone is important, and this value repeats itself every 180° instead of 360°.

Thus the amplitude grows indefinitely as t increases.[20] The result is shown in Fig. 12. This condition is called *resonance*. It is important to note that the motion is a sine function, whereas the force is a cosine function. Hence the displacement lags behind the force by a phase difference of 90° instead of 0 or 180°, as in the case of nonresonant forced vibrations.

The motion described by (34) is an example of a phenomenon called *beat*. It is formed by two harmonic oscillations with the same amplitudes

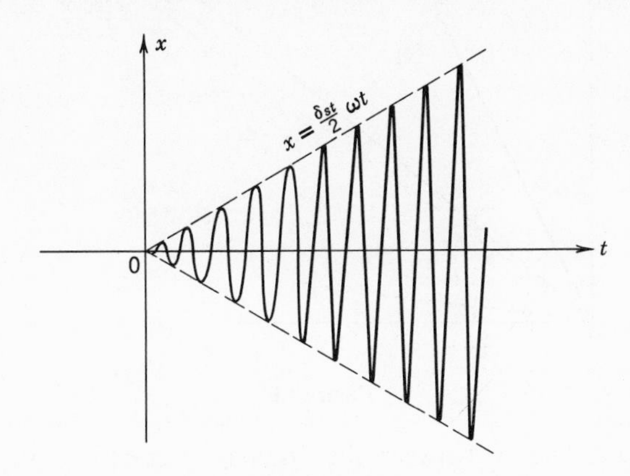

Figure 12

but slightly different frequencies. The phase difference between the two changes continually so that sometimes the two oscillations reinforce each other and at other times they cancel each other. In a more general beat phenomenon the amplitudes of the two need not be the same. The general case is therefore represented by

$$\begin{aligned} x(t) &= A \cos (\omega + \Delta\omega)t + B \cos (\omega - \Delta\omega)t \\ &= (A + B) \cos \Delta\omega\, t \cos \omega t - (A - B) \sin \omega t \sin \Delta\omega\, t \\ &= C \cos (\omega t - \alpha) \end{aligned} \tag{36}$$

where

$$\begin{aligned} C^2 &= A^2 + B^2 + 2AB \cos (2\Delta\omega\, t) \\ \tan \alpha &= \frac{A - B}{A + B} \tan (\Delta\omega\, t) \end{aligned} \qquad (37)^{21}$$

---

[20] This is a more precise statement than the one that asserts that the amplitude is infinite. Aside from physical limitations, such as overstraining and breaking of parts, it takes time to build up large amplitude and infinite time to build up infinite amplitude. True steady-state forced vibration of an undamped system is not possible at resonance.

[21] In electronics we call the variation of C with t *amplitude modulation* and that of α with t, *frequency modulation*.

The foregoing relations are nothing but the law of cosine and the law of tangent applied to the triangle shown in Fig. 13. The maximum and minimum "displacements" are therefore approximately the sum and the difference of the amplitudes A and B, respectively. The *beat frequency* is

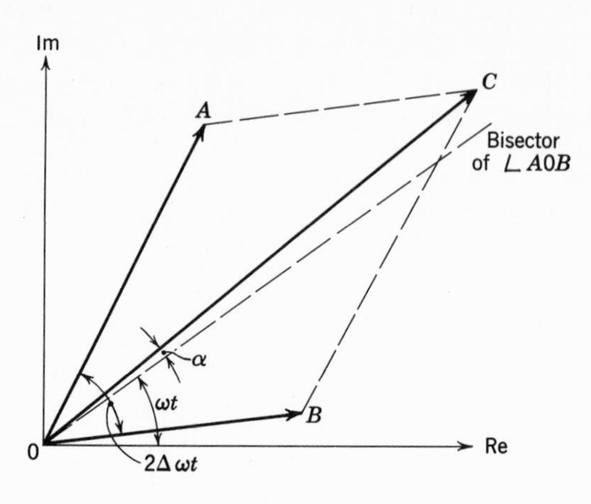

Figure 13

$\Delta\omega/\pi$, or the difference between the original frequencies. In Fig. 14 the two different cases of combined motion are shown: *(a)* $\omega \doteq \Delta\omega$ and *(b)* $\omega \gg \Delta\omega$. It is to be noted that in *(b)* the envelopes are not sine waves, being somewhat "pinched in" in the valleys, especially when A and B are

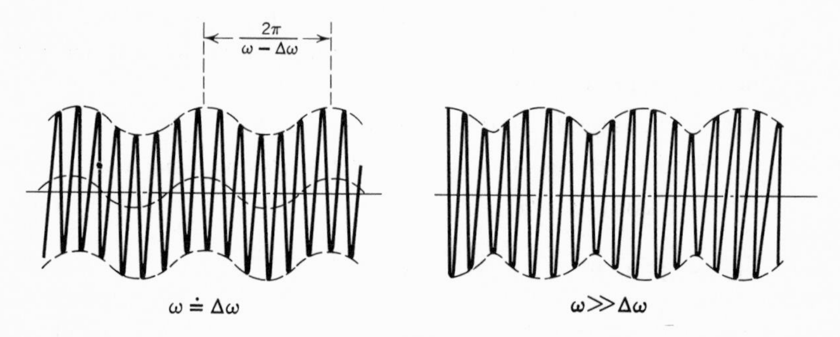

Figure 14

about equal. When A and B are equal and $\alpha = 0$, the bottoms of the valleys become cusps, and the two envelopes are joined there to form sinusoidal envelopes, as shown in Fig. 11.

In forced vibration near resonant frequency, if the system has a slight amount of damping, the beat will die out, since one of its component vibrations is a transient. On the other hand, if the system is subject to slight disturbances from various sources at all times, beats of various amplitudes but the same beat frequency will be observed continually. The important point is that since the transients have a frequency very near to that of the steady-state vibration during their brief time of existence they can make their influence distinctly observable by forming beats with the steady-state vibration.

(B) DAMPED SYSTEM

We consider next the steady-state response to a harmonic force of a system with viscous damping. Let the equation of motion be

$$m\ddot{x} + c\dot{x} + kx = F_0 \cos \omega_f t \tag{38}$$

The solution of this equation is known to be of the form[22]

$$x(t) = C_1 e^{s_1 t} + C_2 e^{s_2 t} + |\lambda| \cos (\omega_f t - \alpha) \tag{39}$$

in which $|\lambda|$ and α are determined by substituting (39) into (38):

$$\begin{aligned} -m\omega_f^2 + k &= (F_0/|\lambda|) \cos \alpha \\ c\omega_f &= (F_0/|\lambda|) \sin \alpha \end{aligned} \tag{40}$$

$$\tan \alpha = \frac{c\omega_f}{-m\omega_f^2 + k} = \frac{2(c/c_c)(\omega_f/\omega)}{1 - (\omega_f/\omega)^2}$$

$$|\lambda| = \frac{F_0}{\sqrt{(-m\omega_f^2 + k)^2 + c^2\omega_f^2}} = \frac{\delta_{st}}{\sqrt{\left(1 - \dfrac{\omega_f^2}{\omega^2}\right)^2 + \left(2\dfrac{c}{c_c}\dfrac{\omega_f}{\omega}\right)^2}} \tag{41}$$

These relationships can be geometrically represented by a parabola, as shown in Fig. 15. The validity of this representation, first given by C. Runge, can be readily verified. By either the analytical expressions of (41) or the graphical construction shown in Fig. 15, graphs of the magnification factor $|\lambda|/\delta_{st}$ and of the phase lag α as functions of ω_f/ω and c/c_c can be plotted as shown in Fig. 16. They represent the so-called *frequency response* of the system. A general discussion on the frequency response of linear system is contained in Art. 1.11.

The maxima and minima of the curves in Fig. 16*a* are of practical

[22] Although (38) can be solved by standard methods for solving differential equations of this type, we employ the following intuitive reasoning. The solution consists of a transient that must be the same as the solution of (14) and a steady-state motion that must be of frequency ω_f. The steady state, however, may or may not be in phase with the force, so we introduce a phase difference α.

interest, as illustrated in Art. 1.15. For $c/c_c < 1/\sqrt{2}$ all the curves possess a maximum lying between frequency ratios of 0 and 1 and a minimum at (0, 1). The point (0, 1) becomes the maxima of all curves with damping ratio greater than $1/\sqrt{2}$. Exercise 1.17 is devoted to the verification of these statements.

The curves for the phase lag α, shown in Fig. 16*b* change gradually from 0 to π as ω_f increases. For different values of c/c_c the curves first diverge from the origin, converge at $(1, \pi/2)$, diverge again, and then approach π asymptotically.

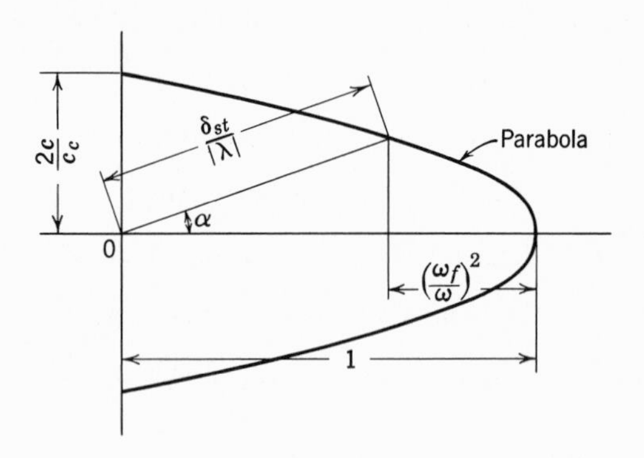

Figure 15

1.7 Complex Number Representation

The amplitude of the steady-state response $|\lambda|$ in (39) is assumed to be a real number. By replacing it with a complex number, it can take into account the phase difference α; and we may write

$$x = \text{Re}\,(\lambda e^{i\omega_f t}) = \text{Re}\,(\zeta)$$

and (42)

$$F_0 \cos \omega_f t = \text{Re}\,(F_0 e^{i\omega_f t})$$

Since (42) satisfies (38)

$$m \frac{d^2}{dt^2} \text{Re}\,(\zeta) + c \frac{d}{dt} \text{Re}\,(\zeta) + k\, \text{Re}\,(\zeta) = \text{Re}\,(F_0 e^{i\omega_f t})$$

Since m, c, and k are real constants and t is a real variable,

$$\text{Re}\,(m\ddot{\zeta} + c\dot{\zeta} + k\zeta) = \text{Re}\,(F_0 e^{i\omega_f t}) \tag{43}$$

Now if we change our "zero point" on the time scale and make the external force $F_0 \sin \omega_f t$ instead of $F_0 \cos \omega_f t$, it is evident that the steady-state

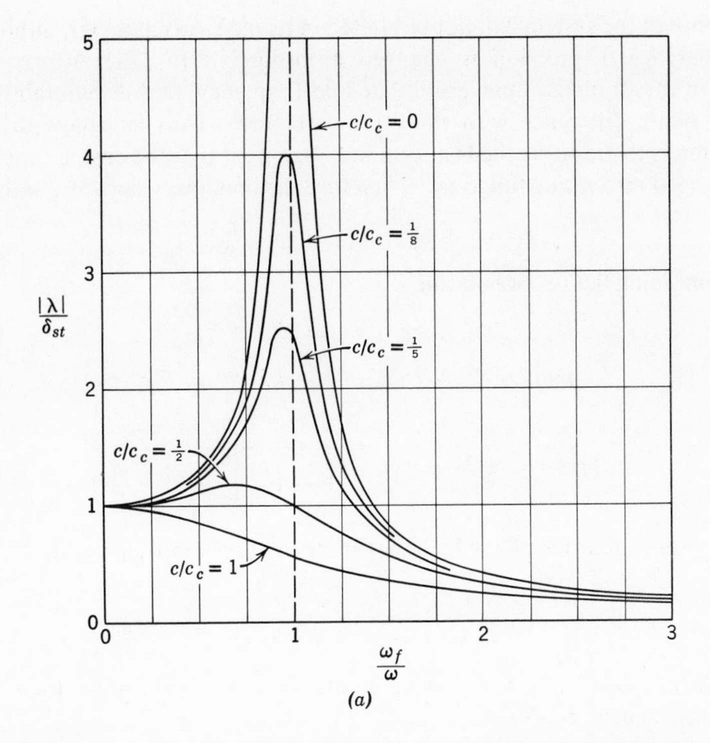

5
4
3
2
1
0
$\frac{|\lambda|}{\delta_{st}}$
$c/c_c = 0$
$c/c_c = \frac{1}{8}$
$c/c_c = \frac{1}{5}$
$c/c_c = \frac{1}{2}$
$c/c_c = 1$
0
1
2
3
$\frac{\omega_f}{\omega}$

(a)

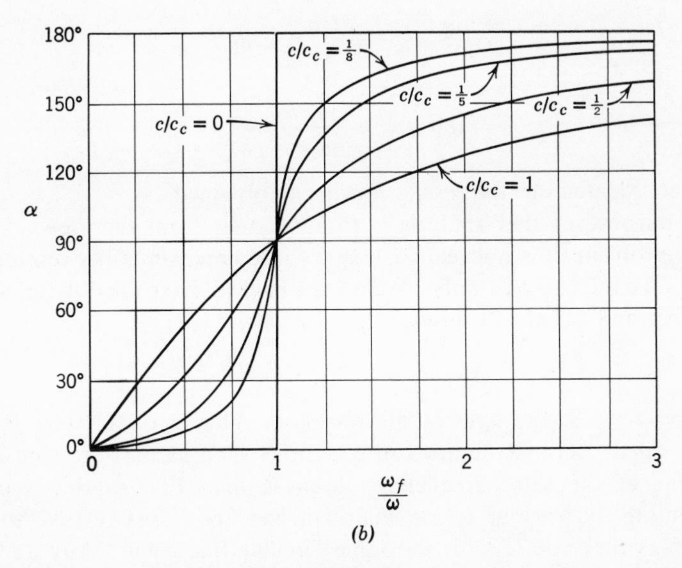

180°
150°
120°
90°
60°
30°
0°
α
$c/c_c = \frac{1}{8}$
$c/c_c = \frac{1}{5}$
$c/c_c = \frac{1}{2}$
$c/c_c = 0$
$c/c_c = 1$
0
1
2
3
$\frac{\omega_f}{\omega}$

(b)

Figure 16

response of the system will not be altered in its physical character, although its analytical expression is changed accordingly. In other words, the motion is still of the same amplitude and frequency, and it maintains the same phase difference with the force as before. Thus its analytical expression is the same as the last term in (39), except that the cosine function is changed into a sine function. Therefore the imaginary part of ζ satisfies

$$\mathrm{Im}\,(m\ddot{\zeta} + c\dot{\zeta} + k\zeta) = \mathrm{Im}\,(F_0 e^{i\omega_f t})$$

By combining the two we obtain

$$m\ddot{\zeta} + c\dot{\zeta} + k\zeta = F_0 e^{i\omega_f t} \tag{44}$$

$$-m\omega_f^2 \lambda e^{i\omega_f t} + ic\omega_f \lambda e^{i\omega_f t} + k\lambda e^{i\omega_f t} = F_0 e^{i\omega_f t} \tag{45}$$

$$\lambda = \frac{F_0}{-m\omega_f^2 + k + ic\omega_f} = \frac{F_0/k}{1 - \left(\dfrac{\omega_f}{\omega}\right)^2 + i\left(\dfrac{2c}{c_c}\dfrac{\omega_f}{\omega}\right)} \tag{46}$$

The absolute value of λ, which we denote by the symbol $|\lambda|$ is then

$$|\lambda| = \frac{F_0}{\sqrt{(-m\omega_f^2 + k)^2 + c^2\omega_f^2}} \tag{47}$$

and the argument of λ, which is the phase difference between the force and the displacement, is

$$-\alpha = \arg(\lambda) = -\tan^{-1}\frac{c\omega_f}{-m\omega_f^2 + k}$$

or

$$\tan\alpha = \frac{c\omega_f}{-m\omega_f^2 + k} \tag{48}$$

These are identical to the results previously obtained.

The purpose of this analysis is to show that from the viewpoint of solving problems it is not really necessary in complex-number representation to take the real part only. We do not have to make the differentiation between x and ζ, and it is just as well if we write (38) as

$$m\ddot{x} + c\dot{x} + kx = F_0 e^{i\omega_f t} \tag{49}$$

with $x = \lambda e^{i\omega_f t}$ as the steady-state response. This is permissible *if, and only if*, all the terms contained in equations such as (38) are sinusoidal functions of the same frequency; because then the rotating vectors, representing the various terms, maintain fixed positions relative to one another as they rotate with the same circular frequency. Any additive relationship existing among their projections must also hold vectorially among themselves. The vectors, which represent the inertia force $m\ddot{x}$, the damping force $c\dot{x}$, and the spring force kx, are shown in Fig. 17. Their vectorial sum is the vector representing the external force.[23]

It cannot be overemphasized that in applying mathematical tools to solve a physical problem a set of "ground rules" is always agreed upon beforehand by the users. Literal interpretation of symbols beyond what the ground rules allow is meaningless.[24] In the present analysis it is understood that we are interested only in getting the amplitude and phase difference of the steady-state response of a linear system to an external force which is a sinusoidal function of time. Under such circumstances, it has been shown that with proper representation complex-number algorism

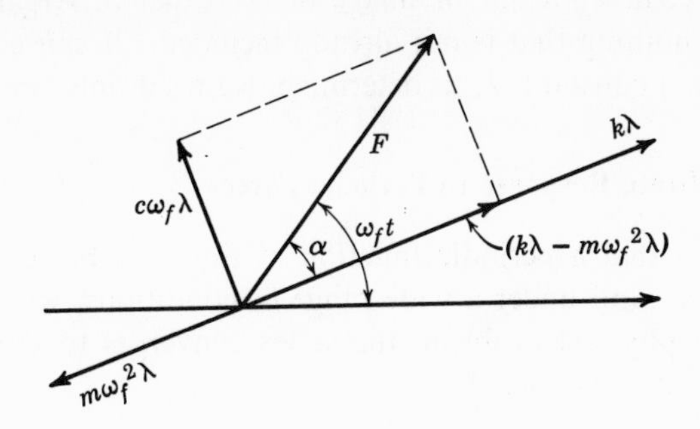

Figure 17

can yield the correct results. No claim is being made that all physical aspects of force and displacement can be adequately described by the mathematical properties of complex numbers.

In the transient analysis we have shown that a damped oscillation can be represented by the real part of a complex number

$$x(t) = \text{Re}\,(\zeta) = \text{Re}\,(\lambda e^{i\sigma t})$$

It is rather simple to verify that the imaginary part of ζ also satisfies (14). Hence the complex number itself also satisfies

$$m\ddot{\zeta} + c\dot{\zeta} + k\zeta = 0 \tag{50}$$

and, with proper understanding, we may dispense with the difference

---

[23] The parallelogram law for the addition of coplanar vectors is equivalent to the addition rule of complex numbers. Using mathematical terminology, one says that coplanar vectors and complex numbers are isomorphic under addition laws.

[24] Even the common practice of representing a scalar physical quantity by a real number involves a prior agreement of units and method of measurement. It is meaningless to say, for instance, that boiling water is 212/32 times as hot as ice.

between x and ζ. Our problem becomes that of looking for a solution of (50) of the type $\zeta = \lambda e^{i\sigma t}$, satisfying the initial condition specified by (23).

$$\zeta_0 = \lambda = x_0 - i\frac{c_c\dot{x}_0 + c\omega x_0}{\omega_c c_c}$$

At this moment some of the keener readers may recall that according to the theory of differential equation a second-order equation requires two, not one, initial values for its complete solution whereas only one is given by (23). There are several ways to explain this discrepancy, but all are based on the fact that in our scheme of things the other solution of (50), viz., $\zeta = \lambda' e^{i\bar{\sigma} t}$ (where $\bar{\sigma}$ is the complex conjugate of σ), can be ignored, since, being a mirror image of the other in Argand's diagram, it represents nothing that is not already included. Because we have only one integration constant, λ, to determine, we need only one initial value.

1.8 Steady-State Response to Periodic Forces

It is known that a periodic function of time can be represented by a Fourier series; and under a wide range of conditions, which are usually satisfied in a physical problem, the series converges to the value of the function almost everywhere.[25]

$$\begin{aligned} F(t) &= \sum_{n=0}^{\infty} (a_n \cos n\omega_f t + b_n \sin n\omega_f t) \\ &= \sum_{n=0}^{\infty} f_n \cos (n\omega_f t - \beta_n) = \sum_{n=0}^{\infty} \mathrm{Re}\, (\phi_n e^{in\omega_f t}) \end{aligned} \tag{51}$$

where $T = 2\pi/\omega_f$ is the period of the function and for each n the constants a_n, b_n, f_n, β_n, and ϕ_n are interrelated in the usual manner. It is well known that the coefficients a_n and b_n are given by

$$\begin{aligned} a_0 &= \frac{1}{T}\int_{-T/2}^{T/2} F(t)\, dt \qquad b_0 = 0 \\ a_n &= \frac{2}{T}\int_{-T/2}^{T/2} F(t) \cos n\omega_f t\, dt \\ b_n &= \frac{2}{T}\int_{-T/2}^{T/2} F(t) \sin n\omega_f t\, dt \end{aligned} \qquad n > 0 \tag{52}$$

[25] See standard mathematics text about Dirichlet's conditions in Fourier-series representation. The term "almost everywhere" has precise mathematical meaning with which we need not be concerned here. Sufficient is it to say that the series will converge to the function at all points of continuity.

A periodic force, when expressed by a convergent Fourier series, is thus the sum of sine and cosine functions. By the principle of superposition, which is discussed fully later, the response of a linear system to a periodic force can be expressed as an infinite series whose terms are the responses to the terms in the Fourier series, provided that both series are convergent. Utilizing the results previously obtained, such as (33), (39), and (41), we see that the steady-state response to a periodic force for an undamped spring-mass system is

$$x = \frac{1}{k} \sum_{n=0}^{\infty} \frac{f_n}{1 - (n\omega_f/\omega)^2} \cos (n\omega_f t - \beta_n) \tag{53}$$

and for a damped spring-mass system,

$$x = \frac{1}{k} \sum_{n=0}^{\infty} \frac{f_n \cos (n\omega_f t - \beta_n - \alpha_n)}{\sqrt{\left(1 - \dfrac{n^2\omega_f^2}{\omega^2}\right)^2 + \left(\dfrac{2c}{c_c}\dfrac{n\omega_f}{\omega}\right)^2}} \tag{54}$$

where

$$\alpha_n = \tan^{-1} \frac{(2c/c_c)(n\omega_f/\omega)}{1 - (n\omega_f/\omega)^2}$$

Both expressions are a Fourier series; the motion they represent is therefore periodic and has the same period as that of the force. In comparing the coefficients of these series with those of (51), it is seen that unless ω is an integral multiple of ω_f the convergence of (53) and (54) is assured. As a matter of fact, the series representing the motion converges much faster than that representing the force, and one need not use too many terms of (51) to obtain approximate answers for x in (53) and (54).[26]

The studying of a periodic phenomenon by resolving it into sinusoidal components is called *harmonic analysis*. Besides the formal mathematical operations expressed in (52), there is a mechanical or electronic device, called *harmonic analyzer* or *wave analyzer*, which will "measure" the coefficients f_n (and sometimes also β_n) of a periodic phenomenon. Numerical procedure for computing the coefficients in the Fourier series, representing a physical phenomenon based on a finite number of measurements taken on the phenomenon, is also available.[27]

---

[26] Note also that $\alpha_n \to \pi$ as $n \to \infty$.

[27] For details see Scarborough, *Numerical Analysis*, Johns Hopkins Press, Baltimore, 1955, 3rd edition, pp. 477–494.

1.9 Work Done by External Forces and Energy Dissipation in Vibratory Systems

The work done in a time period T by a force $F(t)$ acting on a body moving with velocity $\dot{x}(t)$ in the direction of the force is given by the integral

$$W = \int_0^T F(t)\dot{x}(t)\,dt \tag{55}$$

If both the force and the displacement are sinusoidal functions of time having the same frequency ω_f and a phase difference of α, then the work done per cycle of the motion is

$$\begin{aligned} W &= \int_0^{2\pi/\omega_f} F_0 \cos \omega_f t \frac{d}{dt} |\lambda| \cos (\omega_f t - \alpha)\, dt \\ &= \pi F_0 |\lambda| \sin \alpha \end{aligned} \tag{56}$$

Thus it is seen that work done per cycle is not only proportional to the amplitudes of the force and the displacement but also to the sine of phase difference. In addition, there is the constant of proportionality π. In steady-state forced vibration of an undamped system α is 0 or π, except at resonance. The work done per cycle is therefore zero, and no energy is accumulated. At resonance, as discussed in Art. 1.6, α becomes $\pi/2$, and there is a net amount of work gained by the system for each cycle proportional to the amplitude of that cycle. Since the system contains no mechanism for energy dissipation, the amplitude must build up each cycle by an equal amount.[28] This accounts for the straight-line envelopes in Fig. 12. For the steady-state vibration of a damped system $\sin \alpha$ does not vanish, the net work performed by F is dissipated by the damping mechanism in each cycle, and a constant amplitude is maintained. Since the damping force is the only force that can dissipate mechanical energy, the work done by the damping force per cycle must be equal to that by the external force. Hence

$$\begin{aligned} \pi F |\lambda| \sin \alpha &= \int_0^T c\dot{x}(t)\dot{x}(t)\,dt \\ &= c|\lambda|^2 \omega_f^{\,2} \int_0^T \sin^2 (\omega_f t - \alpha)\,dt = \pi c |\lambda|^2 \omega_f \end{aligned} \tag{57}$$

or

$$\frac{F_0}{|\lambda|} = \frac{c\omega_f}{\sin \alpha} \tag{58}$$

[28] The truth of this statement lies with the fact that the total energy of the system, E, is proportional to the square of the amplitude. $E \propto |\lambda|^2$ and $(dE/dt) \propto |\lambda|$; hence, $d|\lambda|/dt =$ constant.

By the use of (47) and (48) it can be readily verified that the foregoing relationship is correct. For systems with a small amount of damping $|\lambda|$ is almost maximum at $\alpha = \pi/2$. (See Fig. 16 and Exercise 1.17.) The damping of the system can thus be measured by exciting the system to vibrate with maximum steady amplitude and compute c from the approximate relationship

$$c = \frac{F_0}{\omega_f |\lambda|_{\max}} \tag{59}$$

The energy relationship also serves as a convenient means for setting up the differential equation of motion, especially when the system contains a number of constraint forces, which do no work and can thus be ignored in the analysis. An example is given in Art. 1.12. The basic energy equation is

$$\frac{d}{dt} T + \frac{d}{dt} V + P = \frac{dW}{dt}$$

in which P is the power of the dissipative force and W is the work done by external forces. The parameters of a single-degree-freedom system can then be defined by

$$m = \frac{1}{\ddot{x}\dot{x}} \frac{dT}{dt} \qquad k = \frac{1}{\dot{x}x} \frac{dV}{dt} \qquad c = \frac{P}{\dot{x}^2} \qquad \text{and} \qquad F = \frac{1}{\dot{x}} \frac{dW}{dt}$$

Depending upon the coordinate variable x chosen, the quantities m, k, c, and F, may or may not have their usual dimensions.

1.10 Response of Linear Systems to a General External Force—Superposition Theorem

The systems discussed so far are called *linear systems* because their equations of motion are linear differential equations having the form

$$\mathsf{L}(x) = F(t) \tag{60}$$

where L is a linear differential operator.

$$\mathsf{L} = a_0(t) \frac{d^n}{dt^n} + a_1(t) \frac{d^{n-1}}{dt^{n-1}} \cdots a_{n-1}(t) \frac{d}{dt} + a_n(t)$$

For the systems studied $n = 2$ and the a's are constants instead of functions of time t. The following discussion is, however, pertinent to general linear systems.

An important property of linear systems is that they follow the *principle of superposition.* This property is derived from the fact that linear operations are distributive; that is,

$$\mathsf{L}(x_1 + x_2) = \mathsf{L}(x_1) + \mathsf{L}(x_2)$$

Thus if $x = x_1(t)$ is a solution of $\mathsf{L}(x) = F_1(t)$, satisfying the initial condition $x(0) = x_{10}$ and $\dot{x}(0) = \dot{x}_{10}$, and $x = x_2(t)$ is a solution of $\mathsf{L}(x) = F_2(t)$, satisfying the initial condition $x(0) = x_{20}$ and $\dot{x}(0) = \dot{x}_{20}$, then $x = \alpha x_1(t) + \beta x_2(t)$ is a solution of the differential equation[29]

$$\mathsf{L}(x) = \alpha F_1(t) + \beta F_2(t)$$

and satisfies the initial condition[30]

$$x(0) = \alpha x_{10} + \beta x_{20} \qquad \dot{x}(0) = \alpha \dot{x}_{10} + \beta \dot{x}_{20}$$

in which α and β are arbitrary constants.

Let the equation of motion of a linear system under the influence of an external force $F(t)$ be

$$\mathsf{L}(x) = F(t) \tag{61}$$

and let $x = u(t)$ be the solution of the differential equation

$$\mathsf{L}(x) = \mathcal{J}(t) \tag{62}$$

satisfying the initial condition $x_0 = 0$, $\dot{x}_0 = 0$, in which $\mathcal{J}(t)$ is a unit step function defined as

$$\mathcal{J}(t) = 0 \qquad \text{for } t < 0$$

$$\mathcal{J}(t) = 1 \qquad \text{for } t \geq 0$$

This function $u(t)$ is called the *indicial response* or *indicial admittance* of the system. It gives the displacement of the system, if it is *initially resting at its equilibrium position* and is suddenly subjected to a constant force of unit magnitude applied at $t = 0$.

From the principle of superposition it can then be seen that the response of a system that is initially at rest and then subject to a constant force A

---

[29] This theorem was also implied in deriving (53).

[30] We assume that the differential equation is of the second order. Otherwise, the initial condition shall contain the values of derivatives up to $(n - 1)$th order. This assumption does not affect the generality of subsequent results.

suddenly applied at $t = 0$ and to another force B suddenly applied at $t = \tau$ is

$$x(t) = Au(t) + Bu(t - \tau) \qquad t \geq \tau \geq 0 \tag{63}$$[31]

We assume here that the system is *time invariant*; that is, the physical property of the system does not vary with t or the operator L does not contain t explicitly. Otherwise u is a function of two variables $u(t, \tau)$ where τ is the time when the force is applied and t is the time when the response is measured. $u(t)$ then stands for $u(t, 0)$. Most physical systems whose properties vary gradually with time because of aging of components

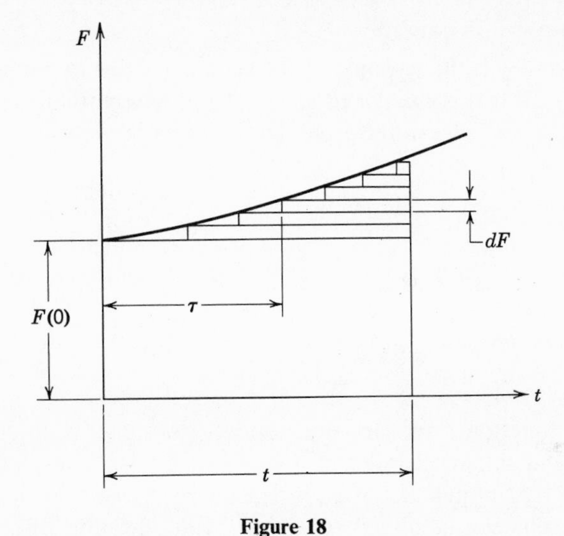

Figure 18

or changes in the environment have become of interest. Such gradual changes, however, do not affect their short-time behavior.

A general time-dependent force $F(t)$, which is applied to a system at time $t = 0$, can be considered as the sum of finite and "infinitesimal" step functions, as shown in Fig. 18. Assuming, for the time being, that

---

[31] The method of defining $u(t)$ previously given leaves it undefined for $t < 0$, so that (63) is valid only for $t \geq \tau \geq 0$. However, if we extend out domain of definition by assigning

$$u(t) = 0 \qquad \text{for } t < 0$$

then (63) is valid for all values of t and $\tau \geq 0$. For what follows this extension is not necessary.

$F(t)$ is continuous and differentiable for $t > 0$, we may write

$$F(t) = F_0 \mathcal{J}(t) + \int_0^t dF \mathcal{J}(t - \tau)$$
$$= F_0 \mathcal{J}(t) + \int_0^t F'(\tau) \mathcal{J}(t - \tau)\, d\tau \tag{64}$$

By the principle of superposition, if this force is applied to a system that is initially at rest at its equilibrium position, the response will be

$$x(t) = F_0 u(t) + \int_0^t F'(\tau) u(t - \tau)\, d\tau \tag{65}$$

in which $u(t - \tau)$ is the response of the system at t due to a unit step force applied at τ. If $u(t)$ is *continuous* at $t = 0$ and differentiable for $t > 0$, as in most problems, we can integrate (65) by parts to yield

$$x(t) = F_0 u(t) + [F(\tau) u(t - \tau)] \Big|_{\tau=0}^{\tau=t} - \int_0^t F(\tau) \frac{d}{d\tau} u(t - \tau)\, d\tau$$

Now $u(0) = 0$ and $(d/d\tau) u(t - \tau) = -u'(t - \tau)$; hence

$$x(t) = \int_0^t F(\tau) u'(t - \tau)\, d\tau \tag{66}$$

Since the function F appears under an integral sign, the requirements of continuity and differentiability of F are not necessary insofar as (66) is concerned.[32] Although these requirements were made in deriving (66), the same results can be directly obtained by another line of reasoning.

Consider a time-invariant linear system that is in equilibrium and at rest prior to $t = 0$. At $t = 0$ the system receives an impulse of force of unit magnitude.[33] The effect of this unit impulse is to produce an initial velocity $\dot{x}_0 = 1/m$. With this initial velocity the system is now set into

[32] If the integral in (65) is considered a Stieljes integral, the requirement on F is not very stringent. At any rate, in an actual physical problem F has at most a finite number of discontinuities and points where F' does not exist; the mathematical difficulties can easily be overcome by adding the term $\Delta F u(t - t_1)$, corresponding to a jump discontinuity ΔF at $t = t_1$, to (65) and splitting the integral to cover ranges where $F'(t)$ exists. After integration by parts, the result is still (66), since the terms corresponding to the discontinuities in F cancel out just as $F_0 u(t)$ term does.

[33] One may speak of a unit impulse of force at $t = 0$ as a force described by the Dirac function $\delta(t)$. Although pure mathematicians are still somewhat uneasy about a precise definition of such a function, applied mathematicians have accepted it with little qualm.

motion. Let the response of the system be such that its displacement is given by the function $h(t)$. That is to say

$$x = h(t)$$

satisfies

$$\mathsf{L}(x) = 0$$

and

$$x_0 = 0 \qquad \dot{x}_0 = \frac{1}{m}$$

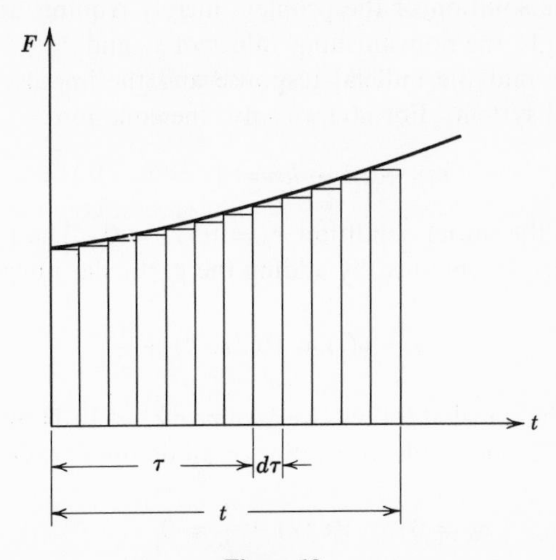

Figure 19

In a more general discussion we must assume that L is of nth order. A unit impulse will then produce the initial condition

$$x_0 = \dot{x}_0 = \cdots x_0^{(n-2)} = 0$$

and

$$x_0^{(n-1)} = \frac{1}{a_0}$$

in which a_0 is the first coefficient in L. For the convenience of visualization we assume that L is second-order without losing important generalization.

Figure 19 shows that the action of a force $F(t)$ on a system may be considered as that of a series of elemental impulses $F(\tau)\, d\tau$ applied successively to the system in the interval $0 \leq \tau \leq t$. According to the principle of superposition, the response of the system at t is the sum of the responses to these impulses. Hence

$$x(t) = \int_0^t F(\tau) h(t - \tau)\, d\tau \tag{67}$$

In comparing (67) with (66), we see that[34]

$$h(t) = u'(t)$$

Thus the displacement response of a linear system to a unit impulse is equal to its velocity response to a unit step force. Either way we define it, the function $u'(t)$ is called the *impulse response* of the system.

In all these derivations it was assumed that at $t = 0$ the initial condition of the system is $x_0 = 0$ and $\dot{x}_0 = 0$. If this is not the case, it is not difficult to see that the solution of the problem merely requires additional terms corresponding to the nonvanishing values of x_0 and $\dot{x}_0$.

Let us now find the indicial response and the impulse response of a linear damped system. For $u(t)$ we solve the equation

$$m\ddot{x} + c\dot{x} + kx = 1 \qquad t \geq 0 \tag{68}$$

together with the initial condition $x_0 = 0$, $\dot{x}_0 = 0$. The general solution of (68) is evidently obtained by adding the particular integral $1/k$ to (21).

$$x = u(t) = \operatorname{Re}(\lambda e^{i\sigma t}) + \frac{1}{k} \tag{69}$$

It appears that in what follows we assume $c/c_c < 1$. However, according to Exercise 1.11, the results are valid for all damping ratios.

$$\begin{aligned} x_0 &= 0 \qquad \operatorname{Re}(\lambda) + \frac{1}{k} = 0 \\ \dot{x}_0 &= 0 \qquad \operatorname{Re}(i\sigma\lambda) = 0 = -\operatorname{Im}(\sigma\lambda) \end{aligned} \tag{70}$$

or

$$\operatorname{Re}(\sigma)\operatorname{Im}(\lambda) = -\operatorname{Re}(\lambda)\operatorname{Im}(\sigma)$$

Since from (27)

$$\sigma = \omega e^{i\delta} = \omega_c + \frac{i\omega c}{c_c}$$

or

$$\begin{aligned} \lambda &= -\frac{1}{k}(1 - i\tan\delta) = -\frac{e^{-i\delta}}{k\cos\delta} \\ u'(t) &= \operatorname{Re}(i\sigma\lambda e^{i\sigma t}) = -\operatorname{Im}(\sigma\lambda e^{i\sigma t}) \end{aligned} \tag{71}$$

[34] The equality of these two functions cannot really be established merely by comparing (66) and (67) because t appears both in the integrands and in the limits. Nevertheless, these functions can be shown to be identical. To prove this fact, utilize the formula to be proved in Exercise 1.32 and remember that $F(\tau)$ can be any arbitrary function.

Utilizing (22), (27), and (71), we have

$$u'(t) = \frac{\omega^2}{\omega_c k} e^{-(c/2m)t} \sin \omega_c t \tag{72}$$

Derivations for the same relationships by the classical method are as follows (see also Exercise 1.24):

$$\begin{aligned} x = u(t) &= Ce^{-(c/2m)t} \cos (\omega_c t - \alpha) + \frac{1}{k} \\ u(0) = 0 \qquad & C \cos \alpha = -\frac{1}{k} \end{aligned} \tag{69a}$$

$$u'(t) = -Ce^{-(c/2m)t}\left[\frac{c}{2m} \cos (\omega_c t - \alpha) + \omega_c \sin (\omega_c t - \alpha)\right]$$

$$u'(0) = 0 \qquad \frac{c}{2m} \cos \alpha = \omega_c \sin \alpha$$

division of the equation by ω and the application of the relations in (27) yield

$$\alpha = \delta \qquad C = -\frac{1}{k \cos \alpha} = -\frac{\omega}{k\omega_c}$$

$$\begin{aligned} u'(t) &= \frac{\omega^2}{k\omega_c} e^{-(c/2m)t} \sin \omega_c t \\ u(t) &= \frac{1}{k}\left(1 - \frac{\omega}{\omega_c} e^{-(c/2m)t} \cos (\omega_c t - \delta)\right) \end{aligned} \tag{69b}$$

Equation (72) can be obtained much more readily if we solve for the problem of free vibration due to an initial velocity $\dot{x}_0 = 1/m$.[35]

In that case we take the general solution (21):

$$x = h(t) = \text{Re}\,(\lambda e^{i\sigma t})$$

As

$$x_0 = 0 \qquad \text{so} \qquad \text{Re}\,(\lambda) = 0$$

Also as

$$\dot{x}_0 = \text{Re}\,(i\sigma\lambda) = -\text{Im}\,(\sigma\lambda) = -\text{Im}\,(\lambda)\,\text{Re}\,(\sigma) = \frac{1}{m}$$

and

$$\text{Re}\,(\sigma) = \omega_c \qquad \text{Im}\,(\lambda) = -\frac{1}{m\omega_c}$$

[35] On the other hand, the reasoning we used in deriving (67) is not mathematically very rigorous, although such rigor can be had by refining some of the arguments.

so

$$\lambda = -\frac{i}{m\omega_c}$$

and

$$h(t) = \text{Re}\left(-\frac{i}{m\omega_c}e^{i\sigma t}\right) = u'(t) \tag{73}$$

It can easily be verified that (73) is the same as (72). The foregoing results contain as a special case the indicial response and impulse response of an undamped system. For such a system let

$$\omega = \omega_c = \sigma \qquad c = \delta = 0$$

Thus (69) and (72) become

$$\begin{aligned} u(t) &= \frac{1}{k}(1 - \cos \omega t) \\ u'(t) &= \frac{\omega}{k}\sin \omega t = \frac{1}{m\omega}\sin \omega t = \frac{1}{\sqrt{mk}}\sin \omega t \end{aligned} \tag{74}$$

Substituting (72) into (66), we have the solution for forced vibration of a damped system, which is initially resting at its equilibrium position.

If the system has an initial displacement and velocity, complementary solutions (19) with the constants determined in (23) must be added. The complete solution is therefore

$$\begin{aligned} x(t) = e^{-(c/2m)t}&\left(x_0 \cos \omega_c t + \frac{c_c\dot{x}_0 + c\omega x_0}{\omega_c c_c}\sin \omega_c t\right) \\ &+ \int_0^t \frac{\omega^2}{\omega_c k} e^{-(c/2m)(t-\tau)} \sin \omega_c(t - \tau)F(\tau)\, d\tau \end{aligned} \tag{75}$$

For an undamped spring-mass system, with $c = 0$ and $\omega_c = \omega$, the solution becomes

$$x(t) = x_0 \cos \omega t + \frac{\dot{x}_0}{\omega}\sin \omega t + \int_0^t \frac{\omega}{k}\sin \omega(t - \tau)F(\tau)\, d\tau \tag{76}$$

In summary, the particular solution satisfying a linear differential equation with constant coefficients and a set of initial values

$$\mathsf{L}(x) = F(t) \qquad \text{when} \quad t = 0 \qquad x = x_0 \qquad \dot{x} = \dot{x}_0$$

etc., is made up of two parts; one part represents the motion[36] which

[36] We use the words "motion" and "force" merely to fit the physical phenomenon under discussion. The theorem is, however, strictly mathematical and can have other applications.

would prevail if $F = 0$, and the other part represents the motion caused by the force $F(t)$ acting on the system subsequent to $t = 0$.[37] In contrast, the classical method illustrated in Arts. 1.7 and 1.9 obtains the general solution to the differential equation first; this consists of a complementary function, representing the transients, and a particular integral, representing the steady-state motion.[38] The particular solution, when needed, is then obtained by determining the constants in the complementary function to satisfy the initial conditions. When the applied force is periodic, and only the long-term behavior of the system is of interest, this method of solution is a natural one. Conversely, when the applied force is of short duration and only the short-term behavior of the system is wanted, the method described in this article is more natural. Nevertheless, as far as mathematics is concerned, either method can be used in either case.

1.11 Signal-Response Relation of Linear Systems in General

The problem we have studied in the last few articles was formulated in a restricted way. We sought the force-displacement relationship in a spring-mass-damper system of a certain arrangement. The essential part of the analyses has, however, much more general applications.

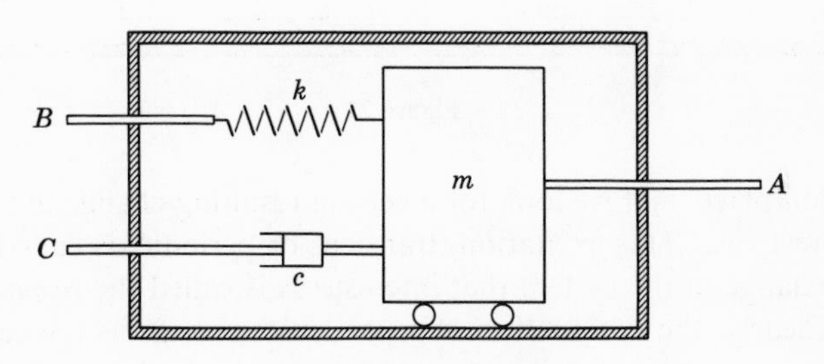

Figure 20

Let us visualize a spring-mass-damper system enclosed in a "black box," as shown in Fig. 20. The three weightless rods, A, B, and C, which are attached to the components of the system, protrude through the walls of the box and can either slide without friction or be locked to the wall. The problem investigated was, "What kind of displacement will be produced

[37] In this approach the condition of the system prior to $t = 0$ is not considered at all.

[38] The terms "transient" and "steady-state motion" are devoid of physical significance when the applied force is *not* a *periodic function* of time, although the two parts of the solution are commonly so designated.

in A by a force applied at A, provided that B and C are locked to the box, which is held fixed?" In other words, "How does the black box transform a force applied at A into a displacement of A?" Evidently, this is not the only behavior of the box that could be of interest. For instance, one may investigate, "What is the force transmitted to the foundation, to which the box is attached?" Or one may change the operating condition of the system by loosening the lock on B and moving B by some external means, and then ask, "What will be the motion transmitted to A?" We can also ask the same questions about a more complex system, such as that shown in Fig. 21. In all of these cases an external disturbance or excitation, such as a force, an impulse, or a displacement, is imparted to the system

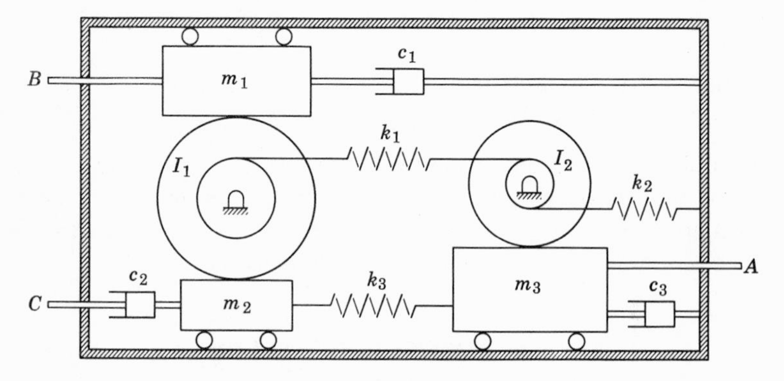

Figure 21

at a certain place, and we look for a certain resulting change in the system that interests us. This excitation, transient or periodic, is called a *signal*, and the change in the system that interests us is called the *response* to the signal. Clearly, the designation of a particular change as the response is purely a subjective matter. What we wish to emphasize here is that many of the analytical results obtained in the preceding articles can be immediately generalized to cover the all-signal-response relationships in linear systems.

(A) TRANSIENT RESPONSE—INDICIAL RESPONSE

Consider the superposition theorem described by (66) and (67). Since in the derivation of these equations no reference is made to the exact make-up of the systems or to the nature of the signal and the response, it is evident that they apply to all linear systems with time-invariant components. Take, for instance, the question of the force transmitted to the foundation of the box of the system in Fig. 20. If $F(t)$ is the force applied at A and

$f(t)$ is the force transmitted to the foundation, the problem can be formulated by the following set of differential equations:

$$\begin{aligned} m\ddot{x} + c\dot{x} + kx &= F(t) \\ c\dot{x} + kx &= f(t) \end{aligned} \tag{77}$$

Although it is possible to eliminate the variable x in the foregoing set of equations to obtain a single equation in the standard form of

$$m\ddot{f} + c\dot{f} + kf = c\dot{F} + kF = G(t) \tag{78}$$

it is not necessary to do so.[39] According to our previous reasoning, if $u_f(t)$ is the force transmitted to the foundation when a unit step force is applied at A, the corresponding force transmitted with $F(t)$ is given by

$$f(t) = \int_0^t u_f'(t - \tau)F(\tau)\, d\tau \tag{79}$$

provided that the system is initially at rest and in equilibrium.

To evaluate $u_f(t)$, we can first evaluate $u_x(t)$, which is the solution to the equation

$$m\ddot{x} + c\dot{x} + kx = \Gamma(t) \qquad \text{with} \quad x_0 = 0 \qquad \text{and} \qquad \dot{x}_0 = 0$$

and then utilize the relationship

$$c\dot{u}_x(t) + ku_x(t) = u_f(t)$$

If we are to analyze the same problem for the system in Fig. 21, the indicial response function $u_f(t)$ will be a more complicated one and will have to be obtained by methods discussed in later chapters; but when it is found the rest of the procedures will be the same.

The most important lesson to be learned from this discussion is that the dynamic property of any linear system is completely specified by its indicial or its impulse response. These functions describe how a system behaves under any given excitation or how it will change any given input signal into an output. In short, they describe the system just as completely as the differential equation itself. Furthermore, for many actual systems, because of the uncertainties in the measurement of such parameters as masses and spring constants, the differential equations themselves are likely to be less reliable than the indicial response functions when the latter can be measured directly.

(B) STEADY-STATE RESPONSE—FREQUENCY RESPONSE

Another way of describing the dynamic property of a linear system is by its steady-state response to sinusoidal inputs. This description is

[39] See also Art. 1.17.

furnished by the so-called *frequency response* of the system, that is, the amplitude and phase difference (lag) of the response as functions of the frequency. Take, for instance, the system shown in Fig. 20. Let the signal be in the form of a sinusoidal motion imposed on B, and let the motion of A be considered as the response, with C clamped to the box. The differential equation relating the displacements of A and B is

$$m\ddot{x}_a + c\dot{x}_a + k(x_a - x_b) = 0$$

Upon letting

$$x_b = |\lambda_b| \cos \omega_f t$$

and

$$x_a = |\lambda_a| \cos (\omega_f t - \alpha)$$

a comparison with (38) shows that the amplitude ratio $|\lambda_a|/|\lambda_b|$ and phase lag α are the same as the magnification factor[40] $|\lambda|/\delta_{st}$ and angle α defined in (41).

It is more convenient, however, to use complex-number representation to describe the signal to response relation so that both the amplitude ratio, generally called the *gain*, and the phase lag are combined in one expression. According to (46), the frequency response in this case is given by the complex number

$$\frac{\lambda_a}{\lambda_b} = \frac{1}{1 - \left(\frac{\omega_f}{\omega}\right)^2 + i\left(\frac{2c}{c_c}\frac{\omega_f}{\omega}\right)}$$

in which λ_a and λ_b are then the complex amplitudes of A and B, respectively.

Consider now the relation between the force transmitted to the foundation f and the force applied to A, that is, F. According to (78), if we let

$$f = f_0 e^{i\omega_f t} \qquad \text{and} \qquad F = F_0 e^{i\omega_f t}$$

we have

$$\frac{f_0}{F_0} = \frac{ic\omega_f + k}{k - m\omega_f^2 + ic\omega_f} = T_r(i\omega_f) \tag{80}$$

The absolute value represented by this ratio, or the gain, is called *transmissibility*.

$$\left|\frac{f_0}{F_0}\right| = \frac{\sqrt{1 + \left(\frac{2c}{c_c}\frac{\omega_f}{\omega}\right)^2}}{\sqrt{\left[1 - \left(\frac{\omega_f}{\omega}\right)^2\right]^2 + \left(\frac{2c}{c_c}\frac{\omega_f}{\omega}\right)^2}} \tag{81}$$

---

[40] In the present connection the name of this factor gives a more graphical description to its physical nature.

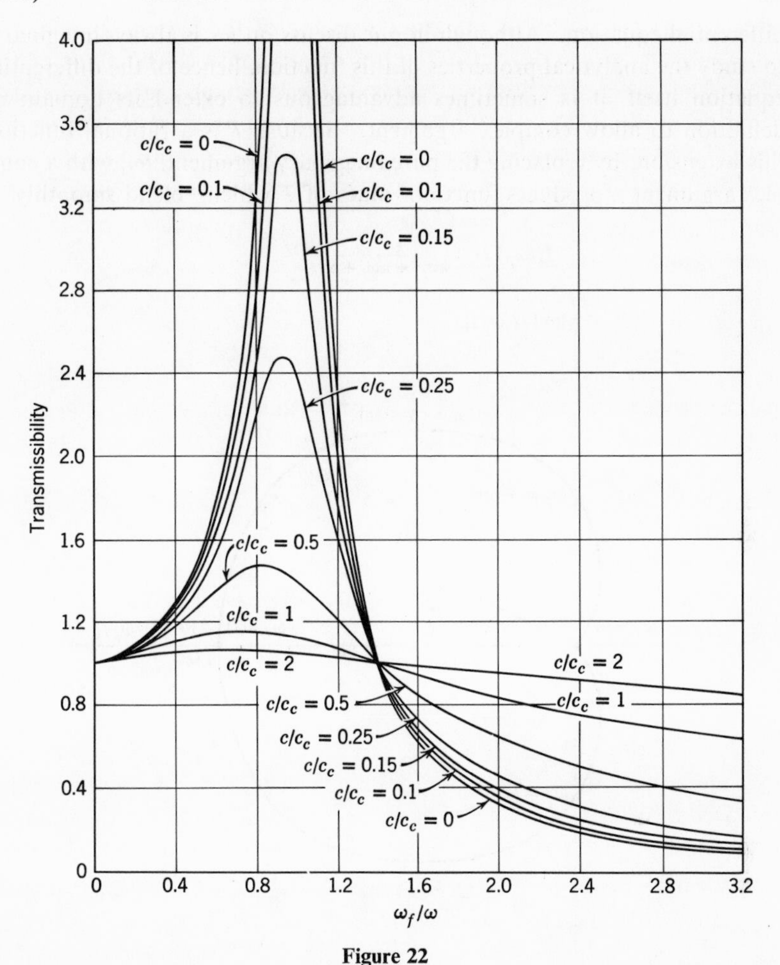

Figure 22

This ratio is plotted in Fig. 22 and is of practical interest in the design of supporting structures for machines susceptible to vibration.

(c) TRANSFER FUNCTION AND TRANSFER LOCUS

In general, if λ_r is the complex amplitude of the response and λ_s is that of the signal, the ratio between the two is a complex function of variable $i\omega_f$, which describes the frequency response of the system

$$\lambda_r = T(i\omega_f)\lambda_s \tag{82}$$

The two examples show that the function T is a ratio of two polynomials of $i\omega_f$ with real coefficients, which are the coefficients in the differential equation. Although in our discussion $i\omega_f$ is always imaginary, to study the analytical properties of this function, hence of the differential equation itself, it is sometimes advantageous to extend its domain of definition to allow complex argument. Because T is a rational function this extension, by replacing the pure imaginary argument, $i\omega_f$ with a complex argument s, produces function values of T which "blend smoothly"[41]

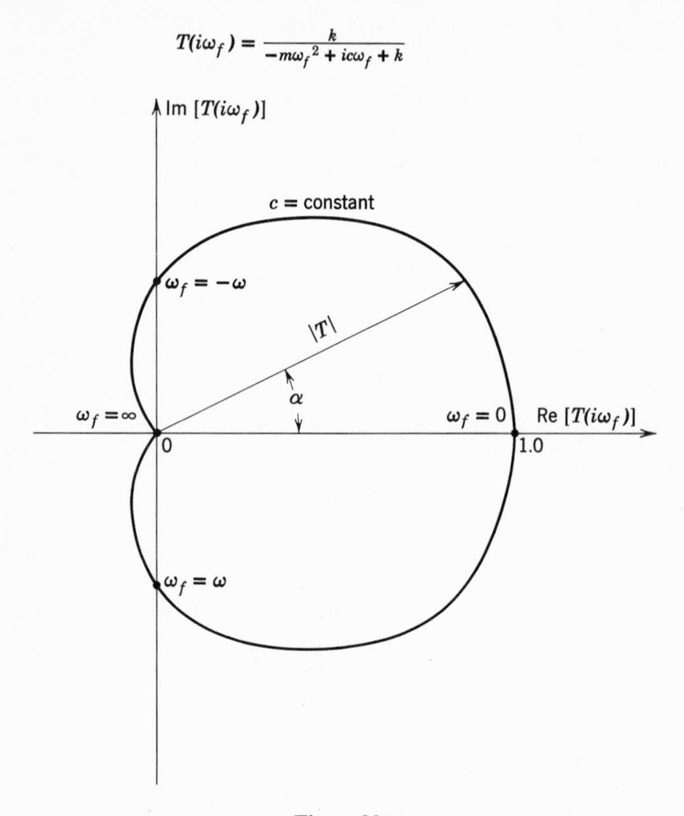

Figure 23a

into the values in its restricted domain of definition. The utility of the function $T(s)$, called the *transfer function*, is connected with the theory of Laplace transformation, a powerful tool in analyzing linear systems, which, unfortunately, cannot be discussed at length here. It is mentioned only to introduce the reader into a casual but logical acquaintance with a

[41] Without entering into the theory of analytical continuation of analytic functions, this is the best we can do to describe this process. The statement is intended merely to convey some rough idea of a process which is not of primary concern to us here.

subject that, it is hoped, he will study more intensively elsewhere. This remark applies also to the rest of the discussion under this heading.

To represent the function $T(i\omega_f)$ graphically, we have been plotting its absolute value (or the gain) and its argument (or the phase lag) as functions of ω_f. This method results in two curves. There is another method of

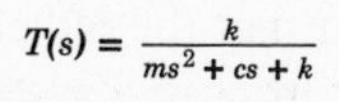

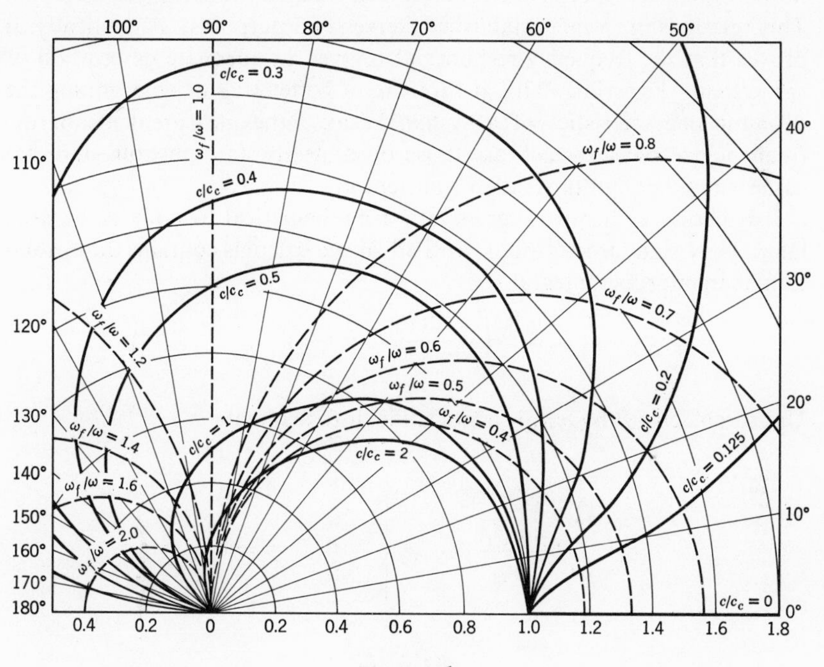

Figure 23*b*

graphical representation which cross-plots the two to give a locus of T in Argand's diagram with ω_f as a parameter. Such a plot is called the *Nyquist diagram* or *Nyquist locus*. The Nyquist locus, representing the frequency response of a simple mass-spring-damper system, is shown in Fig. 23*a*. Figure 23*b* assembles a number of such loci with different values of c/c_c. Consider $T(s)$ as a function of a complex variable s, the Nyquist locus is then the "map" of the imaginary axis of the s-plane on the T-plane.

The generic term *transfer locus* is used to include the Nyquist locus, T, the *inverse Nyquist locus* $1/T$, and the *over-all transfer locus* $T/(1 + T)$. All are useful tools in the analysis and design of linear control systems.

(D) RELATION BETWEEN THE INDICIAL RESPONSE AND THE FREQUENCY RESPONSE OF A LINEAR SYSTEM

We have seen that both the indicial response function and the transfer function can be derived from the differential equation describing the system. We have also shown that the indicial response by itself describes adequately the dynamic properties of a system. We now proceed to show how the indicial response function is directly related to the transfer function. This relationship, when established, serves two purposes. Analytically, it proves that the frequency response also gives an adequate description of the system. Experimentally, it furnishes a better way of determining the dynamic characteristics of a system because the measurements of the frequency response, which are those on a steady-state phenomenon, are easier to make than those on a transient one.

It is necessary here to digress into a mathematical formula to be used later. Any standard textbook[42] on advanced calculus contains the evaluation of an improper integral

$$\int_0^\infty \frac{\sin \theta}{\theta}\, d\theta = \frac{\pi}{2}$$

Upon replacing θ by $\omega_f t$, it is not difficult to see that

$$\int_0^\infty \frac{\sin \omega_f t}{\omega_f}\, d\omega_f = \begin{cases} \dfrac{\pi}{2} & t > 0 \\ 0 & t = 0 \\ \dfrac{-\pi}{2} & t < 0 \end{cases}$$

The step function $\mathcal{J}(t)$ can then be expressed in terms of this improper integral as

$$\mathcal{J}(t) = \frac{1}{2} + \frac{1}{\pi}\int_0^\infty \frac{\sin \omega_f t}{\omega_f}\, d\omega_f \qquad (83)^{43}$$

---

[42] See, for instance, Sokolnikoff, *Advanced Calculus*, McGraw-Hill, New York, 1939, pp. 361, 362.

[43] Strictly speaking, this equation is not valid at one point, viz., $t = 0$, when the left-hand side is defined as 1 and the right-hand side is $\frac{1}{2}$. This difference is, however, of no consequence here.

The indicial response $u(t)$ to a linear system represented by the differential operator L can thus be considered as the solution to the equation

$$\mathsf{L}(x) = \frac{1}{2} + \frac{1}{\pi}\int_0^\infty \frac{\sin \omega_f t}{\omega_f}\, d\omega_f \tag{84}$$

It must be pointed out that replacing (62) by (84) really involves a change in physical considerations as well as in the mathematical description of the problem. The step function $\Gamma(t)$ was previously chosen to characterize a nonperiodic excitation. Although the function value was also defined for $t < 0$, its definition for negative values of t is not essential because our analysis covers only the time period beginning at $t = 0$ when $u(0) = u'(0) = \ldots = u^{(n-1)}(0) = 0$. On the other hand, physical reasoning clearly shows that if we extend the time axis of analysis backward to $t = -\infty$ the fact that $\Gamma(t) = 0$ for all negative t's means that the system has been completely free from excitation since time immemorial and consequently it must be in a completely quiescent state at $t = 0$.[44] Therefore, by utilizing the definition of a unit step function for negative values of t, we have altered our consideration of the indicial response from that due to a nonperiodic excitation to that due to a periodic excitation of infinite period, which, according to (83), is the sum of sinusoidal functions of all frequencies. Each frequency contributes an amount equal to $d\omega_f/\pi\omega_f$, and the contribution of zero frequency is the constant $\frac{1}{2}$.

Let the transfer function associated with the differential operator L be $T(s)$ and the real and imaginary parts of the frequency response function $T(i\omega_f)$ be R and I, respectively,

$$T(i\omega_f) = R(\omega_f) + iI(\omega_f)$$

Equation (82) can then be written as

$$\lambda_r e^{i\omega_f t} = [R(\omega_f) + iI(\omega_f)]\lambda_s e^{i\omega_f t}$$

Let $\lambda_s = 1$, $\lambda_s e^{i\omega_f t} = \cos \omega_f t + i \sin \omega_f t$.

$$\operatorname{Re}(\lambda_r e^{i\omega_f t}) = R(\omega_f)\cos \omega_f t - I(\omega_f)\sin \omega_f t$$

$$\operatorname{Im}(\lambda_r e^{i\omega_f t}) = R(\omega_f)\sin \omega_f t + I(\omega_f)\cos \omega_f t$$

According to the discussion in Art. 1.7, the right-hand sides of the last two equations are the responses to signals equal to $\cos \omega_f t$ and sin

[44] In essence, we are assuming that the system is stable and has energy dissipation mechanism.

$\omega_f t$, respectively. Hence we have the following signal-to-response relationship:

SIGNAL OR EXCITATION	RESPONSE
$\frac{1}{2} = \frac{1}{2}\cos 0t$	$\frac{1}{2}[R(0) \times \cos 0t] = \frac{1}{2}R(0)$
$\sin \omega_f t$	$R(\omega_f)\sin \omega_f t + I(\omega_f)\cos \omega_f t$
$\_\!\!\Gamma(t)$	$u(t)$

The solution to (84) can thus be obtained through superposition:

$$u(t) = \tfrac{1}{2}R(0) + \frac{1}{\pi}\int_0^\infty [R(\omega_f)\sin \omega_f t + I(\omega_f)\cos \omega_f t]\,\frac{d\omega_f}{\omega_f} \tag{85}$$

If the resulting improper integral converges uniformly with respect to t, we may differentiate (85) with respect to t to obtain

$$u'(t) = \frac{1}{\pi}\int_0^\infty [R(\omega_f)\cos \omega_f t - I(\omega_f)\sin \omega_f t]\,d\omega_f \tag{86}$$

Before we proceed, it must be realized that the operations leading to (85) and (86) are strictly formal; that is to say, there is a number of mathematical questions that must be settled before we can accept the results as legitimate. The subject belongs to the theory of Fourier transforms, which is not within the scope of this book. We can, however, deal with the more essential points here.

Let us introduce the symbol L^{-1} to denote the operation that yields the particular integral of a linear differential equation:

$$\mathsf{L}(x) = F(t)$$

$$x = \mathsf{L}^{-1}F(t)$$

This inverse operation can be carried out by a number of methods, including such procedures as Lagrange's variation of parameters. We do not have to be concerned with the exact method used, except that essentially it involves integration processes. The solution to (84) should be of the form

$$u(t) = \mathsf{L}^{-1}\left(\frac{1}{2}\right) + \frac{1}{\pi}\mathsf{L}^{-1}\int_0^\infty \frac{\sin \omega_f t}{\omega_f}\,d\omega_f$$

whereas (85) is in reality

$$u(t) = \mathsf{L}^{-1}\left(\frac{1}{2}\right) + \frac{1}{\pi}\int_0^\infty \mathsf{L}^{-1}\left(\frac{\sin \omega_f t}{\omega_f}\right)d\omega_f$$

Since L^{-1} involves integration with respect to t, the validity of (85) depends upon whether the order of the two integration processes can be reversed.

For the integral in question the sufficient condition for the legitimacy of order reversal is that the integral should be uniformly convergent for any finite ranges of t, $-\infty < a \leq t \leq b < \infty$. Upon examining the integrand, we see that uniform convergence is assured if $I(\omega_f)/\omega_f$ has a finite limit at $\omega_f = 0$, $I(\omega_f)$ approaches 0 at $\omega_f = \infty$, and the absolute value of $T(i\omega_f)$ is always finite. The first two conditions are satisfied when $I(\omega_f)$ is the imaginary part of a transfer function. (See Exercise 1.34.) The last condition is satisfied when the system is damped and has no resonance condition.

However, with more sophisticated mathematical tools, (85) and (86) can be derived without the requirements that $T(i\omega_f)$ be bounded and that the integrals converge uniformly. Instead, these integrals are interpreted as the limits of a sequence of convergent integrals containing a parameter α as α approaches 0. Physically, the procedure is equivalent to introducing an extra damping force so that the resonance condition cannot take place and then letting this force approach zero in the solutions obtained. If the limiting integral converges to a so-called Cauchy's principal value, the result is then valid.

Returning now to (85) and (86), we observe that $u(t)$ and $u'(t)$ should be identically zero for $t < 0$. Hence, if t is a positive number

$$0 = u(-t) = \frac{1}{2} R(0) + \frac{1}{\pi}\int_0^\infty [-R(\omega_f)\sin\omega_f t + I(\omega_f)\cos\omega_f t]\frac{d\omega_f}{\omega_f}$$

Combining this equation with (85), by addition and by subtraction we have

$$u(t) = R(0) + \frac{2}{\pi}\int_0^\infty I(\omega_f)\cos\omega_f t\,\frac{d\omega_f}{\omega_f} \qquad (t > 0)$$

or

$$u(t) = \frac{2}{\pi}\int_0^\infty \left(R(\omega_f)\sin\omega_f t\,\frac{d\omega_f}{\omega_f}\right) \qquad (t > 0) \tag{87}$$

Similarly, $u'(-t) = 0$, if t is a positive number.

$$0 = \frac{1}{\pi}\int_0^\infty [R(\omega_f)\cos\omega_f t + I(\omega_f)\sin\omega_f t]\,d\omega_f \qquad (t > 0)$$

Together with (86), this relation gives

$$\begin{aligned} u'(t) &= \frac{2}{\pi}\int_0^\infty R(\omega_f)\cos\omega_f t\,d\omega_f \\ &= -\frac{2}{\pi}\int_0^\infty I(\omega_f)\sin\omega_f t\,d\omega_f \qquad (t > 0) \end{aligned} \tag{88}$$

The expressions (87) and (88) are *valid only for* $t > 0$. When the transfer functions are determined from the frequency response measured experimentally, the integrals in these expressions can be evaluated by a numerical procedure or by mechanical integrating devices.[45] When the transfer function is known analytically, these integrals cannot be conveniently evaluated as they stand. It is usually necessary to carry out the integration process in the complex plane by the following transformation.

First, let us write (86), which is valid for all t, as

$$u'(t) = \frac{1}{\pi}\int_0^\infty \mathrm{Re}\,[T(i\omega_f)e^{i\omega_f t}]\,d\omega_f \tag{89}$$

Now consider the function

$$T(i\omega_f)e^{i\omega_f t} = T(i\omega_f)\left(1 + i\omega_f t + \frac{(i\omega_f)^2}{2!}t^2 + \frac{(i\omega_f)^3}{3!}t^3 \cdots\right) \tag{90}$$

in which $T(i\omega_f)$ contains only real constants, except for the argument $i\omega_f$ itself. Since i and ω_f enter together as a product in this function, its real part is an even function of ω_f and its imaginary part is an odd function of ω_f. Hence

$$\int_0^\infty \mathrm{Re}\,[T(i\omega_f)e^{i\omega_f t}]\,d\omega_f = \int_{-\infty}^0 \mathrm{Re}\,[T(i\omega_f)e^{i\omega_f t}]\,d\omega_f \tag{91}$$

and

$$\int_0^\infty \mathrm{Im}\,[T(i\omega_f)e^{i\omega_f t}]\,d\omega_f = -\int_{-\infty}^0 \mathrm{Im}\,[T(i\omega_f)e^{i\omega_f t}]\,d\omega_f \tag{92}$$

We can then write (89) as

$$\begin{aligned} u'(t) &= \frac{1}{\pi}\int_0^\infty \mathrm{Re}\,[T(i\omega_f)e^{i\omega_f t}]\,d\omega_f \\ &= \frac{1}{2\pi}\int_{-\infty}^\infty \mathrm{Re}\,[T(i\omega_f)e^{i\omega_f t}]\,d\omega_f \\ &= \frac{1}{2\pi}\int_{-\infty}^\infty [T(i\omega_f)e^{i\omega_f t}]\,d\omega_f \end{aligned} \tag{93}$$

The sign "Re" was dropped in the last integral, since its imaginary part will vanish because of (92). Replacing the dummy variable $i\omega_f$ in (93) by s puts the integration in the complex plane, and we have

$$u'(t) = \frac{1}{2\pi i}\int_{-i\infty}^{i\infty} T(s)e^{st}\,ds \tag{94}$$

[45] "Determination of Transient Response from Frequency Response," by A. Leonhard. *ASME Trans.* Vol. 76, 1954, p. 1215–1236. See also discussion of the paper by A. Tustin.

This is an important relationship in operational calculus. It states that the impulse response is the inverse Laplace transform of the transfer function, or that the Laplace transform of the impulse response is the transfer function. Ordinarily, the relationship is written

$$u'(t) = \frac{1}{2\pi i}\int_{c-i\infty}^{c+i\infty} T(s)e^{st}\,ds \tag{95}$$

The constant c allows a shift in the path of integration from the imaginary axis to another line parallel to the imaginary axis without changing the value of the integral.[46] Such shifts may facilitate the evaluation of the integral and avoid the mathematical difficulty when the system has resonance conditions and $T(i\omega_f)$ becomes infinite for certain values of $i\omega_f$. Similarly, (85) may be transformed to an integral in the complex plane as

$$u(t) = \frac{1}{2\pi i}\int_{c-i\infty}^{c+i\infty} T(s)\,\frac{e^{st}}{s}\,ds \tag{96}$$

This integral is associated with the name of Bromwich.

As a practical matter, let it be pointed out that there are extensive tables available which give the pairing of functions of t with functions of s through Laplace transformation or its inverse. These tables, together with the linear characteristics of the operation, make it unnecessary to carry out actual integration processes for the evaluation of these integrals.

The primary purpose of this discussion is to show that there is a direct connection between the steady-state response and the transient response. In the process of showing this connection, we have taken a peek into the subject of operational calculus, which is the most powerful tool for transient analyses of linear systems. This subject is, however, too large and important to be included in this book. Moreover, from the viewpoint of applications, elaborate analysis of transient phenomena is seldom made in connection with mechanical vibrations, as it is with control systems and instrumentations, which form courses of study by themselves.

In concluding this article let us make one more generalization. At the beginning we chose as a model a signal-to-response relationship governed by an equation of the type

$$\mathsf{L}(x_r) = x_s \tag{97}$$

in which L is a differential operator with constant coefficients. There is

---

[46] The theory of functions of a complex variable has precise things to say about how much of a shift is permissible.

nothing really to prevent us from dealing in exactly the same way with the equation

$$\mathsf{L}_1(x_r) = \mathsf{L}_2(x_s) \tag{98}$$

or with a set of n linear equations in the general form of

$$\sum_{j=1}^{n} \mathsf{L}_{ij}(x_j) = \mathsf{L}_i(x_s) \qquad i = 1, 2, \cdots, n$$

with one of the x's at the left-hand side chosen as the response. In other words, we have never restricted our reasoning to the case of single-degree-freedom systems. Consequently, with minor modifications, the results obtained can be applied immediately to systems with multiple degrees of freedom.

SECTION B. METHODS AND APPLICATIONS

1.12 Examples of Linear Vibratory Systems with a Single Degree of Freedom

It has been pointed out that the systems shown pictorially in Figs. 1 and 5 are merely models of a class of physical systems whose outward appearances may be quite different. In this article we give a few such examples.[47] For this purpose it is necessary that we set up only the differential equations governing the motions of these systems and show that they are of the form of (2) or (14). The solutions to these equations have already been studied.

(A) TORSIONAL VIBRATION OF A DISK ON AN ELASTIC SHAFT

Let an elastic shaft be fixed at one end and carry a disk of moment of inertia I at the other end, as shown in Fig. 24. Assume that the mass of the shaft is negligible. The configuration of the system can then be described by the angle of twist θ. Because the shaft is elastic the torque exerted by the shaft on the disk must be proportional but opposite in direction to the angle θ. Hence

$$I\ddot{\theta} = -k\theta \qquad \text{or} \qquad I\ddot{\theta} + k\theta = 0$$

where k is the torsional stiffness of the shaft.

(B) OSCILLATION OF A LIQUID IN A U-TUBE OF UNIFORM INSIDE DIAMETER

Let the U-tube shown in Fig. 25 be in a vertical plane and filled partially with an incompressible liquid. The liquid levels at the two sides of the

[47] For other examples see Arts. 1.15 and 1.16.

tube may be set into an oscillation by momentarily applying a pressure to one side of the tube and then releasing the pressure. Let $2x$ be the difference in the levels of the two sides. The potential energy of the system is equal to that of elevating a liquid column of length x to a height x. Hence

$$V = \rho g A x^2$$

in which ρ is the density of the liquid and A is the cross-sectional area of the tube. The kinetic energy of the system can be seen to be

$$T = \tfrac{1}{2}\rho A L \dot{x}^2$$

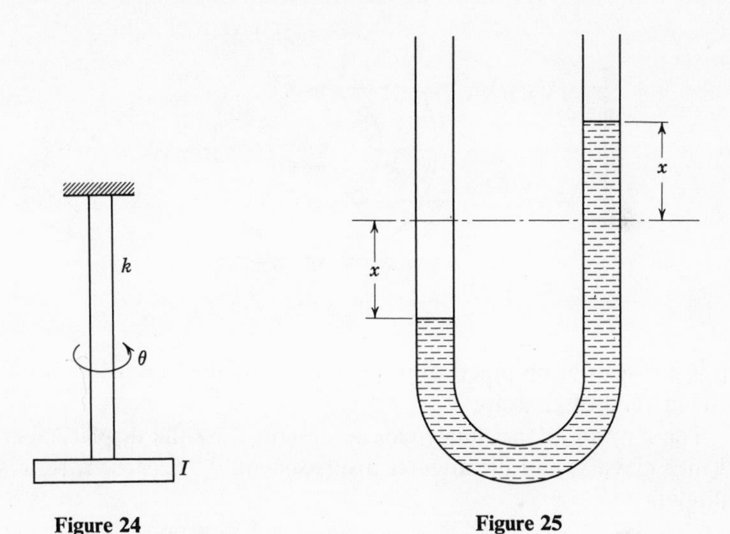

Figure 24 Figure 25

in which L is the total length of the filled tube. If the viscous and capillary forces are neglected, we have

$$\frac{d}{dt}(T + V) = 0 \qquad \text{or} \qquad L\ddot{x} + 2gx = 0$$

If the viscosity has to be taken into account and a laminar flow can be assumed, the viscous force per unit length can be obtained from the well-known Hagen-Poiseuille law as

$$\frac{dF}{dL} = \frac{8\mu\dot{x}}{r^2}$$

in which μ is the dynamic viscosity of the liquid and r is the inside radius of the tube. The differential equation is then

$$\rho A L\ddot{x} + \frac{8L\mu\dot{x}}{r^2} + 2\rho g A x = 0$$

or

$$\ddot{x} + \frac{8\nu}{\pi r^4}\dot{x} + \frac{2g}{L}x = 0$$

in which ν is the kinematic viscosity.

(C) A SYSTEM WITH A MORE COMPLICATED MECHANICAL ARRANGEMENT

The system shown in Fig. 26 consists of two springs and a damper attached to a step pulley that rolls without slipping on a rough surface.

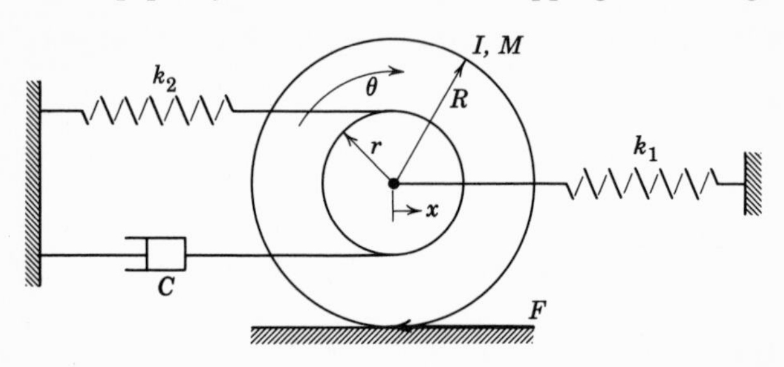

Figure 26

It is a system of no practical utility and is conjured up merely to illustrate our method of analysis.

The motion of the pulley can be described by the displacement of the center mass, x, and the angular displacement, θ. Because it rolls without slipping

$$R d\theta = dx \qquad R\theta = x + \text{constant}$$

in which the integration constant is zero if both θ and x are taken to be zero at the equilibrium configuration of the system. The system has therefore only a single degree of freedom, and either θ or x can be chosen as the coordinate variable of the system.

Let M be the mass of the pulley, I, its moment of inertia about the center of mass, and F, the frictional force at the contact. The two momentum equations, linear and angular, are

$$M\ddot{x} = -k_1 x - k_2(x + r\theta) - C(\dot{x} - r\dot{\theta}) - F$$

$$I\ddot{\theta} = FR + C(\dot{x} - r\dot{\theta})r - k_2(x + r\theta)r$$

Upon substituting x by $R\theta$ and eliminating F from the foregoing equations, we have

$$(MR^2 + I)\ddot{\theta} + C(R - r)^2\dot{\theta} + [k_1R^2 + k_2(R + r)^2]\theta = 0$$

or, if we prefer,

$$(MR^2 + I)\ddot{x} + C(R - r)^2\dot{x} + [k_1R^2 + k_2(R + r)^2]x = 0$$

They are in the standard form of

$$m\ddot{x} + c\dot{x} + kx = 0$$

Let us now analyze the problem by energy considerations, which leads to the observation that

$$\frac{d}{dt}(T + V) + P = 0$$

in which P = power dissipated in damping. For this system

$$T = \tfrac{1}{2}M\dot{x}^2 + \tfrac{1}{2}I\dot{\theta}^2 = \tfrac{1}{2}(MR^2 + I)\dot{\theta}^2$$

$$V = \tfrac{1}{2}k_1x^2 + \tfrac{1}{2}k_2(x + r\theta)^2$$

$$= \tfrac{1}{2}[k_1R^2 + k_2(R + r)^2]\theta^2$$

$$P = C(R - r)^2\dot{\theta}^2$$

Hence

$$(MR^2 + I)\dot{\theta}\ddot{\theta} + C(R - r)^2\dot{\theta}^2 + [k_1R^2 + k_2(R + r)^2]\theta\dot{\theta} = 0$$

Since $\dot{\theta} \not\equiv 0$, it can be canceled out and the same equation is obtained.

1.13 Linearization of Systems in Small Oscillations

Very few physical systems are strictly linear. On the other hand, a large number of them can be so considered if they are in motions representing only small changes from their equilibrium configurations. A general discussion on this subject is taken up in Art. 3.2. At present we shall study a few examples.

(A) SIMPLE AND COMPOUND GRAVITY PENDULUMS

It is well known that the motion of a simple pendulum (Fig. 27*a*) is described by the equation

$$L\ddot{\theta} + g \sin \theta = 0$$

in which L is the length of the pendulum, θ is the angular displacement of the pendulum from the vertical, and g is the gravitational acceleration. Obviously, this differential equation is not linear. Its solution is in the form of an elliptical integral. On the other hand, if the swing of the pendulum is limited to small angles, then $\sin \theta \doteq \theta$, and the equation may be approximated by

$$\ddot{\theta} + \frac{g}{L}\theta = 0$$

Hence the period T of the pendulum is approximately

$$T = \frac{2\pi}{\omega} = 2\pi\sqrt{L/g}$$

The period of a compound pendulum (Fig. 27*b*), having a mass M, a radius of gyration about its center of mass r, and a point of suspension at a distance d from its center of mass, can be found most conveniently by Rayleigh's method if its angular displacement is small. Let θ_m be the amplitude of the swing, which is the maximum angular displacement, and $\dot{\theta}_m$ be the maximum angular velocity, which takes place at $\theta = 0$. The

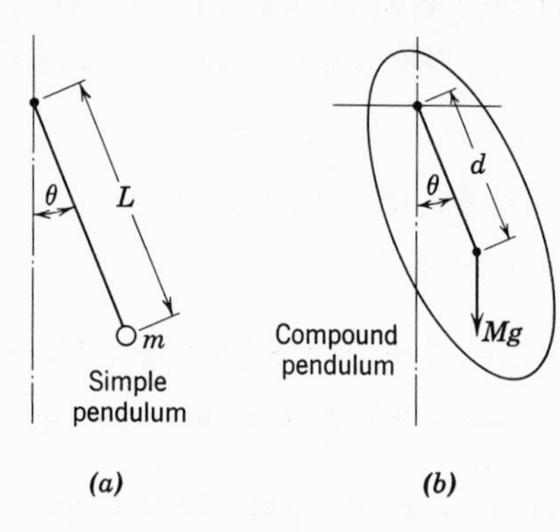

Figure 27

maximum kinetic energy and the maximum potential energy of the system are then

$$T_{\max} = \tfrac{1}{2}M(r^2 + d^2)\dot{\theta}_m^{\,2}$$
$$V_{\max} = Mgd(1 - \cos\theta_m)$$

For small θ_m, $1 - \cos\theta_m \doteq \frac{1}{2}\theta_m^{\,2}$; the system is approximately linear and its motion, approximately simple harmonic. Hence

$$\dot{\theta}_m^{\,2} = \omega^2\theta_m^{\,2}$$

Upon equating the two energy expressions, we have

$$\omega^2 = \frac{gd}{r^2 + d^2} \qquad \text{and} \qquad T = 2\pi\sqrt{\frac{r^2 + d^2}{gd}}$$

(B) A SPRING-LOADED PENDULUM

In Fig. 28 a tension spring is attached to an otherwise simple pendulum of length $2a$. One end of the spring is fastened to a point at a distance a above the suspension point of the pendulum. The other end is attached to the mid-point of the pendulum. The spring constant is k and its natural length is a. Let us assume that the pendulum is heavy and the spring is soft so that the equilibrium position of the pendulum is the vertical. In terms of angular displacement θ, the energy expressions are

$$T = \tfrac{1}{2}m(2a\dot{\theta})^2 = \tfrac{1}{2}(4ma^2\dot{\theta}^2)$$

$$V = 2mga(1 - \cos\theta) + \tfrac{1}{2}k(\Delta L)^2 + C$$

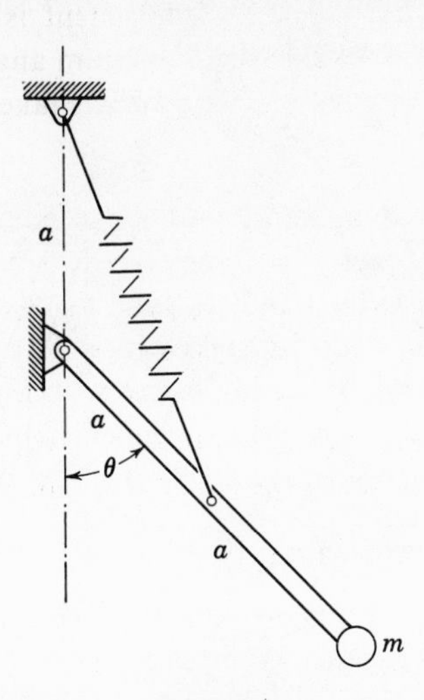

Figure 28

in which ΔL is the change in the length of the spring from its natural length and C is a constant that will make $V(0) = 0$.[48]

$$\Delta L = \sqrt{2a^2 + 2a^2\cos\theta} - a = a\left(2\cos\frac{\theta}{2} - 1\right)$$

At $\theta = 0$, $\Delta L = a$, hence $C = -ka^2/2$. By substitution and simplification, we have, finally,

$$V = 2mga(1 - \cos\theta) - 2ka^2\cos\frac{\theta}{2}\left(1 - \cos\frac{\theta}{2}\right)$$

Now, for small oscillations

$$1 - \cos\theta \doteq \frac{\theta^2}{2} \qquad \cos\frac{\theta}{2} \doteq 1 \qquad 1 - \cos\frac{\theta}{2} \doteq \frac{\theta^2}{8}$$

$$V = \tfrac{1}{2}(2mga - \tfrac{1}{2}ka^2)\theta^2$$

[48] Potential energy expressions are determined only to within an additive constant. In order to use Rayleigh's method, this constant must be such that V vanishes at equilibrium configuration.

Rayleigh's method then yields

$$\omega = \sqrt{\frac{2mga - ka^2/2}{4ma^2}} = \sqrt{\frac{g}{2a} - \frac{k}{8m}}$$

It is interesting to note that the spring in this system exerts an influence, as if it had a negative spring constant, because its potential energy is a maximum instead of a minimum at $\theta = 0$. In order for the system to be stable at $\theta = 0$, it is necessary that

$$2mga > \frac{ka^2}{2}$$

Otherwise ω becomes imaginary, and no oscillation around $\theta = 0$ is possible. As a matter of fact, $\theta = 0$ then would not be a stable equilibrium configuration. On the other hand, as long as this inequality holds, it is possible to obtain a very "soft" system with a very low natural frequency. This scheme of having two restoring forces working against each other to obtain the effect of a soft spring has practical applications, since a single soft spring is usually inconvenient to incorporate in a mechanism.

(c) A BETTER APPROXIMATION

The foregoing examples belong to a class of nonlinear systems whose differential equation of motion is of the type

$$m\ddot{x} + K(x) = 0$$

where $K(x)$ is an odd function that may be represented by

$$K(x) = kx + k'x^3 + R$$

The remainder R is of the order x^5. The corresponding expression for potential energy is then

$$V = \int K(x)\,dx = \frac{1}{2}kx^2 + \frac{k'}{4}x^4 + \int R\,dx$$

As a first approximation, let us take

$$K(x) \doteq kx \qquad \text{and} \qquad V(x) \doteq \tfrac{1}{2}kx^2$$

The frequency ω is then $\sqrt{k/m}$. To get a better approximation, we can take

$$K(x) \doteq kx + k'x^3$$

and

$$V(x) \doteq \tfrac{1}{2}kx^2 + \tfrac{1}{4}k'x^4$$

The first integral of this second-order differential equation is

$$V_m = T + V \qquad T = V_m - V$$

or

$$m\dot{x}^2 = k(x_m{}^2 - x^2) + \frac{1}{2}k'(x_m{}^4 - x^4) = k(x_m{}^2 - x^2)\left[1 + \frac{k'}{2k}(x_m{}^2 + x^2)\right]$$

From this we have

$$dt = \frac{dx}{\sqrt{k(x_m{}^2 - x^2)/m}}\left[1 + \frac{k'}{2k}(x_m{}^2 + x^2)\right]^{-\frac{1}{2}}$$

$$\doteq \frac{dx}{\sqrt{k(x_m{}^2 - x^2)/m}}\left[1 - \frac{k'}{4k}(x_m{}^2 + x^2)\right]$$

If this equation is integrated between the limits $x = 0$ and $x = x_m$, the left-hand side becomes the quarter period

$$\frac{T}{4} = \frac{\pi}{2\omega} - \frac{k'}{4\omega k}\int_0^{x_m} \frac{(x_m{}^2 + x^2)}{\sqrt{x_m{}^2 - x^2}}\, dx$$

$$= \frac{\pi}{2\omega}\left(1 - \frac{3k'}{8k}\, x_m{}^2\right)$$

in which $\omega = \sqrt{k/m}$ is the frequency in the first approximation. The relation

$$T = \frac{2\pi}{\omega}\left(1 - \frac{3k'}{8k}\, x_m{}^2\right)$$

can be considered as a second approximation. To check its accuracy, we take the case of a simple pendulum swinging a total angle of 60°.

$$x_m = \pi/6 \qquad k'/k = -\tfrac{1}{6} \qquad \omega = \sqrt{L/g}$$

$$T = \sqrt{(L/g)}2\pi\left(1 + \frac{\pi^2}{576}\right) = 6.391\sqrt{L/g}$$

The exact answer is

$$T = 4\sqrt{L/g}\int_0^{\pi/2} \frac{d\phi}{\sqrt{1 - \sin^2 15^\circ \sin^2 \phi}} = 6.392\sqrt{L/g}$$

For a 120° swing the formula is in error by 3 per cent.

1.14 Piecewise-Linear Systems

The type of system to be discussed in this article has vibratory motions that are governed by several linear differential equations, each of which is applicable only for a certain range of values of displacement or of velocity. Strictly speaking, such a system is not linear, since it has few of the important properties of linear systems. Its analysis is usually difficult. A few simple cases are introduced here to give us some feeling of such systems.

(A) A SYSTEM WITH AN UNSYMMETRICAL RESTORING FORCE

In Fig. 29 a mass m vibrates between two compression springs k_1 and k_2. The natural lengths of the springs are such that only one of the springs

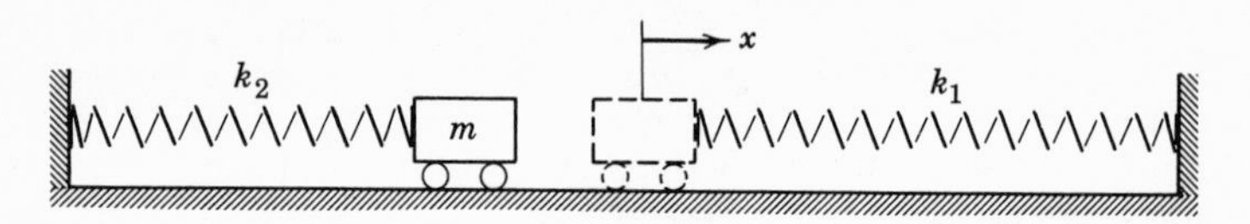

Figure 29

is under stress at any given time. The differential equations governing the motion of m are then

$$m\ddot{x} + k_1 x = 0 \qquad \text{for} \quad x \geq 0$$

and

$$m\ddot{x} + k_2 x = 0 \qquad \text{for} \quad x \leq 0$$

To solve these equations, let us assume $x = 0$ and $\dot{x} = \dot{x}_0 > 0$ at $t = 0$. For the time being, we shall look only for a solution that is valid for a certain time interval containing the instant $t = 0$. It is not difficult to see that

$$x(t) = C_1 \sin \omega_1 t \qquad \text{for} \quad 0 \leq t < t_1$$
$$x(t) = C_2 \sin \omega_2 t \qquad \text{for} \quad 0 \geq t > t_2$$

could be made to satisfy the equations of motion and the initial condition, at least for the certain time interval $t_2 < t < t_1$. Since $\dot{x}_0$ is positive, $\omega_1 = \sqrt{k_1/m}$ and $\omega_2 = \sqrt{k_2/m}$. Since velocity must be a continuous function of t, at $t = 0$,

$$\dot{x}_0 = \omega_1 C_1 = \omega_2 C_2$$

or

$$C_1 = \frac{\dot{x}_0}{\omega_1} \qquad C_2 = \frac{\dot{x}_0}{\omega_2}$$

The limits t_1 and t_2 are determined by the condition that $x(t)$ should not change its sign in $0 \leq t < t_1$, nor in $0 \geq t > t_2$. Hence

$$t_1 = \frac{\pi}{\omega_1} \qquad t_2 = -\frac{\pi}{\omega_2}$$

The solution is therefore

$$x(t) = \frac{\dot{x}_0}{\omega_1} \sin \omega_1 t \qquad \text{for} \quad 0 \le t \le \frac{\pi}{\omega_1}$$

$$x(t) = \frac{\dot{x}_0}{\omega_2} \sin \omega_2 t \qquad \text{for} \quad -\frac{\pi}{\omega_2} \le t \le 0$$

Obviously, the motion is periodic with period

$$T = t_1 - t_2 = \pi\left(\frac{1}{\omega_1} + \frac{1}{\omega_2}\right)$$

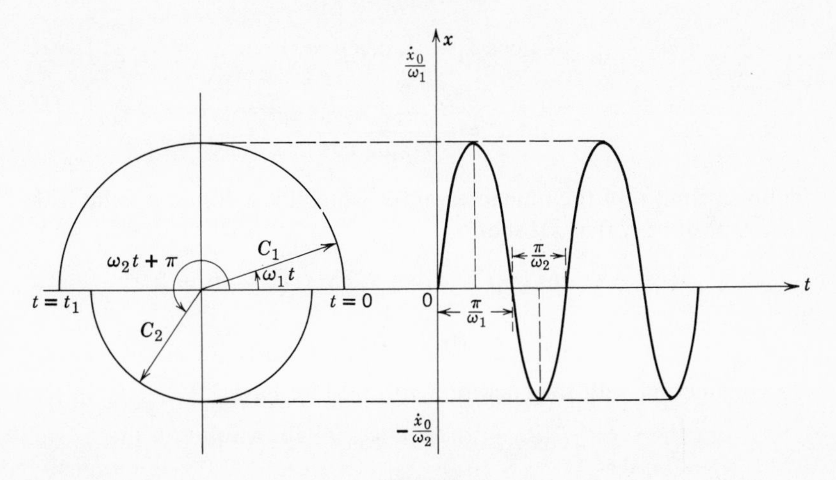

Figure 30

The solution outside the fundamental interval can be expressed as

$$x(t) = \frac{\dot{x}_0}{\omega_1} \sin \omega_1(t - nT)$$

if there is an integer n satisfying

$$0 \le \omega_1(t - nT) \le \pi$$

Otherwise

$$x(t) = \frac{\dot{x}_0}{\omega_2} \sin \omega_2(t - nT)$$

in which n is an integer satisfying

$$-\pi \le \omega_2(t - nT) \le 0$$

A graphical representation of the solution is shown in Fig. 30.

Although the solution for free vibrations of this nonlinear system is comparatively simple, that of forced vibration is algebraically complicated.

Suppose the system is subjected to a harmonic force $F_0 \cos(\omega_f t - \beta)$ and its initial condition is $x(0) = 0$, $\dot{x}(0) = \dot{x}_0 > 0$. The differential equation valid for a certain time interval $0 < t < t_1$ is

$$m\ddot{x} + k_1 x = F_0 \cos(\omega_f t - \beta)$$

The solution of this equation can be written as

$$x(t) = C_1 \cos(\omega_1 t - \alpha_1) + \lambda_1 \cos(\omega_f t - \beta)$$

where

$$\lambda_1 = \frac{F_0}{-m\omega_f^2 + k_1}$$

$$C_1 \cos\alpha_1 + \lambda_1 \cos\beta = 0$$

and

$$\tan\alpha_1 = \frac{\dot{x}_0 - \lambda_1 \omega_f \sin\beta}{-\lambda_1 \omega_1 \cos\beta}$$

The upper limit t_1 of the time interval for which the solution is valid is the smallest positive t_1 that satisfies

$$x(t_1) = C_1 \cos(\omega_1 t - \alpha_1) + \lambda_1 \cos(\omega_f t - \beta) = 0$$

and

$$\dot{x}(t_1) < 0$$

In conjunction with the condition $x(0) = 0$ we have

$$0 = \begin{vmatrix} \cos\alpha_1 & \cos\beta \\ \cos(\omega_1 t_1 - \alpha_1) & \cos(\omega_f t_1 - \beta) \end{vmatrix}$$

Solve for the smallest positive root of t_1 in this equation and obtain $\dot{x}_1 = \dot{x}(t_1)$. Use this as our new initial condition and repeat the process for

$$m\ddot{x} + k_2 x = F_0 \cos[\omega_f(t - t_1) - \beta]$$

with

$$x(t_1) = 0 \qquad \dot{x}(t_1) = \dot{x}_1 \qquad t_1 \le t \le t_2$$

This example shows that for a nonlinear system we cannot always speak of transients or steady states, even when this system is capable of free periodic motion and the applied force is a periodic force.

(B) A SPRING-MASS SYSTEM WITH COULOMB DAMPING

In *Coulomb damping* the damping force is constant in magnitude but always in a direction that resists motion. When there is no motion, its magnitude may assume any lower value that is enough to resist impending motion. Such damping force is an idealization of forces due to dry friction.

Suppose we have a simple spring-mass system subject to a Coulomb damping force of magnitude f, as shown in Fig. 31. Let x be the displacement of mass m from its equilibrium position in the absence of f. The vibration of this system is then governed by the following set of equations:

$$m\ddot{x} + kx = -f \qquad \text{for } \dot{x} > 0$$
$$m\ddot{x} + kx = f \qquad \text{for } \dot{x} < 0$$

Or more concisely,

$$m\ddot{x} + f\,\text{sgn}\,(\dot{x}) + kx = 0$$

The symbol "sgn" stands for "sign of." It denotes a function that takes

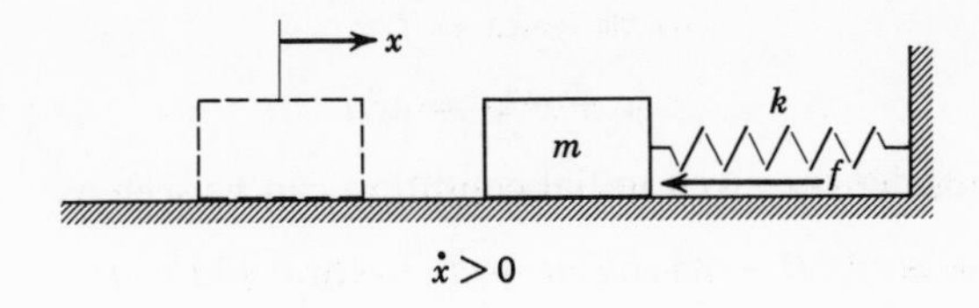

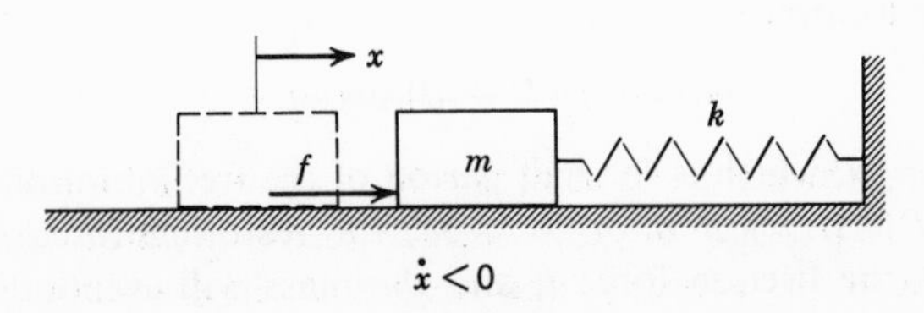

Figure 31

the value $+1$ or -1, according to whether the argument is positive or negative.[49] Hence

$$\text{sgn}\,(\theta) = \theta/|\theta|$$

It is also customary to define $\text{sgn}\,(0) = 0$, although in our case the friction force is undefined when $\dot{x} = 0$. The last way of writing the equation reveals more clearly the nonlinear nature of the system, but it is more convenient to deal with our original way of writing two equations in solving the problem.

Without the loss of generality, let us assume that the system is set into

[49] The second term of (83) is such a function. Also, the differential equation of motion for the system studied in (A) of this article can be written as

$$m\ddot{x} + \left(\frac{k_1 + k_2}{2} + \frac{k_1 - k_2}{2}\,\text{sgn}\,(x)\right)x = 0$$

vibration by giving the mass a positive displacement D and releasing it. The initial condition is then

$$x(0) = D \qquad \text{and} \qquad \dot{x}(0) = 0$$

Let us assume further that

$$D > \frac{f}{k} = d$$

The restoring force kD is thus greater than the friction force f, and in the initial stage the motion will have a negative velocity. The governing equation during a certain time interval $0 \leq t \leq t_1$ becomes

$$m\ddot{x} + kx = f$$

$$\ddot{x} + \omega^2 x = \omega^2 d$$

Its solution under the given initial condition can be seen as

$$x = (D - d)\cos \omega t + d \qquad \text{for } 0 \leq t \leq t_1$$

The vibration is therefore a simple harmonic motion about the point $x = d$, with amplitude $D - d$, and circular frequency ω. This solution is valid only as long as

$$\dot{x} = -\omega(D - d)\sin \omega t \leq 0$$

Hence $t_1 = \pi/\omega$, which is the half period of the free vibration. At $t = t_1$, $x_1 = 2d - D$. If $|x_1| > d$ or $D > 3d$, the restoring force kx_1 is again greater than the friction force f, and the mass will eventually acquire a positive velocity. The subsequent motion is governed by

$$m\ddot{x} + kx = -f$$

$$\ddot{x} + \omega^2 x = -\omega^2 d$$

together with the condition

$$x(t_1) = D - 2d \qquad \text{and } \dot{x}(t_1) = 0$$

For the time interval $t_1 \leq t \leq t_2$ the solution becomes

$$x = (D - 3d)\cos \omega t - d$$

in which $t_2 = 2\pi/\omega$.

Repeating this procedure, we perceive that the motion can be described by patching together simple harmonic motions all having the same frequency ω, which is the natural frequency of the spring-mass system. Each of these motions lasts only for half a cycle during which the velocity does not change sign. After each half cycle the amplitude decreases by an amount equal to $2d = 2f/k$, and the mid-point of the cycle shifts from

$x = d$ to $x = -d$, or vice versa. The motion stops at the end of a half cycle whose amplitude is less than $2d$. A graphical representation of the motion is shown in Fig. 32.

The forced vibration of a system with Coulomb damping is difficult to analyze. An exact analysis by J. P. Den Hartog is too elaborate to be given here. We present instead the following approximate analysis. First, let us observe that if the Coulomb damping force is only of moderate

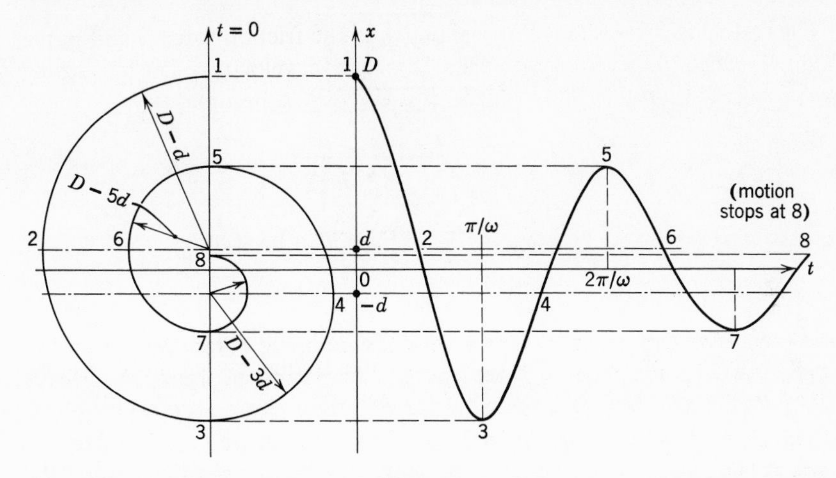

Figure 32

magnitude a harmonic force acting on the system will produce, approximately, a harmonic motion. In other words, we expect motions due to spurious disturbances to die out quickly through the various dissipation mechanisms inherent in any real physical system, whereas a more or less periodic motion will persist through the action of the harmonic force applied. For a small Coulomb damping force this periodic motion can be approximated by a sinusoidal motion. Let the resulting motion be represented by

$$x(t) = |\lambda| \cos (\omega_f t - \alpha)$$

The energy dissipation through Coulomb damping per cycle is evidently $4f|\lambda|$. On the other hand, the energy dissipation per cycle for viscous damping is $\pi c|\lambda|^2\omega_f$, according to (57). Hence we may obtain the equivalent viscous damping coefficient by

$$4f|\lambda| = \pi c|\lambda|^2\omega_f$$

or

$$c = \frac{4f}{\pi|\lambda|\omega_f}$$

Substituting this equivalent damping factor into (41) or (47), we have

$$|\lambda| = \frac{F_0}{\sqrt{(-m\omega_f^2 + k)^2 + \left(\dfrac{4f}{\pi\lambda}\right)^2}}$$

Solving this equation for $|\lambda|$, we have

$$|\lambda| = \frac{\sqrt{F_0^2 - \left(\dfrac{4f}{\pi}\right)^2}}{-m\omega_f^2 + k^2}$$

or

$$\frac{|\lambda|}{\delta_{st}} = \frac{\sqrt{1 - \left(\dfrac{4}{\pi}\dfrac{f}{F_0}\right)^2}}{1 - \left(\dfrac{\omega_f}{\omega_m}\right)^2}$$

In examining this equation we find that the damping parameter is now the ratio between the friction force and the amplitude of the applied force f/F_0. When this ratio reaches the value $\pi/4$, the equation can no longer be used, since it yields imaginary values. Within the range of f/F_0 values for which the equation can be used the amplitude tends to infinity when the frequency of the applied force approaches the natural frequency of the system. The existence of a limiting value of f/F_0 for the validity of the analysis and the occurrence of an infinitely large amplitude in a system with energy dissipation mechanism can be explained as follows. According to (56), the work done per cycle by the external force is $\pi F_0|\lambda| \sin \alpha$ and the work dissipated by friction force is $4f|\lambda|$. Since both are proportional to $|\lambda|$, the system can achieve an energy balance only by adapting its motion to a proper phase lag α.[50]

$$\sin \alpha = \frac{4f}{\pi F_0}$$

If the friction f is so large that $\sin \alpha$ has to be greater than unity, a sinusoidal response is completely out of the question, even as an approximation. Experiments and exact analysis show that for large values of f the response motion has "stops"; that is, during a cycle the mass will come

[50] Here we are accepting a metaphysical principle, which is borne out in a number of physical laws. This principle in essence says that nature is clever but lazy. Within the freedom allowed her, she always finds the way in which she can exert herself the least in reacting to changes imposed on her.

to a complete stop or stops before moving further. Such motions are qualitatively described in Fig. 33. The phase angle α defined by

$$\alpha = \sin^{-1} \frac{4f}{\pi F_0}$$

is multiple-valued. Let the principal values of the foregoing equation be α_1 and α_2 with

$$\alpha_2 > \alpha_1 \qquad \text{and} \qquad \alpha_1 + \alpha_2 = \pi$$

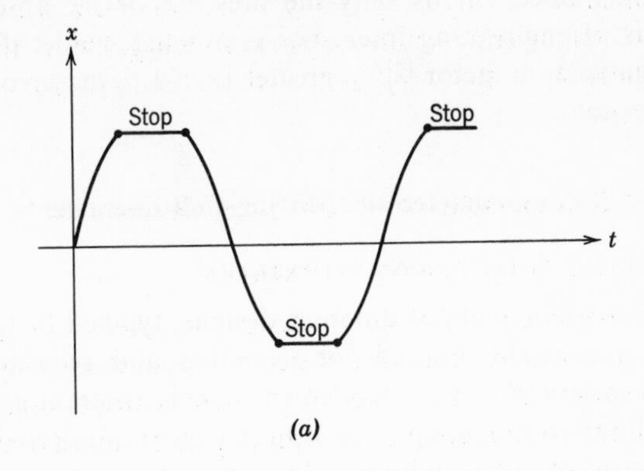

(a)

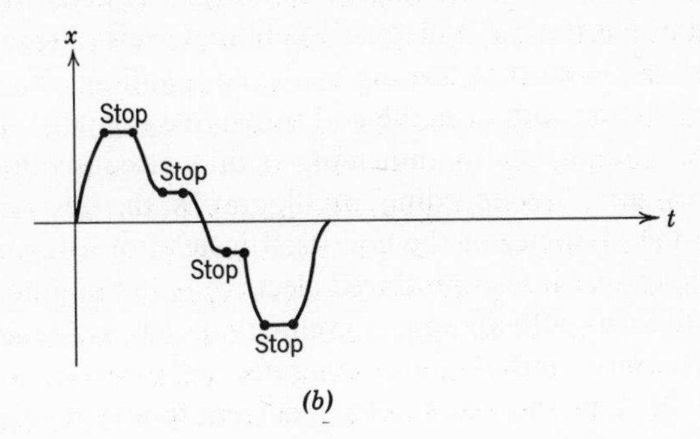

(b)

Figure 33

Analogous to the forced vibration of an undamped system, there is a sudden jump of the phase angle from α_1 to α_2 as the frequency of the force passes through the natural frequency of the system. This jump discontinuity exists even in the exact solution, although there the phase angle also varies with frequency ratio elsewhere. In a real physical system the value of α must change rapidly, and near resonance condition it assumes a value between α_1 and α_2, say α', Since

$$\sin \alpha' > \sin \alpha_1 = \sin \alpha_2$$

the energy input is larger than that which can be dissipated through Coulomb damping, and the amplitude grows excessively.

The accuracy of this approximate analysis depends upon both the friction ratio f/F_0 and the frequency ratio. Generally speaking, the accuracy is good when the amplitude is large. This makes the analysis of practical value, since usually only the presence or the absence of large amplitudes is of engineering interest. As a rough guide, if the analysis yields a magnification factor $|\lambda|/\delta_{st}$ greater than 1.5, the error involved is only a few per cent.

1.15 Theory of Galvanometer and Moving-Coil Instruments

(A) DIFFERENTIAL EQUATION OF OPERATION

Moving-coil instruments of different designs, typified by a D'Arsonval galvanometer, are widely used for detecting and recording electrical signals from a variety of sensing elements, such as strain gages, thermocouples, and vibration pickups. To a high degree of approximation such instruments behave like ideal linear vibratory systems having one degree of freedom.

Basically a D'Arsonval galvanometer movement consists of a moving coil of moment of inertia J, a magnetic field that exerts a torque on the coil proportional to the current flowing in the coil, and an elastic spring that produces a restoring torque as the coil turns (See Fig. 80). The motion of the coil may be damped by immersing it in a viscous oil. In the more delicate types used in recording oscillographs the restoring torque is provided by the elasticity of the coil itself instead of a separate spring.

A damping torque is also produced electrically in the following manner. When the coil turns with an angular velocity, it acts as the armature of an electrical generator and thereby generates a back electromotive force (emf for short). This emf causes a back current to flow if the galvanometer circuit is closed, and this back current produces a torque opposite but proportional to the angular velocity in the same way as a viscous damping torque. Since the back current is inversely proportional to the total resistance in the galvanometer circuit, so is the equivalent damping constant. If the circuit is open, the total resistance in the circuit is infinite, and the oscillation of the coil is therefore not damped electrically. [See also Art. 3.14(B).]

The differential equation of motion of a D'Arsonval galvanometer without viscous damping is therefore

$$J\ddot{\theta} + \frac{BC}{R + R_g}\dot{\theta} + k\theta = \frac{Ce(t)}{R + R_g} \tag{i}$$

θ = deflection angle
J = moment of inertia of the coil
k = spring constant of the meter movement
C = deflecting torque per unit current
$e(t)$ = emf generated by the sensing device
R_g = resistance of the galvanometer coil
R = resistance external to the galvanometer
B = back emf per unit deflection velocity[51]

In practice, it is neither convenient nor necessary to describe the characteristics of a galvanometer by so many constants. The following four quantities are usually given in the specifications:

S = galvanometer constant or sensitivity which is the galvanometer deflection per unit current when both are steady
ω = natural undamped (circular) frequency
R_c = critical damping resistance, that is, external resistance required to produce critical damping
R_g = resistance of the galvanometer coil

The relationships between these two sets of constants are

$$S = \frac{c}{k} \qquad \omega^2 = \frac{k}{J}$$

$$\frac{BC}{R_c + R_g} = c_c = 2\sqrt{Jk} \tag{ii}$$

By dividing the original equation by k and utilizing the foregoing relationships, we have

$$\frac{1}{\omega^2}\ddot{\theta} + \frac{2}{\omega}\left(\frac{R_c + R_g}{R + R_g}\right)\dot{\theta} + \theta = \frac{S}{R + R_g}e(t) \tag{iii}$$

Having written the equation in this form, we realize that the units of measurement of θ can be arbitrary as long as the same unit is used in defining S. For a given set-up of instrumentation we can also lump together $S/(R + R_g)$ as the deflection per unit signal strength and consider e as the signal strength.

[51] The constants B and C are equal. This fact is shown in Art. 3.14, but it is of no consequence here.

(B) FREQUENCY RESPONSE AND OPTIMUM DAMPING

In an ideal instrument the response $\theta(t)$ should be proportional to the signal $e(t)$. In an examination of the differential equation (iii) it is seen that such idealized characteristics can be approached if ω is high enough so that the first two terms in the equation are small. This means that the undamped oscillation of the galvanometer must be relatively fast in comparison with the rate of signal change, or

$$|e| \gg |\dot{e}/\omega| \qquad |e| \gg |\ddot{e}/\omega^2|$$

However, in practice, this desirable condition is not easy to achieve without sacrificing the sensitivity of the meter. This is because a high value of ω implies a stiff spring or a light coil; a lighter coil means fewer turns, smaller coil loop, or finer wire, and finer wire results in higher R_g. Any of these conditions result in less deflection per unit signal strength.[52] Therefore, in choosing galvanometers for instrumentation a compromise has to be made between sensitivity and fidelity of response.

Although the inertia and elastic stiffness of the galvanometer movement cannot be arbitrarily varied because of constructional practicability, the amount of damping is relatively easy to adjust; and, by a proper adjustment of damping force, the performance of the instrument can be much enhanced. First, suppose the galvanometer is to record steady-state sinusoidal signals of different frequencies. Evidently, it is desirable for the amplitude of the response to be proportional to that of the signal, regardless of its frequency. In other words, in the ideal situation the magnification factor should be independent of the frequency ratio. Figure 16, however, shows that this is not exactly realizable in a simple spring-mass damper system. The most we can accomplish is an approximately constant amplitude of response for a limited frequency range. Such a condition exists for instruments with a moderate amount of damping at signal frequencies below the natural undamped frequency of the instruments. Figure 34 shows the magnified lower left portions of the curves in Fig. 16*a*. It is seen that some of the curves are reasonably "flat" within the frequency range shown. We noticed also that for high values of c/c_c the point (0, 1) is a maximum and for low values of c/c_c it is a minimum. As shown in Exercise 1.17, the transition takes place at $c/c_c = 1/\sqrt{2}$ when the point (0, 1) becomes a minimax, so that both the slope and the curvature are zero, and the curve has a broad plateau. This value of damping is

[52] A way of compensating the loss sensitivity in using a lighter coil and stiffer suspension is to increase the magnetic-field strength of the pole pieces. This usually results in bulkier instruments. Compactness is of importance in such instruments as oscillographs, which contain scores of galvanometers in a small enclosure.

then a theoretical optimum. In practice, a lower damping ratio is usually chosen because, by allowing the curve first to go up a little and then to come down, the usable frequency range is further extended, although it is not so flat at the beginning as the curve corresponding to the theoretical optimum damping of 0.707. For instance, with 65 per cent of critical

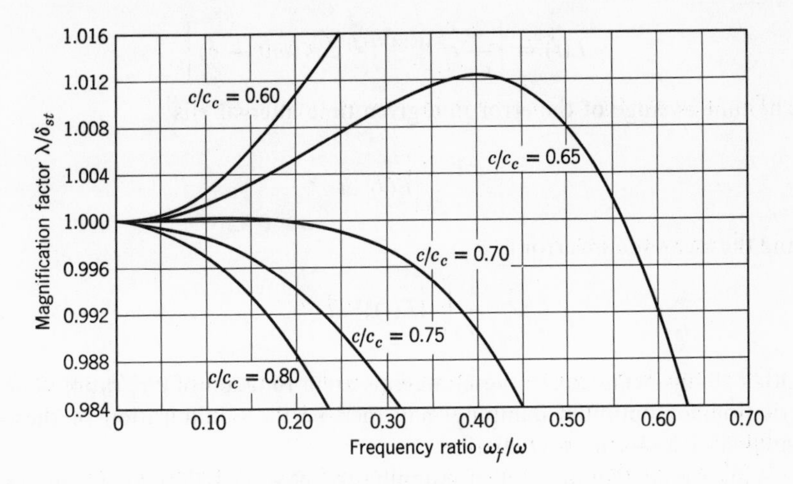

Figure 34

damping, the variation in frequency response for signal frequencies up to 60 per cent of the natural frequency of the instrument is within ± 1.3 per cent.

It must be emphasized that even within the frequency range, where the frequency response is relatively constant, the phase difference between the signal and the response varies appreciably. Hence, if the signal contains harmonics of different frequencies, their phase differences will not be preserved in the response. This results in a distortion of the waveform called a *phase shift*. This type of distortion may or may not be important in a given application of the instrument.

The criterion for optimum damping can also be based upon the response of the instrument to step signals. This is especially appropriate if the instrument is to record transient signals faithfully. Let S be the sensitivity of the instrument. The response of an ideal instrument to a step function $\mathcal{J}(t)$ is then $S\mathcal{J}(t)$, or simply S for $t > 0$.[53]

[53] We assume here that the signal is in the form of a current. If it should be a step voltage, replace S by $S/(R + R_g)$. In any event, by sensitivity or meter constant one means the response per unit signal strength when both are constant with respect to time.

The response of the actual instrument is $u(t)$, which is given by (69*b*) with $1/k$ replaced by S. We can then define the error $E(t)$ as

$$E(t) = 1 - \frac{u(t)}{S}$$

It can be verified that

$$E(t) = \left[\frac{\omega}{\omega_c} e^{-(\tan\delta)(\omega_c t)} \cos(\omega_c t - \delta)\right]$$

The time average of the error in a given time interval τ is

$$\frac{1}{\tau}\int_0^\tau |E(t)|\, dt$$

and the mean square error is

$$\frac{1}{\tau}\int_0^\tau \{E(t)\}^2\, dt$$

Other things being equal, these integrals are a function of c/c_c ratio. The criterion for optimum damping may then be the minimization of these integrals in a specific interval.

With a moderate amount of damping the error function $E(t)$ becomes quite small after t reaches a value equal to a few times the natural period of the instrument, so it is quite reasonable to optimize the amount of damping by minimizing either of the following two integrals:

$$\int_0^\infty |E|\, dt \qquad \text{and} \qquad \int_0^\infty E^2\, dt$$

Both of these improper integrals are convergent.

The first integral cannot be evaluated conveniently.[54] Since this criterion is somewhat arbitrary and since the results, if carried out, cannot differ much from those by minimizing the second integral, we choose the second criterion instead. This leads to an optimum damping ratio of $c/c_c = \frac{1}{2}$. The details of this procedure are left to the readers as an exercise.

Another and perhaps commoner procedure of choosing an appropriate damping ratio is by minimizing the so-called *response time*, that is, the

---

[54] In case one wishes to evaluate it, the integral can be expressed as an infinite series of definite integrals, each covering an interval of time in which the cosine function does not change sign. Except for the first term, the values of the succeeding integrals form a geometrical progression with a common ratio of $e^{\Delta/2}$. The sum of the series can thus be computed.

time required for the instrument to settle down into an oscillation between prescribed limits. This procedure usually amounts to the determination of the minimum damping ratio, so that the maximum "overshoot" is less than the amount prescribed, although the two criteria are based on two slightly different physical considerations.[55] For example, with a prescribed error of ± 5 per cent, the shortest response time is 43 per cent of the period of natural oscillation, and it corresponds to a damping ratio of 0.69, which is also the value of the minimum damping ratio for a maximum overshoot of 5 per cent. This overshoot takes place at $t = 0.65T$.

The different considerations involved in selecting an optimum damping ratio, as discussed, lead to the observation that for a general purpose instrument a damping ratio of 0.65 is a good compromise.

In concluding this article, let us remark that although a moving coil galvanometer was chosen for this study many of the results, observations, and methods of analysis are applicable to other types of instruments and control equipment.

1.16 Seismic Instruments and Transducers

The type of device discussed in this article is essentially a single-degree-freedom vibratory system mounted on a frame or in an enclosure which can be attached to a moving body whose motion is to be measured or converted into an output signal. The total mass of the system and its mounting must be relatively small so that it will not affect the motion of the body to which it is attached.

(A) SEISMOGRAPH

The oldest instrument of this type is the seismograph, an instrument for detecting the motion of the earth's surface. In its simplest form it consists of a spring-mass system of very low natural frequency enclosed in a frame attached to the ground, as schematically shown in Fig. 35.[56] The input to the system is the motion of the ground (hence of the frame), and the output is the relative displacement between the frame and the mass. This relative displacement can be recorded by attaching a tracing pen to the mass and attaching graph paper to the frame.

Let x be the displacement of m, x_s, the displacement of the frame, and

[55] See Draper, Mckay, and Lees, *Instrument Engineering*, Vol. II, McGraw-Hill, New York, 1953, pp. 264–265.

[56] We assume in Fig. 35 that the motions are in the vertical direction. The mass could be suspended to have freedom in three dimensions. However, since the three motions are independent of one another, the principles involved are essentially those of a single-degree-freedom system.

x_r, the relative displacement $x_s - x$. The differential equation of motion is then

$$m\ddot{x} + k(x - x_s) = 0$$

or

$$m\ddot{x}_r + kx_r = m\ddot{x}_s$$

$$\ddot{x}_r + \omega^2 x_r = \ddot{x}_s$$

From this equation it can be inferred that if the natural frequency of the system is very low, relative to the two accelerations, then

$$\ddot{x}_r \doteq \ddot{x}_s$$

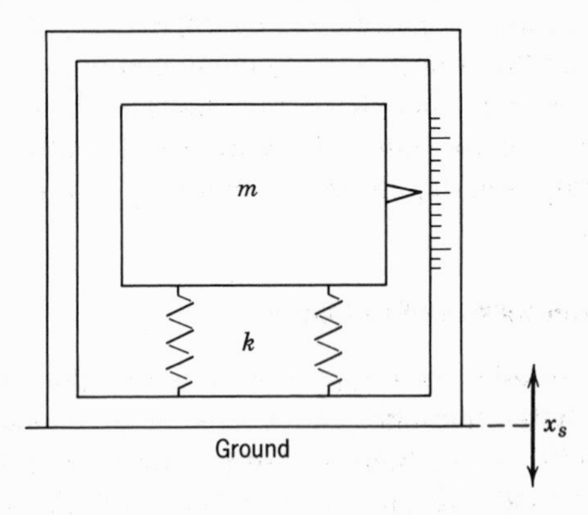

Figure 35

This implies that the response is equal to the signal when everything starts from a rest condition at $t = 0$. To achieve this approximate relationship physically, we need to have a very heavy mass[57] suspended by very soft springs. As the frame moves because of earthquake or underground explosion, the heavy mass stands almost still, and any rapid vibration of the ground is reflected directly by the relative motion between the mass and the frame. The principle of a seismograph is similar to that of certain vibration pickups.

(B) VIBRATION PICKUPS

There are several types of vibration pickups whose construction is essentially a spring-mass system (with or without a damper), mounted in a housing which can be attached to a vibrating machine or structure, as shown in Fig. 36. We give them the generic name *seismic instruments* because they are related to seismographs in their operational principle.

---

[57] Even a very heavy mass is still not heavy enough to affect the motion of the earth's surface.

The characteristic feature of a seismic instrument is that its output or response is generated by the relative motion between its housing and the mass inside. This output may be in the form of a mechanical movement, a

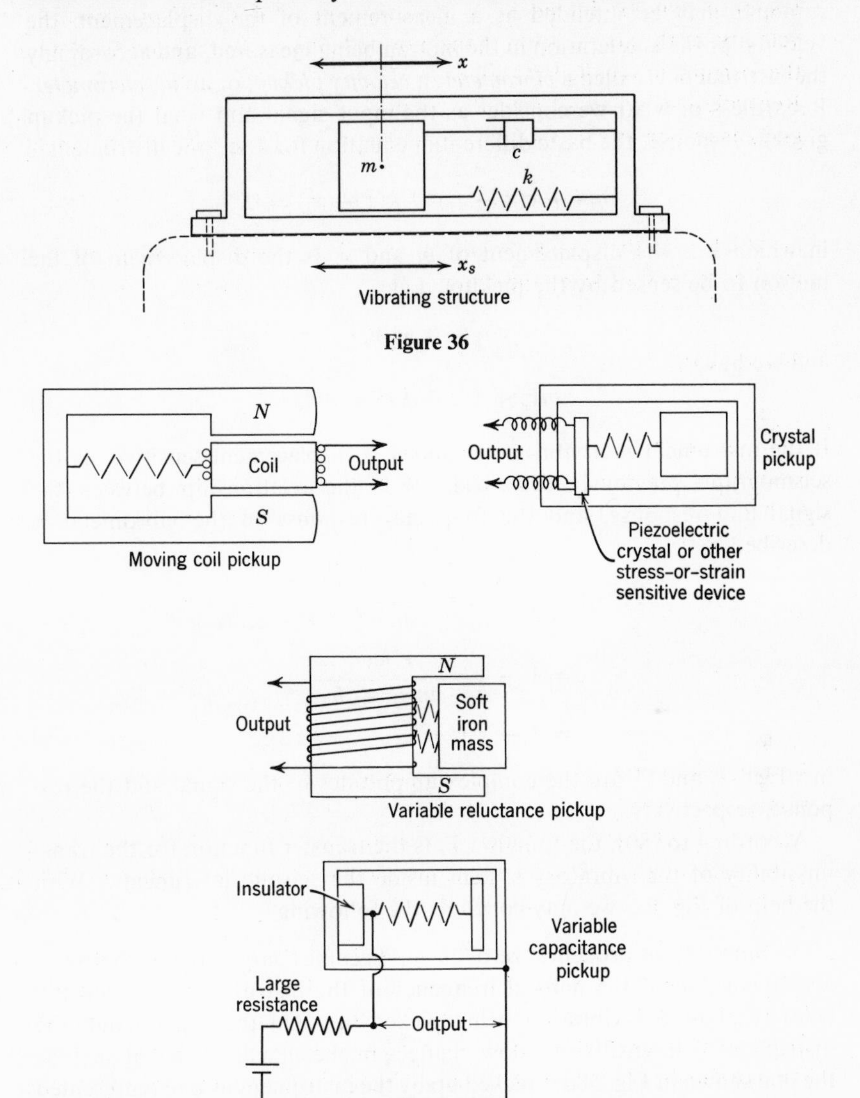

Figure 36

Figure 37

moving light beam, or an electrical voltage. Figure 37 shows schematically some typical instruments whose output is in electrical form.

The strength of the output may depend upon the relative displacement or the relative velocity between the housing and the mass, and accordingly the pickup is said to be *displacement-sensitive* or *velocity-sensitive*. The response may be intended as a measurement of the displacement, the velocity, or the acceleration in the motion being measured, and accordingly the instrument is called a *vibrometer*, a *velocity pickup*, or an *accelerometer*. Regardless of what we consider as the input signal and what the pickup gives as response, the basic differential equation for a seismic instrument is

$$m\ddot{x} + c(\dot{x} - \dot{x}_s) + k(x - x_s) = 0$$

in which x is the displacement of m and x_s is the displacement of the motion to be sensed by the pickup. Let

$$x_s - x = x_r$$

and we have

$$m\ddot{x}_r + c\dot{x}_r + kx_r = m\ddot{x}_s \tag{i}$$

If the instrument is a vibrometer and it is displacement-sensitive, as the seismograph previously described, (i) is the relationship between the signal and response, and the frequency response of the vibrometer is described by

$$\begin{aligned} T(i\omega_f) = \left(\frac{\lambda_r}{\lambda_s}\right)_{\text{vib}} &= \frac{-m\omega_f^2}{-m\omega_f^2 + k + ic\omega_f} \\ &= 1 - \frac{k + ic\omega_f}{k - m\omega_f^2 + ic\omega_f} \\ &= 1 - T_r(i\omega_f) \end{aligned} \tag{ii}$$

in which λ_s and λ_r are the complex amplitudes of the signal and the response, respectively.

According to (80), the function T_r is the transfer function for the transmissibility of the vibratory system inside the seismic instrument. With the help of Fig. 22, we may conclude the following:

(1) Since T_r approaches zero as ω_f becomes large, the response is nearly constant if the natural frequency of the instrument is sufficiently below that of the vibration being picked up. On the other hand, the instrument is insensitive to slow changes in the signal. A signal such as the one shown in Fig. 38*a* is picked up by the instrument as one represented by Fig. 38*b*. This can be an advantage or a disadvantage, depending upon applications. Note that the situation here is exactly the opposite of galvanometer response.

(2) Since T_r approaches zero faster with less damping, there is no

advantage in introducing any damping in the system. Therefore, a vibrometer is designed with a minimum amount of damping.

Let us now take the case of a velocity pickup whose output is proportional to the relative velocity of the motion inside. The signal is then taken to be $v_s = \dot{x}_s$ and the response to be $v_r = \dot{x}_r$. Evidently, by differentiating (i) with respect to t, we have

$$m\ddot{v}_r + c\dot{v}_r + kv_r = m\ddot{v}_s$$

So if this time we let our signal $\lambda_s e^{i\omega_f t}$ be v_s and the response $\lambda_r e^{i\omega_f t}$,

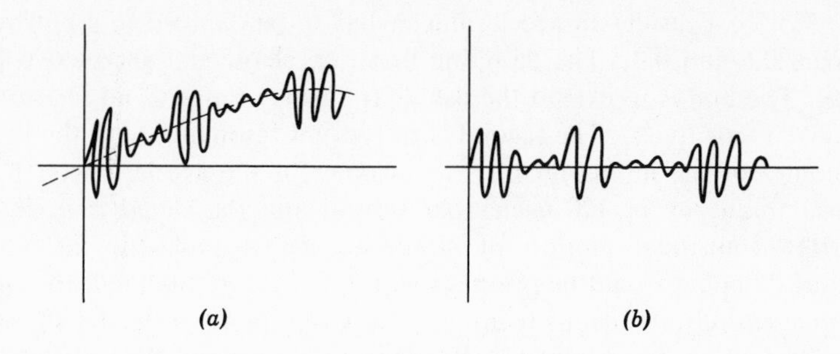

(a) (b)

Figure 38

v_r, the relation between λ_r and λ_s would be the same as before, and all the observations we made about a vibrometer would hold true for a velocity-sensitive velocity pickup.

Now let us suppose that the instrument is an accelerometer and its output is proportional to the relative displacement. The input signal is then

$$\lambda_s e^{i\omega_f t} = \ddot{x}_s$$

and the response is

$$\lambda_r e^{i\omega_f t} = x_r$$

According to (i), the relationship between λ_r and λ_s is then

$$(-m\omega_f^2 + ic\omega_f + k)\lambda_r = m\lambda_s$$

$$T_a(i\omega_f) = \left(\frac{\lambda_r}{\lambda_s}\right)_{\text{acc}} = \frac{m}{k - m\omega_f^2 + ic\omega_f}$$

$$= \frac{\dfrac{1}{\omega^2}}{1 - \dfrac{\omega_f^2}{\omega^2} + i\dfrac{2c}{c_c}\dfrac{\omega_f}{\omega}} \tag{iii}$$

The denominator in this expression is the same as that of (46), and the numerator is a constant of the instrument. The response of an accelerometer is therefore proportional to its magnification factor, and the situation is the same as a D'Arsonval galvanometer. To repeat what we said about a galvanometer:

(1) A displacement sensitive accelerometer should have a natural frequency that is high in comparison with that of the signal. On the other hand, by making its natural frequency high, one sacrifices its sensitivity, which, according to (iii), is proportional to $1/\omega^2$.

(2) For best results an accelerometer has to be damped to a c/c_c value between 0.6 and 0.7. The damping in an accelerometer serves two purposes. The first is to extend the usable frequency range of an instrument of a given sensitivity. The second is to prevent resonance with the higher harmonics of the input signal. For instance, if the accelerometer has a natural frequency of 120 cycles per second and the signal is a slightly distorted sinusoidal motion of 40 cycles per second, the instrument without damping would be resonant with the third harmonic of the signal and give entirely erroneous readings. Note that in a vibrometer the same situation will not be obtained if the natural frequency of the instrument is below that of the fundamental frequency of the signal.

Another remark we made about the phase shift in a galvanometer with damping also applies here; that is, by extending the frequency range of the instrument through proper damping, we do not eliminate the phase-shift distortion, which is important only when the waveform of the signal is of interest.

(c) COMPENSATION AND EQUILIZATION

Most modern instruments give their outputs in the form of electrical signals. These have to be converted by external means into the motions of a pointer or recording pen. The conversion device is in itself a signal-transferring system. It is then possible to introduce an electrical network into this device, which has a signal-transfer characteristic compensating in part for the inaccuracies in the sensing instrument. For instance, if an accelerometer is damped to 70 per cent of the critical, its response falls off for signal frequencies above 20 per cent of its natural frequency. By introducing a network whose response shows a proper rise above the same frequency, we can extend the usable frequency range of the combination. Another familiar example is a magnetic phonograph pickup, which is essentially a velocity-sensitive seismic instrument in which the arm is equivalent to a seismic mass and the needle is equivalent to a mounting frame. Since most records are cut to be played by displacement sensitive pickups, the use of magnetic pickups requires compensation in the playback amplifier.

The point to be emphasized is that with the available flexibility in compensating network design a flat frequency response of a sensing device may not always be of the utmost importance as long as its response characteristics are known.

1.17 Vehicle Suspension

The suspension system of a vehicle may be analyzed in the first approximation as a vibratory system having a single degree of freedom. As shown

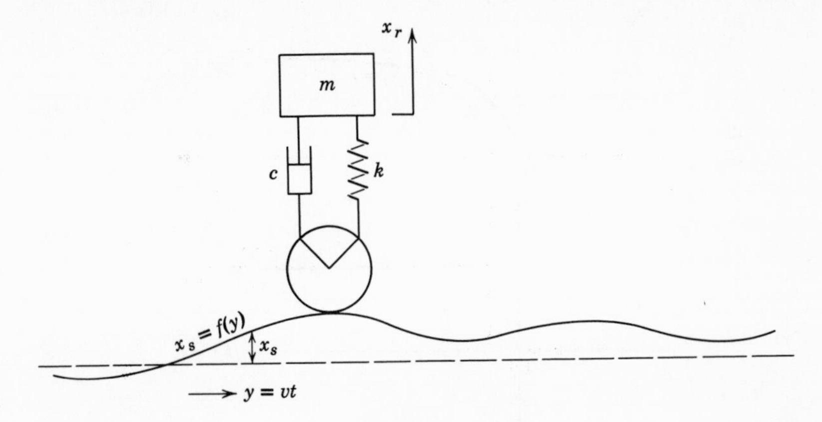

Figure 39

in Fig. 39, the system is equivalent to a seismic instrument, and its differential equation of motion is

$$m\ddot{x}_r + c(\dot{x}_r - \dot{x}_s) + k(x_r - x_s) = 0 \tag{i}$$

or

$$m\ddot{x}_r + c\dot{x}_r + kx_r = c\dot{x}_s + kx_s \tag{ii}$$

where x_s and x_r are the vertical displacements of the wheel and the vehicle, respectively. If the profile of the road surface is given by $x_s = f(y)$ and the velocity of the vehicle is v, then

$$x_s = f(vt) \qquad \text{and} \qquad \dot{x}_s = vf'(vt) \tag{iii}$$

So the left-hand side of (ii) is a function of t. When the road surface irregularity is more or less periodic, the frequency response of the system is of immediate interest. It must be pointed out that although the differential equation is the same as that for a seismic instrument the response of the system is taken to be the motion of the vehicle body rather than the relative displacement. The frequency response is then

$$\left(\frac{\lambda_r}{\lambda_s}\right)_{\text{veh}} = \frac{k + ic\omega_f}{k - m\omega_f^2 + ic\omega_f} = T_r(i\omega_f)$$

which is the transmissibility of a spring-mass-damper system. The frequency ω_f is determined by the profile of pavement irregularities as well as the speed of the vehicle v. A look at Fig. 22 enables us to make the following observations:

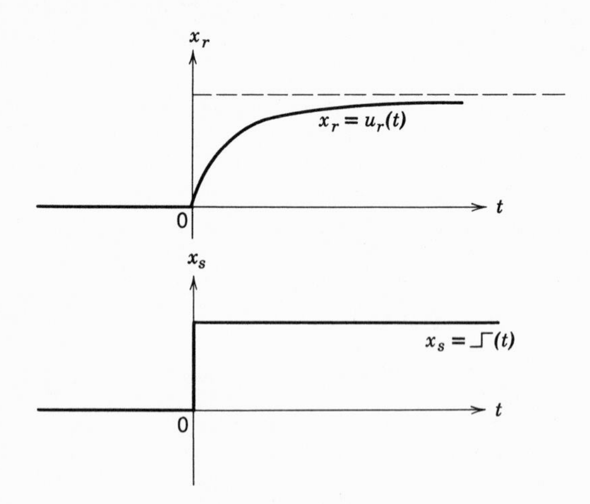

Figure 40

(1) Insofar as vibration absorption is concerned, it is desirable to use soft suspension springs to lower the natural frequency of the system. Very soft suspension springs, of course, have problems of their own. These include lateral instability and excessive changes in road clearance and vehicle height between loaded and unloaded conditions.

(2) At low speeds, which correspond to frequency ratios below $1/\sqrt{2}$, damping is necessary to cut down the vibration transmitted from the wheel to the body, whereas at higher speeds the existence of damping is actually disadvantageous insofar as steady-state road disturbances are concerned.

An important consideration in the design of vehicle suspension concerns its ability to absorb bumps and holes in the pavement. This ability can best be assessed by its indicial response. By definition, the indicial response in this case is the solution to (ii) for $x_s(t) = \mathcal{J}(t)$ with $x_r(0) = 0$. There is, however, a mathematical difficulty in solving this problem by the classical method, since with x_s being a step function $c\dot{x}_s$ is infinite at $t = 0$, although it is zero at all other times. There are other methods, including the use of (96), whereby this difficulty can be removed. But we have dealt with this problem before in Art. 1.11, in which it is shown that the differential equation (78) is equivalent to a pair of equations (77). Borrowing the subsequent results, together with (69*b*), we have

$$u_r(t) = c\left(\frac{1}{m\omega_c} e^{-(c/2m)t} \sin \omega_c t\right) + \left(1 - \frac{\omega}{\omega_c} e^{-(c/2m)t} \cos (\omega_c t - \delta)\right)$$

With the help of (27), this expression can be simplified to yield

$$u_r(t) = 1 - \frac{\omega}{\omega_c} e^{-(c/2m)t} \cos (\omega_c t + \delta) \qquad \text{(iv)}$$

From this we have

$$u_r'(t) = \frac{\omega^2}{\omega_c} e^{-(c/2m)t} \sin (\omega_c t + 2\delta) \qquad \text{(v)}$$

Now we see that at $t = 0$ the foregoing expression does not vanish, since

$$u_r'(0) = \frac{\omega^2}{\omega_c} \sin 2\delta = \frac{2\omega c}{c_c} = \frac{c}{m}$$

Hence this does not satisfy the initial condition $\dot{x}_r(0) = 0$. However, when we examine the physical meaning of indicial response, we see that the system is assumed to have zero displacement and zero velocity for all $t < 0$. They are zero at $t = 0$ only if they are both continuous at $t = 0$. Such continuity exists if the signal-response relationship is of the form (97); but, when the relationship is of the form (98), the derivatives of the indicial response may not be continuous. Returning to the problem on hand, we see that when the wheel is suddenly given a displacement the body of the vehicle will suddenly acquire a velocity of c/m. This statement is true also for $c/c_c > 1$, since (iv) and (v) are true if ω_c and δ are allowed to be complex.

This sudden velocity change[58] of the vehicle body represents a shock or impact which should be kept small. This means that the value for c/c_c should not be too large. On the other hand, to prevent large oscillation, c/c_c should not be too small. A good compromise is for $c/c_c = 1$.

---

[58] In reality, the tire and wheel structure is not absolutely rigid so that the acceleration will not be infinite.

1.18 Structural Damping and the Concept of Complex Stiffness

In a real vibratory system the restoring force of the "spring" is not entirely conservative. Thst is to say, cyclic deformation of the spring consumes mechanical energy. The dissipative forces involved originate either in the interior of the spring material or at regions between two parts of a built-up spring. The outward manifestation of such dissipative forces is described by the general term *structural damping*. As a rule, forces due

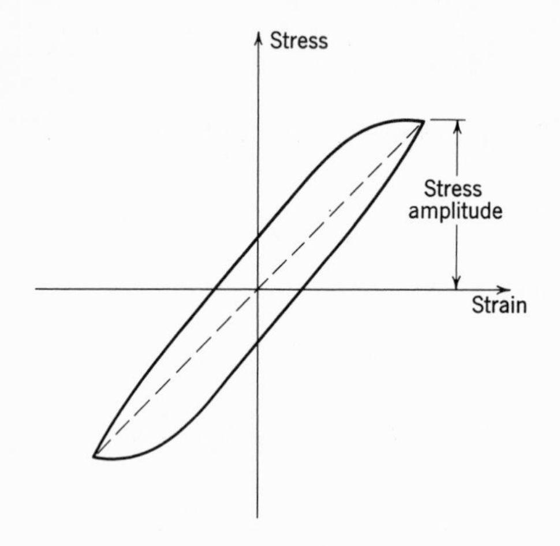

Figure 41

to structural damping are small, but often their presence affects the dynamic behavior of a vibratory system, especially if the vibration is self-excited.[59]

In this article we discuss a simple form of structural damping and its effects on the vibratory motion of a single-degree-freedom system.

It is generally accepted that when structural damping is caused by the material of the spring in a spring-mass system the hysteresis of the spring material under cyclic deformation is responsible for the energy dissipation. Hence we have the term *hysteresis* or *hysteretical damping*. Precise measurements on the stress-strain relationship of most real materials show that even at stress levels much below their accepted elastic limits cyclic straining produces hysteresis loops such as that shown in Fig. 41. The area enclosed by the loop represents the mechanical energy dissipated by the material during one complete stress-strain cycle.

[59] A vibration is said to be self-excited when the external force becomes a periodic excitation by virtue of the vibration itself. For instance, the stroking of a bow on a string produces a periodic force on the string as the latter vibrates. Also, the flutter of an airfoil is excited by aerodynamic forces which become periodic as the airfoil flutters.

(A) EXPERIMENTAL EVIDENCE

Using a rotating beam loaded by a dead weight, Kimball and Lovell[60] showed that for most materials the energy dissipated per cycle is independent of frequency over a wide frequency range and proportional to the square of the stress (or strain) amplitude of the cycle. This observation can be translated to mean that the hysteresis loop is not affected by the rate of straining and that a change in the stress amplitude produces a change in the size of the loop but not its shape. More modern measurements by Lazan[61] indicate that the foregoing statement is approximately true for many materials in a limited range of frequencies and stress amplitudes. The actual phenomenon, of course, is exceedingly complex and is dependent upon a host of mechanical and metallurgical factors.

(B) STRUCTURAL DAMPING FORCE IN STEADY-STATE VIBRATION

When a spring-mass system with a small amount of structural damping is excited by an external harmonic force, it is reasonable to expect that the resulting steady-state vibration will be a harmonic oscillation with the frequency of the excitation ω_f. Let the amplitude of this oscillation be $|\lambda|$. The law of structural damping, according to Kimball and Lovell, then states that the energy dissipation E_d per cycle is

$$E_d \propto |\lambda|^2 \tag{i}$$

In the meantime, according to (57), the energy dissipation per cycle by viscous damping under the same circumstance is

$$E_d = \pi c \omega_f |\lambda|^2$$

Therefore, a system with structural damping in steady-state vibration may be analyzed as a viscously damped system having a damping constant *c inversely proportional* to the frequency. In other words, the linear equation

$$m\ddot{x} + \frac{h}{\omega_f}\dot{x} + kx = F_0 \cos \omega_f t \tag{ii}$$

has a steady-state harmonic solution in which the energy dissipation per cycle is independent of the frequency ω_f although proportional to the square of the amplitude. The constant h is determined by the property of

---

[60] "Internal Friction in Solids" by A. I. Kimball and D. E. Lovell, *Physical Review*, Vol. 30, December 1927.

[61] "A Study with New Equipment of the Effects of Fatigue Stress on Damping Capacity and Elasticity of Mild Steel" by B. J. Lazan, *Trans. Am. Soc. Metals*, Vol. 4, 1950.

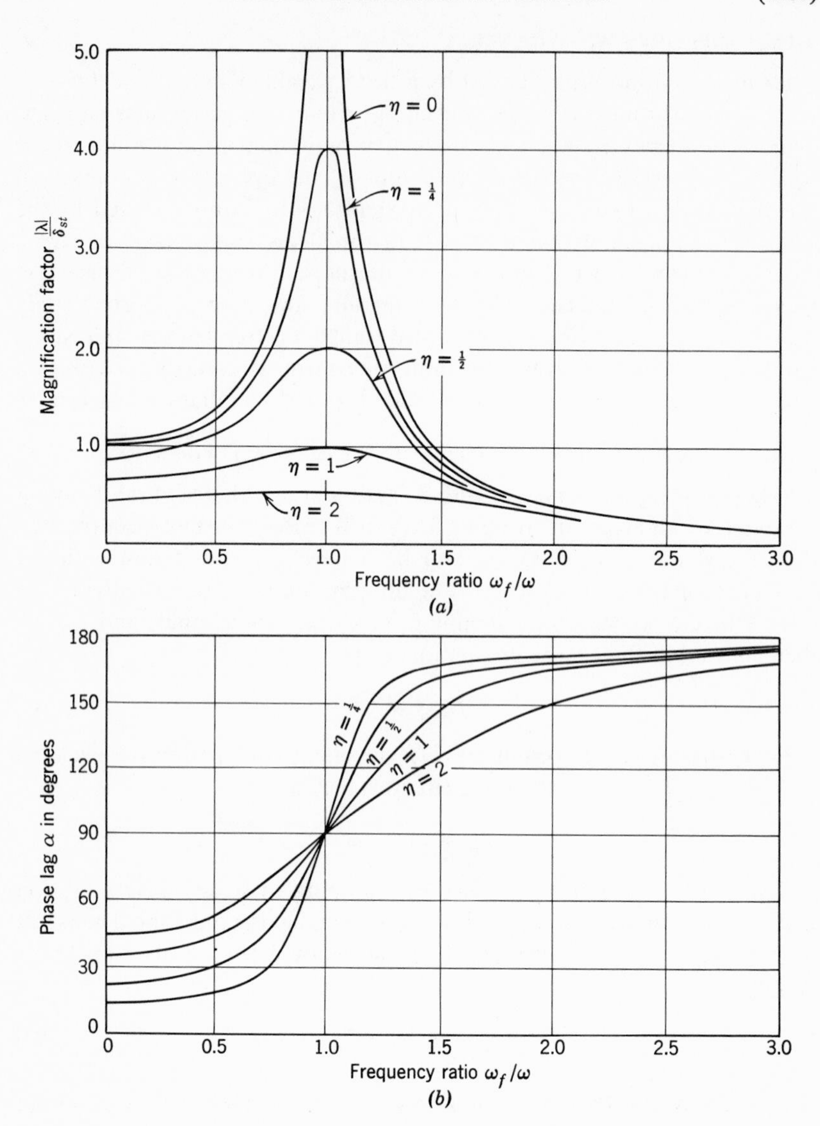

5.0
4.0
3.0
2.0
1.0
Magnification factor $\frac{|\lambda|}{\delta_{st}}$
$\eta = 0$
$\eta = \frac{1}{4}$
$\eta = \frac{1}{2}$
$\eta = 1$
$\eta = 2$
0
0.5
1.0
1.5
2.0
2.5
3.0
Frequency ratio ω_f/ω
(a)
180
150
120
90
60
30
0
Phase lag α in degrees
$\eta = \frac{1}{4}$
$\eta = \frac{1}{2}$
$\eta = 1$
$\eta = 2$
Frequency ratio ω_f/ω
(b)

Figure 42

the spring-material, and it has the dimension of k. Often one writes

$$h = k\eta$$

in which η is a nondimensional quantity called the *structural damping coefficient* and is usually less than unity. The steady-state solution for (ii) can thus be obtained by replacing c with h/ω_f in (41) of Art. 1.6. The result is

$$x = |\lambda| \cos(\omega_f t - \alpha)$$

$$\tan \alpha = \frac{h}{-m\omega_f^2 + k} = \frac{\eta}{1 - \left(\dfrac{\omega_f}{\omega}\right)^2}$$

$$|\lambda| = \frac{F_0}{\sqrt{(-m\omega_f^2 + k)^2 + h^2}} = \frac{\delta_{st}}{\sqrt{\left(1 - \dfrac{\omega_f^2}{\omega^2}\right)^2 + \eta^2}} \tag{iii}$$

Plots of the magnification ratio $|\lambda|/\delta_{st}$ and the phase lag α versus the frequency ratio ω_f/ω for different value of η are shown in Fig. 42. It is instructive to compare these plots with Fig. 16, which is designed for a viscously damped system. An interesting feature of Figure 42*a* is that the peaks of all the curves are at $\omega_f/\omega = 1$.

(C) COMPLEX NUMBER REPRESENTATION IN THE CASE OF STEADY-STATE VIBRATION WITH STRUCTURAL DAMPING

Since (ii) is a linear differential equation having a solution of the form (iii), we can use a complex number representation

$$x = \lambda e^{i\omega_f t} \tag{iv}$$

by rewriting the differential equation of motion as

$$m\ddot{x} + \frac{h}{\omega_f}\dot{x} + kx = F_0 e^{i\omega_f t} \tag{v}$$

Upon differentiating (iv) and putting into (v), we obtain

$$\dot{x} = i\omega_f \lambda e^{i\omega_f t} = i\omega_f x$$

$$m\ddot{x} + (ih + k)x = F_0 e^{i\omega_f t}$$

or

$$m\ddot{x} + k(1 + i\eta)x = F_0 e^{i\omega_f t} \tag{vi}$$

Writing the equation of motion in the form of (vi) has the advantage of simplicity as well as the disappearance of ω_f from the left-hand side of the equation. The complex quantity

$$\kappa = k + ih = k(1 + i\eta)$$

is called the *complex stiffness*.[62] This complex quantity represents the elastic and the structural damping forces of the spring at the same time. Such representation is particularly advantageous in dealing with systems having many degrees of freedom. The vectorial representation of (vi) is shown in Fig. 43.

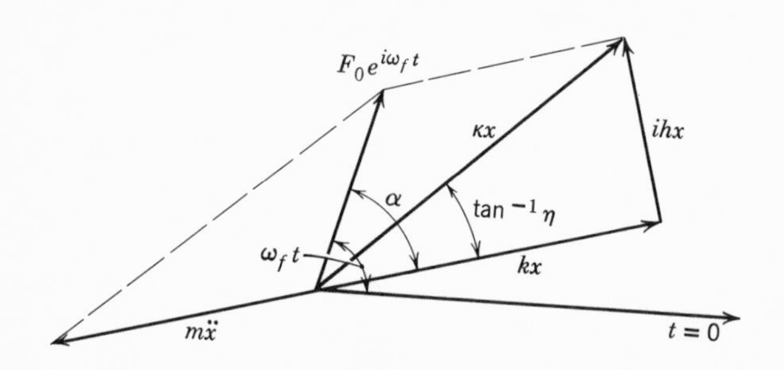

Figure 43

(D) VIBRATION OF STRUCTURALLY DAMPED SYSTEM IN THE ABSENCE OF EXTERNAL EXCITATION

It must be emphasized that all the results presented are valid only when the vibration is known to be a harmonic oscillation. It is obvious from (ii) that in the absence of external excitation the homogeneous differential equation

$$m\ddot{x} + \frac{h}{\omega_f}\dot{x} + kx = 0$$

has no physical meaning, since it includes an undefined quantity ω_f. Unfortunately, ω_f does not appear at the left-hand side of (vi), and this fact led some investigators into trying to solve the problem by solving the equation

$$m\ddot{x} + k(1 + i\eta)x = 0 \tag{vii}$$

We must realize that (v) can be replaced by (vi) only because we know the solution to be of the form (iv).[63]

---

[62] As a matter choice, some authors call it the *complex damping*.

[63] See the discussion following (49) in Art. 1.7. Also, for a physical problem meaningfully described by (vii), see Art. 2.14(c).

The experimental evidence presented in (A) was from a steady-state phenomenon. We really have no adequate physical data to analyze a damped oscillation. It is, however, reasonable to believe that if the structural damping force is small, so that the decay of the resulting damped oscillation is gradual, the motion may be assumed to be the same as that of a viscously damped system with an equivalent damping constant given by

$$c = \frac{h}{\omega_c}$$

The equation to be solved is then

$$m\ddot{x} + \frac{h}{\omega_c}\dot{x} + kx = 0 \tag{viii}$$

where ω_c is the damped frequency of the vibration. This approach was originally suggested by Collar.[64] The solution to (viii) can be obtained by replacing c with h/ω_f in (19) and (19a).

$$x(t) = Ce^{-(ht/2m\omega_c)}\cos(\omega_c t - \alpha) \tag{ix}$$

The damped frequency ω_c is to be determined by (20)

$$\omega_c = \frac{\sqrt{4mk\omega_c^2 - h^2}}{2m\omega_c}$$

Solving for ω_c, we obtain

$$\omega_c = \sqrt{\frac{k + \sqrt{k^2 - h^2}}{2m}} = \omega\sqrt{\frac{1 + \sqrt{1 - \eta^2}}{2}} \tag{x}$$

The oscillatory solution (ix), of course, can be valid only for $\eta < 1$. An aperiodic solution for $\eta > 1$ has no physical meaning because we know nothing of the law of structural damping for such motion. It appears that according to (x) the limiting value of ω_c for oscillatory motion is $\omega/\sqrt{2}$ instead of zero. This is not so mathematically. There is a second solution to (ix) which corresponds to the use of minus signs instead of the plus signs under the radicals in (x). The branch point corresponds to a logarithmic decrement of 2π, a decaying rate too rapid to justify the extrapolation of Kimball-Lovell's law, as stated.

A more lucid way of expressing the relationship between ω_c and η is by the use of the angle δ defined in (27).

$$\frac{\omega_c}{\omega} = \cos\delta = \sqrt{\frac{1 + \cos 2\delta}{2}}$$

---

[64] See "The Treatment of Damping Forces in Vibration Theory" by R. E. D. Bishop, *Journal of Royal Aeronautical Society*, Vol. 59, No. 539, November 1955.

In comparing this expression with (x), evidently

$$\eta = \sin 2\delta \tag{xi}$$

(E) COMPLEX NUMBER REPRESENTATION OF DAMPED OSCILLATION

In complex number representation the solution to (viii) is in the form of

$$x = \lambda e^{i\sigma t}$$

where the complex frequency σ is defined in (22) as

$$\sigma = \omega_c + i\frac{c}{c_c}\omega = \omega_c(1 + i\tan\delta)$$

Hence

$$\dot{x} = i\sigma x = i\omega_c(1 + i\tan\delta)x$$

By substituting this into (viii), we obtain

$$m\ddot{x} + ih(1 + i\tan\delta)x + kx = 0$$

or

$$m\ddot{x} + k(1 - \eta\tan\delta + i\eta)x = 0$$

Because of (xi)

$$1 - \eta\tan\delta = 1 - 2\sin^2\delta = \cos 2\delta = \sqrt{1 - \eta^2}$$

We have, finally,

$$m\ddot{x} + k(\sqrt{1 - \eta^2} + i\eta)x = 0$$

$$m\ddot{x} + ke^{2i\delta}x = 0$$

or

$$m\ddot{x} + \kappa_1 x = 0 \tag{xii}$$

Therefore, in this case the complex stiffness is the quantity

$$\kappa_1 = k(\sqrt{1 - \eta^2} + i\eta) = ke^{2i\delta}$$

Here the structural damping coefficient η enters not only into the imaginary part but also into the real part of the complex coefficient. This came about because of our scheme of representation and not because structural damping force has any physical effects on the conservative force of the spring. This observation is clear, as we examine the original differential equation (viii).

We see, therefore, that for a given system with structural damping the complex stiffness κ in the case of steady-state forced vibration is different from that in the case of a damped oscillation κ_1.[65] For small η the difference is, of course, small. It arises out of the difference in the structural

[65] For another complex number representation of the same hysteresis characteristic see Art. 2.14(c).

damping laws used to analyze the two types of motion. The use of κ for κ_1 in (xii) leads to (vii), which gives inadmissible results.[66] Myklestad,[67] by a different method of derivation, however, arrived at an equation for steady-state vibrations in which κ_1 appears instead of κ.

$$m\ddot{x} + ke^{2i\delta}x = F_0 e^{i\omega_f t} \qquad \text{(xiii)}$$

He stated that certain features of his solution agree better with experimental observations, but there is some question[68] about the physical reasoning underlying his method of derivation. As a practical matter, since the structural damping force is generally small, the numerical results obtained from (viii) and (xiii) have no significant difference.

(F) OTHER TYPES OF STRUCTURAL DAMPING

The structural damping law of Kimball and Lovell has only limited validity. It has the advantage of yielding a linear differential equation. Therefore, whenever reasonable, this law is used for analysis. There are many actual systems with structural damping whose oscillations cannot be described by linear equations without gross error. For example, for a certain built-up beam Pian and Hallowell[69] found that hysteresis loss caused by slipping between its parts is approximately proportional to the third power of deformation while it is independent of the stress amplitude. Naturally, the analysis of such a system is more complicated. Since structural damping force can originate from a number of different physical phenomena, no unifying treatment of such forces is possible.

Exercises

1.1. Write the differential equations of motion for small oscillations of the systems shown.

---

[66] For instance, the solution to (vii) is oscillatory for all values of η and ω_c increases with η. The solution is given in Art. 2.14(c).

[67] "The Concept of Complex Damping", N. O. Myklestad, *Journal of Applied Mechanics*, Vol. 19, No. 3 (September 1952)

[68] See "Concept of Complex Stiffness Applied to Problems of Oscillations with Viscous and Hysteretic Damping" by S. Neumark, Royal Aircraft Establishment, Report No. Aero. 2592 (V.D.C. No. 533.6.013.42) September 1957.

[69] "Structual Damping in a Simple Built-Up Beam", by T. H. H. Pian and F. C. Hallowell, *Proceedings of First U.S. National Congress of Applied Mechanics*, pp. 97–102, 1951. See also "Structural Damping" by T. H. H. Pian, Chapter 5 of *Random Vibration*, edited by S. H. Crandall, MIT Technology Press, Cambridge, Massachusetts, 1958.

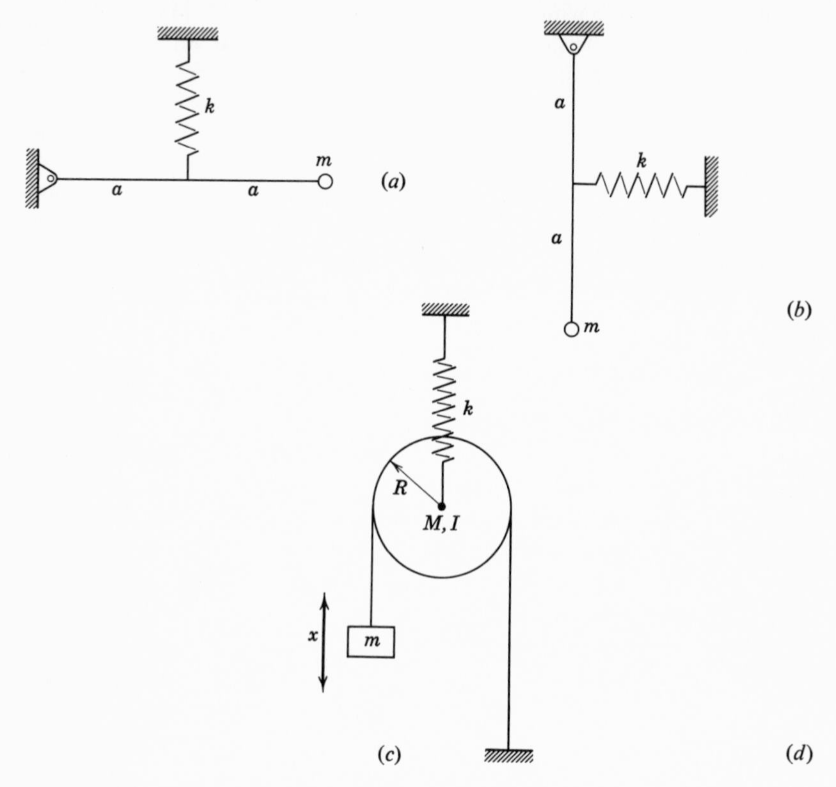

Exercise 1.1

1.2. A torsion-bar suspension system for vehicles may be approximately represented by a weight hanging on an L-shaped round bar as shown. Find the natural frequency of the system in terms of a, b, d, E, G, and W.

E = Young's modulus G = Modulus of rigidity

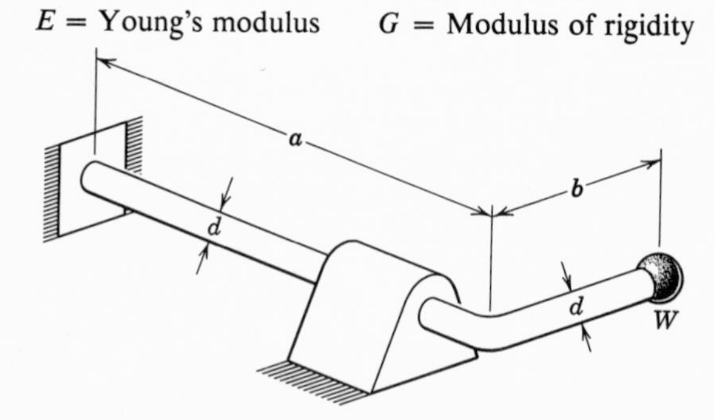

Exercise 1.2

1.3. To find the moment of inertia of a flywheel, a certain engineer hangs the wheel on a nail and measures the period of swing. The wheel weighs 60 lb, the point of suspension is 10 in. from the center of the wheel. If the period of the swing is 1.45 sec, what is the moment of inertia of the wheel about its centroidal axis? The wheel is assumed to be well balanced.

1.4. A spring-loaded cam follower follows an eccentric radius r and eccentricity e. The mass of the follower is m, and the spring has a spring constant k and a natural length that is longer than its maximum length in position by an amount equal to $2e$.

(*a*) Show that for small e/r the follower has a simple harmonic motion when the eccentric rotates with uniform angular speed ω_f.

(*b*) What is the maximum allowable ω_f so that the follower will not leave the cam?

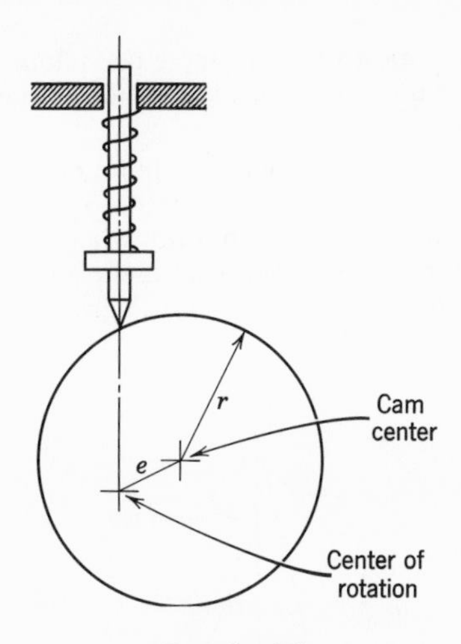

Exercise 1.4

1.5. Show that

$$A \cos (\omega t - \alpha) + B \cos (\omega t - \beta) = C \cos (\omega t - \gamma)$$

where A, B, and C are three sides of a triangle with the respective opposite angles being $\pm(\gamma - \beta)$, $\pm(\alpha - \gamma)$, and $\pi \pm (\alpha - \beta)$.

1.6. A system consists of four uniform identical rigid bars each of length a and mass m, linked together by frictionless pin joints and a linear spring of spring constant k and natural length a. Find the natural frequency of the system by Rayleigh's principle. Assume that the mechanism lies on a smooth horizontal table so that its center of mass is stationary during oscillation.

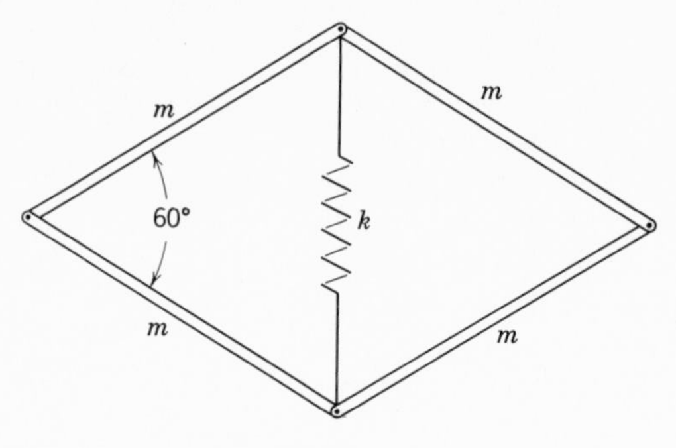

Exercise 1.6

1.7. Draw the phase trajectory of a simple pendulum of length L swinging a total angle of 180°. Compare its shape with that of an ellipse having the same major and minor axes.

1.8. A plumb bob of effective length l is hung on a nail on a vertical wall. Directly under the nail of suspension is another nail which catches the string when the plum bob swings to one side but not when it swings to the other side. If the distance between the nails is $l/4$, what is the period for small angle swing and what is the ratio of the two maximum angles the string makes with the vertical?

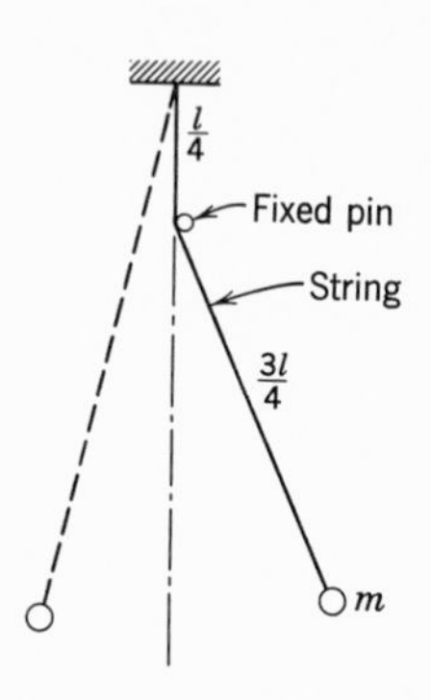

Exercise 1.8

1.9. A piston of mass m "floats" in a cylinder of height h and cross-sectional area A; the cylinder contains a perfect gas. Assuming that the compression and rarefication of the gas are reversible adiabatic as the piston is set into small up-and-down oscillation, find an expression for the frequency of such oscillation.

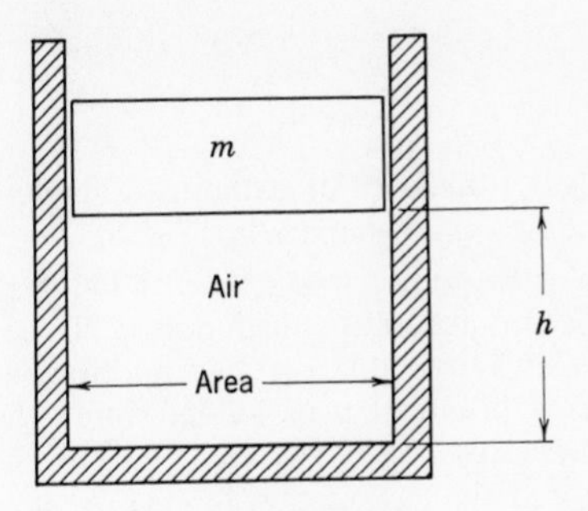

Exercise 1.9

1.10. A small ring slides back and forth without friction along a wire bent to a curve in a vertical plane described by the equation

$$y = \frac{x^2}{2a} - \frac{x^4}{a^3}$$

Find the period of its oscillation when $x_{\max}$ is $0.2a$.

Hint.

$$T = \tfrac{1}{2}m\left(\frac{ds}{dt}\right)^2 = \tfrac{1}{2}m(1 + y'^2)\dot{x}^2$$

$$V = mg(y - y_m) \qquad T + V = 0$$

$$\frac{d}{dt}\left(\frac{T + V}{1 + y'^2}\right) = 0 \qquad x + g\frac{d}{dx}\left(\frac{y - y_m}{1 + y'^2}\right) = 0$$

For small y'

$$\ddot{x} + g(y' - y'^3 + 2y_m y'y'' - 4y_m y'^3 y'' - 2yy'y'') \doteq 0$$

Neglect all terms higher than third order of x.

1.11.

(*a*) The solution expressed by (15) can also be written as

$$x(t) = e^{-(c/2m)t}(A \cosh wt + B \sinh wt)$$

in which $w = \sqrt{(c^2/2m) - 4mk} = i\omega_c$. By the usual method, determine the constants A and B in terms of x_0 and $\dot{x}_0$.

(*b*) Utilize the formula

$$\cos i\theta = \cosh \theta \qquad \text{and} \qquad \sin i\theta = i \sinh \theta$$

to show that (19) and (23) will lead to the same answer as (*a*).

(*c*) Show that, as in Fig. 7, a hyperbola may be used to relate c/c_c and w/ω. If we let $c/c_c = \cosh \epsilon$ and $w/\omega = \sinh \epsilon$, what is the geometrical meaning of ϵ?

(*d*) Show that (18) can be obtained by letting ω_c approach to zero in (19) or by letting $s_1 = \omega$ and s_2 approach s_1.

1.12. Show that the angle δ in Fig. 8 is the δ in (27).

1.13. Show that

$$\ln \frac{\dot{x}(t)}{\dot{x}(t+T)} = \Delta$$

1.14. Draw the phase trajectory of a damped single-degree-freedom system with $c/c_c = 0.5$ and compare its shape with Fig. 8.

1.15. A suspension galvanometer has the following periods of swing: open circuit 3.00 sec; 2000 ohms across the terminals, 3.20 sec; 1000 ohms across the terminals, 3.60 sec. What is the coil resistance and the damping resistance of the galvanometer? Is this a practical way to determine the two resistances of a galvanometer experimentally? Why?

1.16. Plot two cycles of the envelope C in (36) for $B = 0.7A$.

1.17. In Fig. 15, if a circle is drawn with its center at the origin and tangent internally to the parabola, the radius of the circle and the point of tangency correspond to the maximum frequency response and its phase lag for a given damping ratio. Using methods in analytical geometry, show that

(*a*) The radius of the tangent circle is $\sin 2\delta$, hence the maximum frequency response is

$$\lambda_m/\delta_{st} = \csc 2\delta$$

(*b*) The corresponding phase lag α_m is

$$\alpha_m = \tan^{-1}(\sqrt{\cos 2\delta}\csc \delta)$$

(*c*) The frequency response curve has a peak only when

$$\delta \leq \frac{\pi}{4} \qquad \text{or} \qquad \frac{c}{c_c} \leq 1/\sqrt{2}$$

1.18. Improve the accuracy of the period obtained by Rayleigh's method for the system shown in Fig. 28, when the θ has an amplitude of 30° and $(g/a) = (k/m)$.

1.19. A spherical ball of weight w and radius r rolls back and forth without slipping in a plane motion inside a bowl whose surface is a surface of revolution formed by the sinusoidal curve

$$y = r\left(1 - \cos \frac{\pi x}{4r}\right)$$

Find the Rayleigh's method its period for small oscillations.

1.20. An overdamped single-degree-freedom system is set into motion with initial displacement x_0 and initial velocity $\dot{x}_0$. Show that the condition for $x(t) > 0$ at all $t < \infty$ is that $\dot{x}_0 > s_2 x_0$.

1.21. A damped single-degree-freedom system has zero initial velocity. Show that, other things being equal, the integral

$$\int_0^\infty x^2\, dt$$

is a minimum for $c = 0.5c_c$.

Hint. Use (15) and (17) for your analysis.

1.22. The signal from a 4-arm Wheatstone strain gage bridge is to be recorded by an oscillograph using a suspension coil galvanometer which has the following specifications: galvanometer coil resistance 60 ohms, critical damping resistance 140 ohms, and natural frequency 120 cycles. If the gage resistance is 360 ohms and the record shows a steady-state sinusoidal signal of 90 cycles per sec, what is the percentage error in the record? Assume that the bridge and the oscillograph are properly calibrated by static tests.

1.23. Let the signal input to a galvanometer be

$$x_s(t) = 0 \qquad t \leq 0$$
$$x_s(t) = Kt \qquad t > 0$$

in which K is a constant.

(*a*) Find the expression for galvanometer response $x_r(t)$, assuming that the galvanometer is calibrated for static readings.
(*b*) Show that the error $x_r - x_s$ approaches a constant value.
(*c*) What would you estimate to be the optimum damping ratio in this galvanometer operation?

1.24. The indicial response function $u(t)$ may be represented by

$$a_n u(t) = 1 - e(t)$$

where $e(t)$ satisfies

$$L(e) = 0 \qquad t \geq 0$$

and $e(0) = 1$, $e'(0) = 0 \cdots$ etc.

(*a*) Use this approach to derive (69*b*) by the use of (19) and (23).
(*b*) Use the same approach to find $u(t)$ of a spring-mass-damper system for $c/c_c > 1$ and $c/c_c = 1$.
(*c*) Obtain the answer for (*b*) by letting $\omega_c = iw$ for $c/c_c > 1$ and by letting ω_c approach zero for $c/c_c = 1$.

1.25. Draw the phase trajectory of the system in Fig. 27 with the initial condition

$$x(0) = 0 \qquad \dot{x}(0) = \dot{x}_0$$

1.26. A conservative system consisting of n mass particles $m_1, m_2, \ldots, m_n$ is constrained to move with a single degree of freedom so that the spatial coordinates of the particles are differentiable functions of a single configuration variable θ, that is, $x_i = x_i(\theta)$ $y_i = y_i(\theta)$ $z_i = z_i(\theta)$; $i = 1, 2, 3, \ldots, n$.

Show that the kinetic energy of the system is given by

$$T = \tfrac{1}{2}m(\theta)\dot{\theta}^2$$

in which m is a function of θ only.

1.27. A suspension coil galvanometer, whose movement constitutes a spring-mass system, has an undamped natural period of 3.6 sec and a sensitivity of 1 in. deflection per microvolt. If this galvanometer is used in a circuit having a resistance equivalent to 64 per cent of the critical damping, and an emf of 1 microvolt suddenly appears across the galvanometer terminal, find

(*a*) the time required for the galvanometer to deflect 1 in.,
(*b*) the maximum overshoot,
(*c*) the time-deflection curve for the first 10 sec.

1.28. The idealized vehicle in Fig. 39 hits a bump on a pavement which is otherwise level and smooth. Let the profile of the bump be represented by one period of a cosine wave:

$$x_s = a\left(1 + \cos\frac{2\pi y}{L}\right) \qquad -\frac{L}{2} < y < \frac{L}{2}$$

$x_s = 0$ elsewhere.

Assume that a and R are small in comparison with L and that $c/c_c = 1$.

(*a*) Find the vertical motion of the vehicle.

(*b*) What is the maximum horizontal velocity v the vehicle may have in passing over the bump without the wheel leaving the pavement?

1.29. A platform of weight w is supported by a spring k and a shock absorber c. At $t = 0$ the system is at rest and a weight W is suddenly placed on the platform.

(*a*) At what position will the platform finally come to rest again?

(*b*) Using this position as the new equilibrium position of the system and the displacement from this position as the variable of configuration x, analyze the motion of the system.

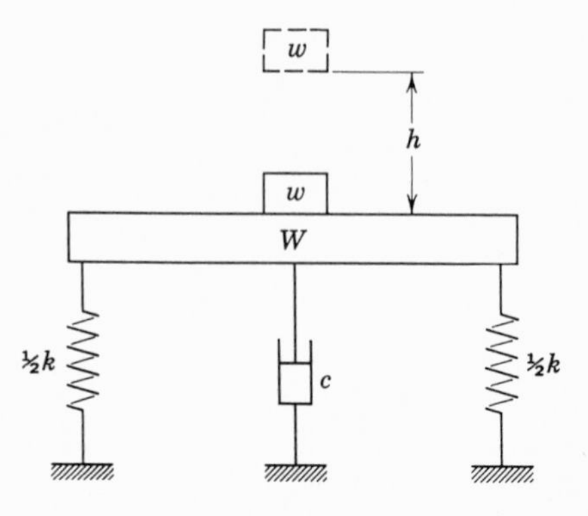

Exercise 1.29

1.30. If the weight W in Exercise 1–29 is dropped onto the platform from a height h, instead of being placed on the platform, what changes will you have to make in the analysis? (Assume that the weight does not bounce on impact.) What is the maximum force transmitted to the foundation in terms of W and h? (Assume $c/c_c = 0.5$.)

1.31. What is the damping ratio the system in Exericse 1–29 should have if the requirement is that

$$|x| \leq 0.02\,(W + w)/k$$

for $t \geq 3T$ where $T = 2\pi\sqrt{kg/(W + w)}$.

1.32. Show that

$$\int_0^t F(\tau)h(t - \tau)\,d\tau = \int_0^t F(t - \tau)h(\tau)\,d\tau$$

1.33. Find the transfer functions between x_r and x_s for the systems shown.

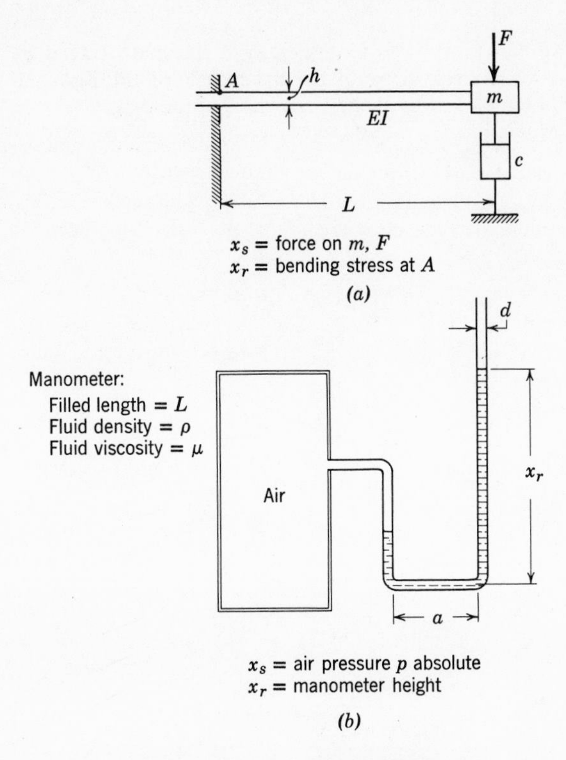

Exercise 1.33

1.34. If the general form of a transfer function is

$$T(s) = \frac{a_0 s^m + a_1 s^{m-1} + \cdots a_m}{b_0 s^n + b_1 s^{n-1} + \cdots b_n}$$

where a's and b's are real, $b_0 \neq 0$, and $n > m$ show that

$$\mathrm{Re}\,[T(i\omega_f)] = R(\omega_f)$$

is an even function of ω_f and

$$\mathrm{Im}\,[T(i\omega_f)] = I(\omega_f)$$

is an odd function of ω_f. Furthermore

$$\lim_{\omega_f \to 0} \frac{I(\omega_f)}{\omega_f} < \infty \qquad \text{and} \qquad \lim_{\omega_f \to \infty} \frac{I(\omega_f)}{\omega_f} = 0$$

1.35. A heavy disk with a diametric groove rotates in a vertical plane. A small mass particle m slides without friction in the groove under the influence of gravity force, centrifugal force, and the force of a linear spring in the groove of constant k. The disk is driven by external means to rotate at a constant speed ω_f.

(a) Show that if we call $k/m = \omega^2$, for $\omega_f^2 < \omega^2/2$, the path traced by the particle in space is a circle lying in the lower half of the disk and for $\omega^2 > \omega_f^2 > \omega^2/2$ the circle lies in the upper half of the disk.

(b) What happens when $\omega_f^2 = \omega^2/2$ and $\omega_f^2 > \omega^2$?

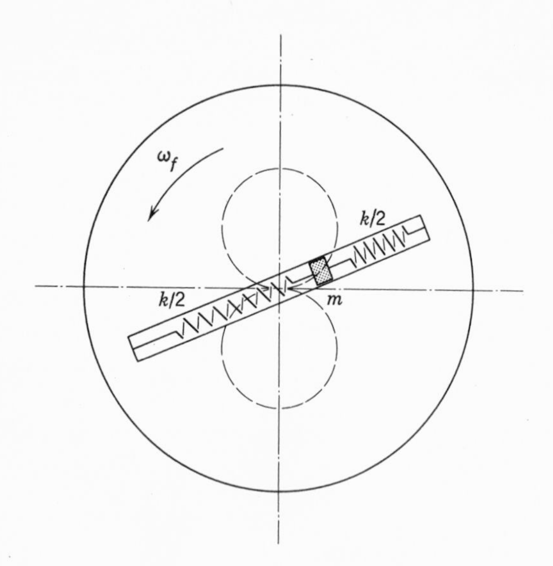

Exercise 1.35

1.36. It is known that

$$\frac{1}{2\pi i}\int_{c-i\infty}^{c+i\infty}\frac{e^{st}}{s-\alpha}\,ds = e^{\alpha t}$$

in which c is any real number greater than the real part of complex number α

$$c > \text{Re}\,(\alpha)$$

(a) Use partial fractions to show that

$$\frac{1}{2\pi i}\int_{c-i\infty}^{c+i\infty}\frac{e^{st}}{(s-\beta)(s-\gamma)}\,ds = \frac{e^{\beta t}-e^{\gamma t}}{\beta-\gamma}$$

and

$$\frac{1}{2\pi i}\int_{c-i\infty}^{c+i\infty}\frac{s+a}{(s-\beta)(s-\gamma)}\,e^{st}\,ds = \frac{(a+\beta)e^{\beta t}-(a+\gamma)e^{\gamma t}}{\beta-\gamma}$$

where c is any real number greater than the real parts of both β and γ.

(*b*) Use the results in (*a*) to show that

$$\frac{1}{2\pi i}\int_{c-i\infty}^{c+i\infty}\frac{e^{st}}{s^2+\omega^2}\,ds = \frac{1}{\omega}\sin\omega t$$

and

$$\frac{1}{2\pi i}\int_{c-i\infty}^{c+i\infty}\frac{se^{st}}{s^2+\omega^2}\,ds = \cos\omega t$$

where ω is real and $c > 0$.

(*c*) Derive (74) and (72) by (94) and the foregoing results.

(*d*) Derive the impulse response for (78) by (94) and the results in (*a*) and compare with results given in Art. 1.17.

CHAPTER 2

Systems with Two Degrees of Freedom

SECTION A. THEORY AND PRINCIPLES

2.0 Introduction

All of the systems studied so far contain only a single variable of configuration, say $x(t)$, and are therefore called single-degree-freedom systems. When a system requires two variables or coordinates, say $x_1(t)$ and $x_2(t)$, to specify its configuration at any instant t, it is said to have two degrees of freedom.[1] Such a system serves as a simple model for the study of the general oscillation characteristics of systems with several degrees of freedom. The purpose of this chapter is to introduce the reader to the more general analysis contained in Chapter 3.

2.1 Free Undamped Vibration—A Model and Its Equation of Motion

Consider the system shown in Fig. 44. It consists of two masses constrained to move in a horizontal line. The masses are connected to a stationary frame and to each other by three linear springs.

Using the displacements of the two masses from their respective equilibrium positions, x_1 and x_2, as the coordinates, we have the following equations of motion for the two masses:

$$m_{11}\ddot{x}_1 = -k_{11}x_1 - k_{12}(x_1 - x_2)$$
$$m_{22}\ddot{x}_2 = -k_{22}x_2 - k_{12}(x_2 - x_1)$$

[1] A detailed discussion of degrees of freedom and its associated number of coordinates is to be postponed till Chapter 3. For the present an intuitive understanding of the terms is sufficient.

or

$$\begin{aligned} m_{11}\ddot{x}_1 + (k_{11} + k_{12})x_1 - k_{12}x_2 &= 0 \\ -k_{12}x_1 + m_{22}\ddot{x}_2 + (k_{22} + k_{12})x_2 &= 0 \end{aligned} \tag{1}$$

This is a set of linear homogeneous differential equations with constant coefficients. In the absence of first order (or velocity) terms, it is known that the solution consists of linear combinations of sine and cosine

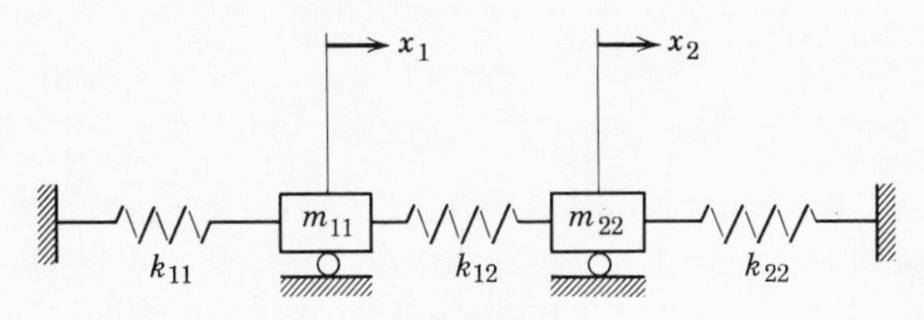

Figure 44

functions with four constants of integration to be determined by the four initial conditions of the system, which specify the displacements and the velocities of the two masses at $t = 0$. Standard methods for obtaining the solution are available. However, we shall take a physical approach that will help us to understand the problem better.

2.2 Principal or Normal Modes

Before proceeding with our analysis, let us recall that of the three quantities that characterize the free vibration of a single-degree-freedom system, only the frequency is an inherent property of the system, whereas the other two (amplitude and time-phase angle) are determined by how and when the system is set into motion by external agents. Consequently, it interests us here to find out if there is also some behavior mode that is inherent in a system with two degrees of freedom and is independent of the manner in which the system is put into motion.

Since the system is conservative, a periodic motion may be possible. This leads us to ask the question, "Can the system vibrate in such a way that the motions of the two masses are simple harmonic motions of equal frequencies?"

Assuming that this is possible, we set as usual

$$x_1 = \lambda_1 e^{i\omega t} \qquad x_2 = \lambda_2 e^{i\omega t} \tag{2}$$

in which λ_1 and λ_2 are complex amplitudes. The substitution of (2) into (1) results in a set of linear homogeneous equations in λ_1 and λ_2.

$$\begin{aligned}(-m_{11}\omega^2 + k_{11} + k_{12})\lambda_1 - k_{12}\lambda_2 &= 0\\ -k_{12}\lambda_1 + (-m_{22}\omega^2 + k_{22} + k_{12})\lambda_2 &= 0\end{aligned} \tag{3}$$

It is possible to satisfy (3), hence (1), other than by choosing the trivial solution $\lambda_1 = \lambda_2 = 0$, if and only if the determinant of the coefficients vanishes; that is,

$$\begin{vmatrix} -m_{11}\omega^2 + k_{11} + k_{12} & -k_{12} \\ -k_{12} & -m_{22}\omega^2 + k_{22} + k_{12} \end{vmatrix} = 0 \tag{4}$$

This is a quadratic equation in ω^2 and is called the *frequency* or *characteristic equation* of the system. Its roots are determined only by the constants of the system. Simple algebraic operation shows further that the two roots of ω^2 are real, nonnegative, and distinct. Hence we conclude the following:

(i) The system is capable of motions describable by the equations in (2), where ω is real, hence the motions of the two masses are simple harmonic in nature and have the same frequency.

(ii) There are two possible values of ω that satisfy the conditions prescribed. These become the *natural frequencies*[2] of the system. To *each* natural frequency there corresponds an *amplitude ratio* $\mu = \lambda_2/\lambda_1$.

$$\mu = \frac{-m_{11}\omega^2 + k_{11} + k_{12}}{k_{12}} = \frac{k_{12}}{-m_{22}\omega^2 + k_{22} + k_{12}} \tag{5}$$

These ratios are also real. In other words, although the λ's themselves are not determined by the system, their relative magnitudes are; furthermore, since the ratio between the two is real, the displacements of the two masses corresponding to a given natural frequency are in phase (or 180° out of phase if the ratio is negative).

2.3 General Solution

Therefore, we have seen that there are two basic ways in which the system can vibrate; they are called the *principal modes* of vibration. Each is characterized by a nature frequency ω and a corresponding amplitude ratio μ. These two modes can operate alone; and, since the

[2] As before, we call ω frequency for short, instead of the more exact term circular frequency, when there is no ambiguity involved.

system is a linear system in which superposition rule holds, the two modes can operate simultaneously yet independently. Let the two natural frequencies be ω' and ω'' and the corresponding amplitude ratios, μ' and μ''. A possible solution of the equations in (1) is

$$\begin{aligned} x_1(t) &= \lambda_1' e^{i\omega' t} + \lambda_1'' e^{i\omega'' t} \\ x_2(t) &= \lambda_1' \mu' e^{i\omega' t} + \lambda_1'' \mu'' e^{i\omega'' t} \end{aligned} \tag{6}$$

in which λ_1' and λ_1'' are two arbitrary complex numbers. Using standard representation, we have

$$\begin{aligned} x_1(t) &= C_0' \cos(\omega' t - \alpha') + C_0'' \cos(\omega'' t - \alpha'') \\ x_2(t) &= \mu' C_0' \cos(\omega' t - \alpha') + \mu'' C_0'' \cos(\omega'' t - \alpha'') \end{aligned} \tag{7}$$

in which C_0', C_0'', α', and α'' are the absolute values and the arguments of λ_1' and λ_1'', respectively. Altogether there are four arbitrary constants, or constants of integration, which may be adjusted to fit any initial conditions. Thus (7) is the general solution of the differential equations of motion, since it satisfies the equations and has the necessary number of constants of integration. To give expressions of these constants, in terms of the initial displacements and velocities of the two masses, involves only routine algebraic operations, which can be dispensed with here.

The use of the displacements from the equilibrium positions of the masses as the variables of configuration is arbitrary though convenient. Any pair of independent geometrical quantities, which specifies the location of the two masses, can be used as the variables of configuration. We call a pair of such variables the *generalized coordinates* of the system. In particular, any two independent linear combinations of $x_1(t)$ and $x_2(t)$ can be chosen as the coordinates.

Suppose we choose a set of coordinates p', p'', to satisfy

$$\begin{aligned} x_1 &= p' + p'' & \qquad & p' = \frac{(\mu'' x_1 - x_2)}{(\mu'' - \mu')} \\ & & \text{or} & \\ x_2 &= \mu' p' + \mu'' p'' & & p'' = \frac{(\mu' x_1 - x_2)}{(\mu' - \mu'')} \end{aligned} \tag{8}$$

Then, from (7),

$$\begin{aligned} p'(t) &= C_0' \cos(\omega' t - \alpha') \\ p''(t) &= C_0'' \cos(\omega'' t - \alpha'') \end{aligned} \tag{9}$$

Thus p' and p'' are two sinusoidal harmonic functions, each of which has its own amplitude,[3] frequency, and time-phase angle; they are called the *principal coordinates* and represent the principal modes of vibration of the system.

If we had prior knowledge of μ' and μ'' and chose at the very beginning p' and p'' as the coordinates, we would have obtained two differential equations of motion for the system, with each equation having only one

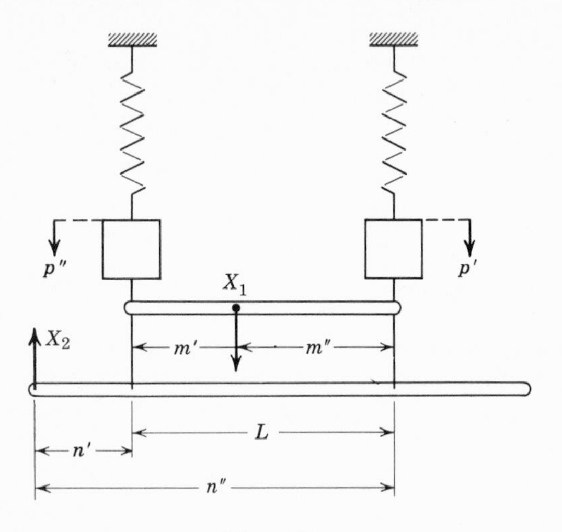

Figure 45

variable. Since their solution is known to be given by (9), they would be of the form (see Exercise 2–4)

$$\begin{aligned} \ddot{p}' + (\omega')^2 p' &= 0 \\ \ddot{p}'' + (\omega'')^2 p'' &= 0 \end{aligned} \tag{10}$$

In this way the two degrees of freedom are *mathematically separated.*

Because of the lack of clairvoyance in the values of μ' and μ'' we cannot take advantage of this transformation of coordinates from x's to p's at the very beginning. However, the existence of a transformation that reduces (1) into (10) is of importance to our later discussions.

A mechanical model for the separation of the two modes can also be conceived. In Fig. 45 we have two spring-mass systems of natural frequencies ω' and ω''. Two weightless levers are attached to the masses, as shown. For small oscillations the displacements of the masses are given by (9).

---

[3] It will become evident that the amplitude of p's has no intrinsic physical meaning because in defining p's arbitrary multiplication factors may be introduced.

Let X_1 and X_2 be two points located somewhere on the levers, as shown. The displacements of these points are then

$$X_1(t) = \frac{m'}{L}p'(t) + \frac{m''}{L}p''(t)$$

$$X_2(t) = \frac{n'}{L}p'(t) - \frac{n''}{L}p''(t)$$

Evidently, by making

$$\mu' = \frac{n'}{m'} \qquad -\mu'' = \frac{n''}{m''}$$

these equations are equivalent to (7), except for a multiplication factor.

In other words, with proper choices of ω', ω'', n'/m', and n''/m'', the free vibrations of the system in Fig. 45 can be made to simulate those of any undamped systems having two degrees of freedom.

2.4 Formulation by Energy Consideration—A General Analysis for the Free Vibration of Systems with Two Degrees of Freedom

The two differential equations in (1) were set up by considering the dynamic equilibrium of the masses. An alternate approach is by considering the conservation of energy in the system. This approach is often more convenient for systems with complicated constraints because of the following reasons. The first is that energy expressions, being scalar and nonnegative, can be written down with less reference to the geometry or the kinematics of the system. The second is that constraint forces, which do no work, will never appear in the resulting equations, whereas they often appear in the equilibrium equations and have to be eliminated.[4] The kinetic energy and the potential energy expressions for the system in Fig. 44 are

$$T = \tfrac{1}{2}(m_{11}\dot{x}_1^2 + m_{22}\dot{x}_2^2)$$

$$V = \tfrac{1}{2}(c_{11}x_1^2 + 2c_{12}x_1x_2 + c_{22}x_2^2)$$

in which

$$c_{11} = k_{11} + k_{12} \qquad c_{22} = k_{22} + k_{12} \qquad c_{12} = -k_{12}$$

The absence of the term $\dot{x}_1\dot{x}_2$ in the first expression is due to the particular choice of coordinates. In general, for a linear system whose configuration is specified by a pair of generalized coordinates q_1 and q_2 will have the

[4] See examples in Art. 2.11.

following quadratic forms for the expressions of its kinetic and potential energies:[5]

$$\begin{aligned} T &= \tfrac{1}{2}(a_{11}\dot{q}_1^{\,2} + 2a_{12}\dot{q}_1\dot{q}_2 + a_{22}\dot{q}_2^{\,2}) \\ V &= \tfrac{1}{2}(c_{11}q_1^{\,2} + 2c_{12}q_1q_2 + c_{22}q_2^{\,2}) \end{aligned} \tag{11}$$

This statement is amplified in the next chapter. In the meantime, we shall consider (11) as the definition of a linear system. Since the system is in free vibration, the principle of conservation of energy requires

$$\frac{d}{dt}(T + V) = 0$$

Upon differentiating (11) and rearranging the terms, we obtain

$$(a_{11}\ddot{q}_1 + c_{11}q_1 + a_{12}\ddot{q}_2 + c_{12}q_2)\dot{q}_1 + (a_{12}\ddot{q}_1 + c_{12}q_1 + a_{22}\ddot{q}_2 + c_{22}q_2)\dot{q}_2 = 0 \tag{12}$$

This relation must hold for all possible vibrations of the system and at all times. However, the values of $\dot{q}_1$ and $\dot{q}_2$ at a given instant are not related by dynamics to the rest of the terms.[6] For instance, the system can be set into motion with arbitrary combinations of q_{10}, q_{20}, $\dot{q}_{10}$, and $\dot{q}_{20}$. Hence the coefficients of $\dot{q}_1$ and $\dot{q}_2$ in (12) must vanish independently, or

$$\begin{aligned} a_{11}\ddot{q}_1 + c_{11}q_1 + a_{12}\ddot{q}_2 + c_{12}q_2 &= 0 \\ a_{12}\ddot{q}_1 + c_{12}q_1 + a_{22}\ddot{q}_2 + c_{22}q_2 &= 0 \end{aligned} \tag{13}$$

This is the set of differential equations that describes the motion of the system.[7] These equations contain the same set of coefficients as the energy expressions. The a_{12} terms represent the *inertia coupling between the coordinates*, and the c_{12} terms represent the *elastic coupling*.[8]

By either of the two approaches illustrated, we find that the frequency equation of the system is

$$\begin{vmatrix} -a_{11}\omega^2 + c_{11} & -a_{12}\omega^2 + c_{12} \\ -a_{12}\omega^2 + c_{12} & -a_{22}\omega^2 + c_{22} \end{vmatrix} = 0 \tag{14}$$

or

$$(a_{11}a_{22} - a_{12}^{\,2})\omega^4 - (a_{11}c_{22} + c_{11}a_{22} - 2a_{12}c_{12})\omega^2 + (c_{11}c_{22} - c_{12}^{\,2}) = 0$$

---

[5] The change of the notation from the m's to the a's and from the x's to the q's is in keeping with the common usage. The a's and c's are called the *inertia constants* and the *elastic constants*, respectively. Note also the appearance of the term a_{12} in the general system.

[6] In contrast, the displacement q's produce spring forces that in turn produce acceleration $\ddot{q}$'s and are thereby dynamically related to the accelerations.

[7] Those who are familiar with Lagrange's equation of motion can easily verify that (11) leads to (13).

[8] Note that the presence or absence of coupling terms depends on the choice of coordinates. When no coupling terms appear, the coordinates become the principal coordinates.

This quadratic equation of ω^2 can be solved in the routine manner. However, a particularly interesting representation of its solution is given below.

Let us define

$$a = \begin{vmatrix} a_{11} & a_{12} \\ a_{12} & a_{22} \end{vmatrix}$$

$$\omega_{11}{}^2 = \frac{1}{a}\begin{vmatrix} c_{11} & a_{12} \\ c_{12} & a_{22} \end{vmatrix} \qquad \omega_{22}{}^2 = \frac{1}{a}\begin{vmatrix} a_{11} & c_{12} \\ a_{12} & c_{22} \end{vmatrix} \tag{15}$$

$$\omega_{12}{}^2 = \frac{1}{a}\left[\begin{vmatrix} a_{11} & c_{11} \\ a_{12} & c_{12} \end{vmatrix}\begin{vmatrix} a_{22} & c_{22} \\ a_{12} & c_{12} \end{vmatrix}\right]^{1/2}$$

It can then be verified that the two roots of ω^2 in (14) are

$$\begin{matrix}\omega'^2 \\ \omega''^2\end{matrix} = \tfrac{1}{2}[\omega_{11}{}^2 + \omega_{22}{}^2) \pm \sqrt{(\omega_{11}{}^2 - \omega_{22}{}^2)^2 + 4(\omega_{12}{}^2)^2}] \tag{16}$$

This is the familiar expression for the principal stresses in plane stress problems. Hence Mohr's construction, shown in Fig. 46, can be used here as well. The reason for bringing Mohr's circle into this discussion is to point out that there is an intimate mathematical connection between the analysis of the principal modes of vibration and of the principal stresses, although the problems are physically unrelated.[9] Incidentally, the expressions in (15) will not look so complicated if the inertia coupling is absent, or $a_{12} = 0$. In that case we may take the system in Fig. 44 as a model and find

$$\omega_{11}{}^2 = \frac{c_{11}}{m_{11}} \qquad \omega_{22}{}^2 = \frac{c_{22}}{m_{22}}$$
$$\omega_{12}{}^2 = \frac{c_{12}}{\sqrt{m_{11}m_{22}}} \tag{17}$$

Substituting (17) into (5) yields

$$\frac{\sqrt{m_{22}}\lambda_2}{\sqrt{m_{11}}\lambda_1} = \frac{\omega_{11}{}^2 - \omega^2}{-\omega_{12}{}^2} = \frac{-\omega_{12}{}^2}{\omega_{22}{}^2 - \omega^2} \tag{18}$$

From Fig. 46 it can be seen that the amplitude ratios corresponding to the two principal modes can be represented by the tangents of the angles θ' and θ'' indicated

$$\frac{\sqrt{m_{22}}\lambda_2'}{\sqrt{m_{11}}\lambda_1'} = \tan\theta' \qquad \frac{\sqrt{m_{22}}\lambda_2''}{\sqrt{m_{11}}\lambda_1''} = -\tan\theta'' \tag{19}$$[10]

where $\theta' + \theta'' = 90°$.

[9] Another problem having the same mathematical connection with these two is the one dealing with the principal moments of inertia about centroidal axes.

[10] The negative sign stems from the fact that ω is less than either ω_{11} or ω_{22}.

Thus in the absence of inertia coupling the principal modes of vibration can be represented by two perpendicular vectors in a proper coordinate system, as shown in Fig. 47. A more generalized orthogonality relation-

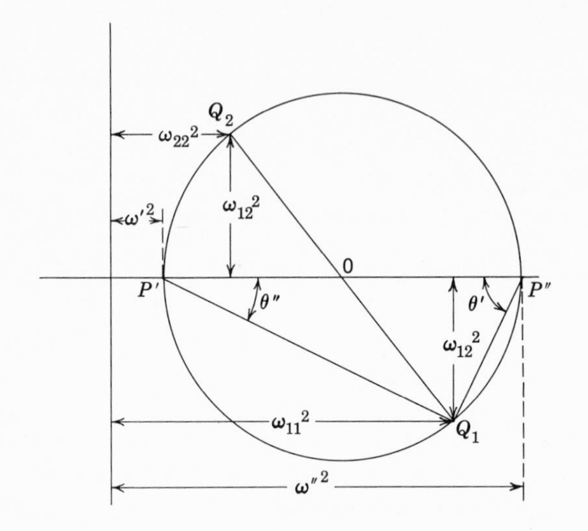

Figure 46

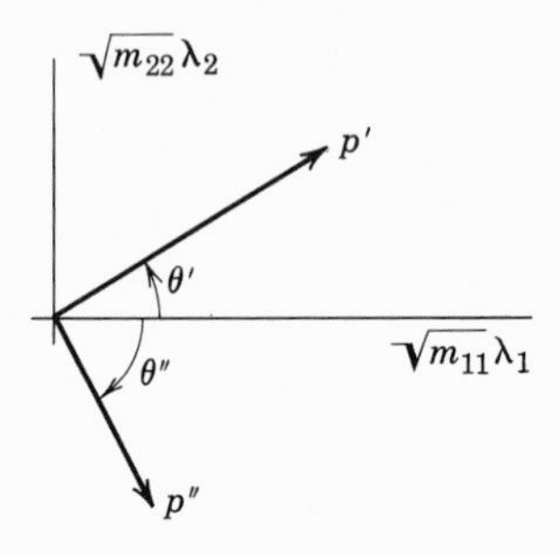

Figure 47

ship also exists in systems containing the "inertia coupling" terms, as discussed in Chapter 3.

2.5 The Use of Influence Coefficients

The elastic property of a system is often more conveniently expressed by a set of quantities called the *influence coefficients*. The influence coefficient γ_{12} is defined as the displacement of the system at point 1 owing to a unit force applied at point 2.[11] The coefficients, γ_{11}, γ_{21}, γ_{22}, etc., are similarly defined. It is stipulated, however, that at a given point all displacements have to be measured in the same direction as the unit forces applied at this point, although they may not be in the same direction of the displacements and the forces at the other point. The meanings of the words "displacements" and "force" are generalized later to cover other things. At present, it suffices to use them in their restricted sense.

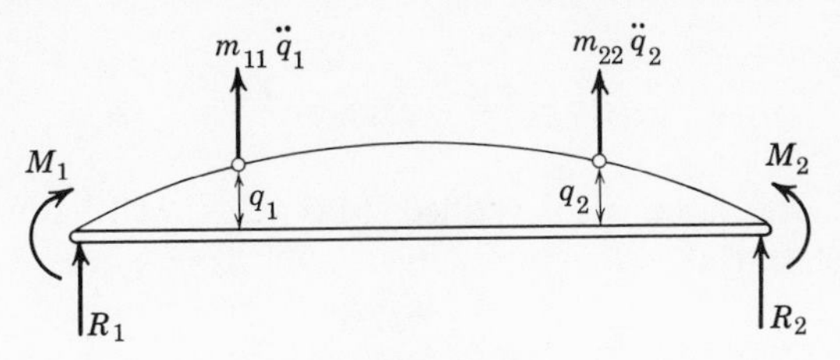

Figure 48

To illustrate the use of influence coefficients in vibration analysis, let us consider a system consisting of a weightless beam supported in some way and carrying two concentrated masses at points 1 and 2, as shown in Fig. 48. Let q_1 and q_2 be the transverse displacements of the beam at the location of the masses at the instant t. Taking the beam as a free body, we see that the two masses exert inertia forces of $m_{11}\ddot{q}_1$ and $m_{22}\ddot{q}_2$ to the beam.[12] These forces with the necessary reactions at the supports produce q_1 and q_2.

Hence

$$\begin{aligned} -q_1 &= \gamma_{11}m_{11}\ddot{q}_1 + \gamma_{12}m_{22}\ddot{q}_2 \\ -q_2 &= \gamma_{21}m_{11}\ddot{q}_1 + \gamma_{22}m_{22}\ddot{q}_2 \end{aligned} \tag{20}$$

By expressing the $\ddot{q}$'s in terms of the q's, we have

$$\begin{aligned} m_{11}\ddot{q}_1 &= \frac{1}{\gamma}(-\gamma_{22}q_1 + \gamma_{12}q_2) \\ m_{22}\ddot{q}_2 &= \frac{1}{\gamma}(-\gamma_{11}q_2 + \gamma_{21}q_1) \end{aligned} \tag{21}$$

---

[11] It is implied here that the system is supported in such a way that forces can be applied to it without producing accelerations; otherwise, the influence coefficients cannot be immediately defined. (See Art. 2.9.)

[12] With the beam as the free body under consideration, the forces exerted by the masses are opposite to the accelerations of the masses. The forces shown in Fig. 48 are in their positive directions consistent with the positive directions of the displacements. The actual directions of the forces are in the reverse, but this fact is to come from the solution of the problem and need not be assumed beforehand. This is very elementary, although at times confusing.

where

$$\gamma = \begin{vmatrix} \gamma_{11} & \gamma_{12} \\ \gamma_{21} & \gamma_{22} \end{vmatrix}$$

By comparing (21) with (1) and recalling the definition of the spring constants c's, we see that

$$\begin{aligned} c_{11} &= \frac{\gamma_{22}}{\gamma} & c_{22} &= \frac{\gamma_{11}}{\gamma} \\ -c_{12} &= \frac{\gamma_{12}}{\gamma} & -c_{12} &= \frac{\gamma_{21}}{\gamma} \end{aligned} \tag{22}$$

Incidentally, we have also verified Maxwell's well-known *reciprocal theorem* which states

$$\gamma_{12} = \gamma_{21}$$

The relationship between the influence coefficients and the elastic constants of a system, as represented by (22), has certain symmetry. We can easily verify that

$$\gamma_{11} = \frac{c_{22}}{c} \qquad \gamma_{22} = \frac{c_{11}}{c} \qquad \gamma_{12} = -\frac{c_{12}}{c}$$

in which

$$c = \begin{vmatrix} c_{11} & c_{12} \\ c_{12} & c_{22} \end{vmatrix} \tag{23}$$

Thus in the language of matrix algebra the influence coefficients and the elastic constants of a system form matrices that are inverse to each other.

The transformation of (20) into (21) shows that it is not often easy to say what kinds of coupling exist between the coordinates by looking at the differential equation. In this problem there is no inertia coupling between q_1 and q_2, even though both accelerations appear in both equations of (20). This is obvious if we write down the kinetic energy expression for the system and observe the absence of a $\dot{q}_1 \dot{q}_2$ term.

Equation (20) can be directly solved without converting the influence coefficients into the elastic constants. Setting, as usual,

$$q_1 = \lambda_1 e^{i\omega t} \qquad q_2 = \lambda_2 e^{i\omega t}$$

in (20), we have, after multiplying the equations by $-1/\omega^2$,

$$\begin{aligned} \left(m_{11}\gamma_{11} - \frac{1}{\omega^2}\right)\lambda_1 + (m_{22}\gamma_{12})\lambda_2 &= 0 \\ (m_{11}\gamma_{12})\lambda_1 + \left(m_{22}\gamma_{22} - \frac{1}{\omega^2}\right)\lambda_2 &= 0 \end{aligned} \tag{24}$$

The frequency equation is then obtained by the condition for the existence of nontrivial solutions, namely, the vanishing of the determinant

$$\begin{vmatrix} m_{11}\gamma_{11} - \dfrac{1}{\omega^2} & m_{22}\gamma_{12} \\ m_{11}\gamma_{12} & m_{22}\gamma_{22} - \dfrac{1}{\omega^2} \end{vmatrix} = 0 \tag{25}$$

2.6 Rayleigh's Quotient

In dealing with systems having a single degree of freedom, it was found that the natural frequencies can be obtained directly by equating the maximum values of the two energies.

$$T_m = V_m$$

We shall now determine where this procedure will lead us in dealing with systems having two degrees of freedom. Let us assume that the system vibrates in one of its principal modes with

$$q_1 = \lambda_1 \cos(\omega t - \alpha) \qquad q_2 = \lambda_2 \cos(\omega t - \alpha)$$

Hence[13]

$$\begin{aligned} T_m &= \tfrac{1}{2}\omega^2(a_{11}\lambda_1^2 + 2a_{12}\lambda_1\lambda_2 + a_{22}\lambda_2^2) = f\omega^2 \\ V_m &= \tfrac{1}{2}(c_{11}\lambda_1^2 + 2c_{12}\lambda_1\lambda_2 + c_{22}\lambda_2^2) \end{aligned} \tag{26}$$

$$\omega^2 = \frac{V_m(\lambda_1, \lambda_2)}{f(\lambda_1, \lambda_2)} \tag{27}$$

Since V_m and f are homogeneous quadratic forms of λ_1 and λ_2, ω^2 is a function of the amplitude ratio $\mu = \lambda_2/\lambda_1$. Without knowing the correct value of μ, ω cannot be found by Rayleigh's method, and if μ is to be found by the method previously discussed we shall have found ω already. The matter, however, bears further discussion.

Let us consider the ratio of the quadratic forms as a function of μ and call it *Rayleigh's quotient*.

$$Q(\mu) = \frac{c_{11} + 2c_{12}\mu + c_{22}\mu^2}{a_{11} + 2a_{12}\mu + a_{22}\mu^2} \tag{28}$$

$Q(\mu)$ becomes ω^2 when μ is the amplitude ratio of a natural mode; otherwise it is always positive and finite, since the energy expressions themselves are always positive and finite for any finite values of λ_1 and λ_2. It is therefore bounded both from above and from below. If these bounds can be established, they will at least give us an estimate of the natural frequencies of the system.

[13] λ_1 and λ_2 are real quantities in this discussion.

It is not difficult to reason out that a plot of Q-versus-μ relationship will result in a curve having the features shown in Fig. 49. Rayleigh's quotient thus has two *stationary values*, one a maximum and the other a minimum. These can be located by setting

$$\frac{dQ}{d\mu} = 0$$

which is equivalent to

$$\frac{\partial Q}{\partial \lambda_1} = 0 \qquad \frac{\partial Q}{\partial \lambda_2} = 0 \tag{29}$$

Substituting (27) for Q in (29), we have

$$\frac{\partial Q}{\partial \lambda_1} = \frac{1}{f^2}\left(f\,\frac{\partial V_m}{\partial \lambda_1} - V_m\,\frac{\partial f}{\partial \lambda_1}\right) = 0$$

$$\frac{\partial Q}{\partial \lambda_2} = \frac{1}{f^2}\left(f\,\frac{\partial V_m}{\partial \lambda_2} - V_m\,\frac{\partial f}{\partial \lambda_2}\right) = 0$$

Multiplication by Qf^2 yields

$$Qf\,\frac{\partial V_m}{\partial \lambda_1} - V_m\,\frac{\partial}{\partial \lambda_1}(Qf) = 0$$

$$Qf\,\frac{\partial V_m}{\partial \lambda_2} - V_m\,\frac{\partial}{\partial \lambda_2}(Qf) = 0$$

Since $Qf = T_m = V_m$,

$$\frac{\partial}{\partial \lambda_2}(V_m - T_m) = 0$$

$$\frac{\partial}{\partial \lambda_1}(V_m - T_m) = 0 \tag{30}$$

Note that these are not trivial identities, even though $T_m - V_m = 0$.

In combining (30) with (26), we have

$$\begin{aligned} (-a_{11}Q^2 + c_{11})\lambda_1 + (-a_{12}Q^2 + c_{12})\lambda_2 &= 0 \\ (-a_{12}Q^2 + c_{12})\lambda_1 + (-a_{22}Q^2 + c_{22})\lambda_2 &= 0 \end{aligned} \tag{31}$$

The condition for this set of homogeneous equations to be consistent is that the determinant formed by the coefficients must vanish. This condition is the frequency equation (14) exactly.

Thus we have shown that *the two stationary values of Rayleigh's quotient are the natural frequencies of the system.*

Perhaps it is worthwhile here to add a physical model to our analysis. Take again the system consisting of two masses and three springs. Let us incorporate into the system some device, such as a gear train, that constrains the motions of the two masses to a given displacement ratio. In so doing we reduce the system to one with a single degree of freedom. Equations (26), (27), and (28), however, are still valid, except that $\mu = \lambda_2/\lambda_1$ is now a given ratio and the frequency of the constrained vibration

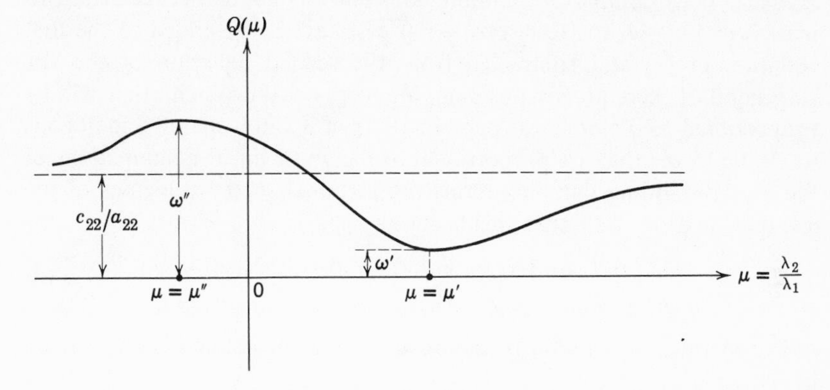

Figure 49

is determined by it. In general, if the ratio imposed by the constraining device changes a little, the frequency of the constrained vibration changes accordingly, But, when the ratio imposed is such that the frequency is a maximum or a minimum, $dQ/d\mu = 0$, a small change in the ratio produces a change in the frequency which is of a smaller order. The various elastic and inertia forces in the existing vibration are therefore in an equilibrium by themselves without the help of the forces exerted by the constraining device. Hence, if the constraints are removed, the vibration remains unchanged, and it is one of the normal modes of the system.

We have shown that the natural frequencies of vibration can be found by maximizing or minimizing Rayleigh's quotient. However, to carry out the process in its entirety requires almost the same algebraic steps as those involved in the standard procedure. The practical value of the analysis just presented is then lost. To apply Rayleigh's method in a practical way, the amplitude ratio corresponding to a given mode instead of being determined exactly is only estimated. The frequency is computed from Rayleigh's quotient by using the estimated amplitude ratio. This procedure gives surprisingly good results because, as we have seen, near a natural frequency of the system the value of Rayleigh's quotient is insensitive to small changes in the amplitude ratio. (See Art. 2.12.) In systems with two degrees of freedom the exact value of the natural frequencies can be obtained without much computation. The practical utility of Rayleigh's method and its modification is in systems with many degrees of freedom, but it is more clearly illustrated when applied to a simpler system.

2.7 Vibration of Damped Systems

If a viscous damper of damping constant c is added between the two masses in Fig. 44, the term $c(\dot{x}_1 - \dot{x}_2)$ will have to be added to the first equation of (1) and subtracted from the second equation of the set. In general, if there are viscous damping forces in the system, they will be proportional to $\dot{q}$'s or linear combinations of $\dot{q}$'s in a manner analogous to elastic forces that are proportional to the q's or linear combinations of the q's. By adding damping terms proportional to the velocities of the $\dot{q}$'s, the equation of motion (13) becomes

$$\begin{aligned} a_{11}\ddot{q}_1 + b_{11}\dot{q}_1 + c_{11}q_1 + a_{12}\ddot{q}_2 + b_{12}\dot{q}_2 + c_{12}q_2 = 0 \\ a_{12}\ddot{q}_1 + b_{12}\dot{q}_1 + c_{12}q_1 + a_{22}\ddot{q}_2 + b_{22}\dot{q}_2 + c_{22}q_2 = 0 \end{aligned} \tag{32}$$[14]

The method of solution is analogous to that of solving (13); that is, by letting

$$q_1 = \lambda_1 e^{st} \qquad \text{or} \qquad q_1 = \lambda_1 e^{i\sigma t}$$

and (33)

$$q_2 = \lambda_2 e^{st} \qquad \text{or} \qquad q_2 = \lambda_2 e^{i\sigma t}$$

in (32). This leads to the *frequency* or *characteristic equation*

$$\begin{vmatrix} a_{11}s^2 + b_{11}s + c_{11} & a_{12}s^2 + b_{12}s + c_{12} \\ a_{12}s^2 + b_{12}s + c_{12} & a_{22}s^2 + b_{22}s + c_{22} \end{vmatrix} = 0 \tag{34}$$

which is a biquadratic equation in s or $i\sigma$, hence possesses four roots: s_1, s_2, s_3, and s_4; the solution of (32) is then

$$\begin{aligned} q_1 = \lambda_{11}e^{s_1t} + \lambda_{12}e^{s_2t} + \lambda_{13}e^{s_3t} + \lambda_{14}e^{s_4t} \\ q_2 = \lambda_{21}e^{s_1t} + \lambda_{22}e^{s_2t} + \lambda_{23}e^{s_3t} + \lambda_{24}e^{s_4t} \end{aligned} \tag{35}$$

in which the ratios $\lambda_{11}/\lambda_{21}$, $\lambda_{12}/\lambda_{22}$, $\lambda_{13}/\lambda_{23}$, and $\lambda_{14}/\lambda_{24}$ are determined by s_1, s_2, s_3, and s_4, respectively.

$$\begin{aligned} \frac{\lambda_{11}}{\lambda_{21}} = -\frac{a_{12}s_1^2 + b_{12}s_1 + c_{12}}{a_{11}s_1^2 + b_{11}s_1 + c_{11}} = -\frac{a_{22}s_1^2 + b_{22}s_1 + c_{22}}{a_{12}s_1^2 + b_{12}s_1 + c_{12}} \\ \frac{\lambda_{12}}{\lambda_{22}} = -\frac{a_{12}s_2^2 + b_{12}s_2 + c_{12}}{a_{11}s_2^2 + b_{11}s_2 + c_{11}} = -\frac{a_{22}s_2^2 + b_{22}s_2 + c_{22}}{a_{12}s_2^2 + b_{12}s^2 + c_{12}} \end{aligned} \tag{36}$$

etc.

[14] We assume here that $b_{12} = b_{21}$, a fact which is discussed further in Art. 3.8.

The initial displacements and velocities of the system and the relations in (36) determine the eight constants of integration in (35). If all the roots of (34) are real, the ratios in (36) are real; and with real initial values of displacements and velocities, all the λ's are real. The resulting motion is nonoscillatory or aperiodic, and the system is overdamped. Furthermore, since the damping forces dissipate energy, the motions must decay with time and the real roots of (34) must be negative.

If (34) has complex roots, they must come in complex conjugate pairs, since all the coefficients in this algebraic equation are real. Let

$$s_1 = s \qquad \text{and} \qquad s_2 = \bar{s}$$

be a pair of such roots. Then

$$e^{s_1 t} = e^{st} \qquad e^{s_2 t} = e^{\bar{s}t}$$

will also be complex conjugate to each other, and, in order to yield real values of q_1 and q_2,[15] the first two coefficients in each of the equations in (35) must also be complex conjugates.

$$\lambda_{11} = \lambda \qquad \lambda_{12} = \bar{\lambda}$$

If in (36) we let

$$\frac{\lambda_{11}}{\lambda_{21}} = \frac{1}{r}$$

$$\lambda_{21} = r\lambda_{11} = r\lambda \qquad \lambda_{22} = \bar{\lambda}_{21} = \bar{r}\bar{\lambda}$$

The part of the solution represented by the first two terms of (35) is then

$$q_1 = \lambda e^{st} + \bar{\lambda} e^{\bar{s}t}$$

$$q_2 = r\lambda e^{st} + \overline{r\lambda} e^{\bar{s}t}$$

Let

$$s = i\sigma = i\omega_c - \eta \qquad \lambda = \tfrac{1}{2}Ce^{-i\alpha} \qquad \text{and} \qquad r = \mu e^{-i\theta}$$

Then

$$\bar{s} = -i\omega_c - \eta \qquad \bar{\lambda} = \tfrac{1}{2}Ce^{i\alpha} \qquad \bar{r} = \mu e^{i\theta}$$

Substituting these into the expressions for q_1 and q_2, we have

$$q_1 = Ce^{-\eta t}\cos(\omega_c t - \alpha)$$

$$q_2 = \mu Ce^{-\eta t}\cos(\omega_c t - \alpha - \theta)$$

If (34) has two pairs of complex roots, the solution (35) may be expressed by

$$\begin{aligned} q_1 &= C'e^{-\eta' t}\cos(\omega_c' t - \alpha') + C''e^{-\eta'' t}\cos(\omega_c'' t - \alpha'') \\ q_2 &= \mu' C'e^{-\eta' t}\cos(\omega_c' t - \alpha' - \theta') \\ &\quad + \mu'' C''e^{-\eta'' t}\cos(\omega_c'' t - \alpha'' - \theta'') \end{aligned} \tag{37}$$

---

[15] Note that (35) is a conventional representation for solutions of (32). Under any real initial conditions it must yield real solutions.

in which $-\eta' \pm i\omega_c'$ and $-\eta'' \pm i\omega_c''$ are the roots of (34); μ', μ'', θ', and θ'' are determined by (36); and C', C'', α', and α'' are determined by the initial conditions.

It is evident from (37) that the oscillation of a slightly damped system with two degrees of freedom may be decomposed into two characteristic damped oscillations in a manner analogous to the decomposition of undamped vibrations into principal modes. In other words, by choosing a pair of coordinates p' and p'', which are certain linear combinations of q_1 and q_2, the set of equations (32) can be transformed into another set in which the two variables are separated. The coefficients for this transformation are determined by (36) and will be complex numbers if the roots of (34) are complex. The numerical computation involved in this transformation is, however, very tedious.

To sum up, the nature of free vibration of a two-degree-freedom system depends upon the roots of the characteristic equation (34). Since all the coefficients of this equation are real, it may be factored into two quadratic factors:

$$(s^2 + 2\eta' s + \omega'^2)(s^2 + 2\eta'' s + \omega''^2) = 0$$

The constant terms in the factors are the squares of the natural frequencies of the undamped system because, if all the b's in (34) are zero, $\eta' = \eta'' = 0$, and the equation is identical to (14). The two η's are the same as those in (37). If there are damping forces, η' and η'' in general will be positive, although in special cases one of the two may be zero. To each of the quadratic factors there corresponds a mode of vibration. In each factor the condition $\eta < \omega$ indicates a damped oscillation with damped frequency $\omega_c^2 = \omega^2 - \eta^2$, the condition $\eta = 0$ indicates a sinusoidal oscillation, and the condition $\eta \geq \omega$ indicates an aperiodic motion. The condition $\omega = 0$ is discussed in Art. 2.9.

To factor the biquadratic equation, a numerical method must be used. For such well-known methods as *Graeffe's root-squaring method* and *Lin's iteration method* and its modifications the readers are referred to textbooks on numerical analysis. It may be added that the general method of solution for biquadratic equations is not convenient to use.

2.8 Forced Vibration

If a two-degree-freedom system is subjected to external excitation, the differential equations of motion will no longer be homogeneous. The external excitations may be forces applied to the mass particle in the system or in motions imposed on certain parts of the system. In either case, the excitations are known functions of time, and the general form for the differential equations of motion is

$$\begin{aligned} a_{11}\ddot{q}_1 + b_{11}\dot{q}_1 + c_{11}q_1 + a_{12}\ddot{q}_2 + b_{12}\dot{q}_2 + c_{12}q_2 &= Q_1(t) \\ a_{12}\ddot{q}_1 + b_{12}\dot{q}_1 + c_{12}q_1 + a_{22}\ddot{q}_2 + b_{22}\dot{q}_2 + c_{22}q_2 &= Q_2(t) \end{aligned} \tag{38}$$

This set of equations can be solved by a number of standard methods. Here we will treat special cases of the most practical interest.

(A) STEADY-STATE VIBRATION UNDER PERIODIC FORCES

It is known that periodic functions can be expanded into a Fourier series of sinusoidal functions. Since the system is linear and the principle of superposition holds, the solution for periodic forces can be built up from solutions for sinusoidal forces. We need therefore deal here only with sinusoidal forces. Let

$$Q_1(t) = F_1 e^{i\omega_f t} \qquad \text{and} \qquad Q_2(t) = F_2 e^{i\omega_f t} \tag{39}$$

in which F_1 and F_2 are in general complex numbers. The steady-state solution must be of the form

$$q_1 = \lambda_1 e^{i\omega_f t} \qquad \text{and} \qquad q_2 = \lambda_2 e^{i\omega_f t} \tag{40}$$

By substituting (39) and (40) in (38), we have

$$\begin{aligned} (-\omega_f^2 a_{11} + i\omega_f b_{11} + c_{11})\lambda_1 + (-\omega_f^2 a_{12} + i\omega_f b_{12} + c_{12})\lambda_2 &= F_1 \\ (-\omega_f^2 a_{12} + i\omega_f b_{12} + c_{12})\lambda_1 + (-\omega_f^2 a_{22} + i\omega_f b_{22} + c_{22})\lambda_2 &= F_2 \end{aligned} \tag{41}$$

This set of equations possesses a pair of complex solutions for λ_1 and λ_2, which are to be interpreted in accordance with the discussion in Art. 1.7. They are given by

$$\begin{aligned} \lambda_1 &= \frac{1}{D}\begin{vmatrix} F_1, & -\omega_f^2 a_{12} + i\omega_f b_{12} + c_{12} \\ F_2, & -\omega_f^2 a_{22} + i\omega_f b_{22} + c_{22} \end{vmatrix} \\ \lambda_2 &= \frac{1}{D}\begin{vmatrix} -\omega_f^2 a_{11} + i\omega_f b_{11} + c_{11}, & F_1 \\ -\omega_f^2 a_{12} + i\omega_f b_{12} + c_{12}, & F_2 \end{vmatrix} \end{aligned} \tag{42}$$

where

$$\begin{aligned} D &= \begin{vmatrix} -\omega_f^2 a_{11} + i\omega_f b_{11} + c_{11}, & -\omega_f^2 a_{12} + i b_{12}\omega_f + c_{12} \\ -\omega_f^2 a_{12} + i\omega_f b_{12} + c_{12}, & -\omega_f^2 a_{22} + i b_{22}\omega_f + c_{22} \end{vmatrix} \\ &= (\omega_f^2 - i\eta'\omega_f - \omega'^2)(\omega_f^2 - i\eta''\omega_f - \omega''^2) \end{aligned} \tag{43}$$

It is to be noted that if both η' and η'' are not equal to zero the determinant D cannot vanish and λ_1 and λ_2 are always finite. On the other hand, if one or both of the η's are zero and the determinant D vanishes for one or two values of ω_f, namely, ω' and/or ω'', the correspondent λ_1 and λ_2 will in general become infinitely large.

A frequency response curve for each coordinate in a two-degree-freedom system can be obtained from (42) for any appropriate set of parameters. It is not difficult to see that if the damping coefficients are not too large all the curves will have two peaks near the natural frequencies of the system. (See Fig. 58).

(B) ANALYSIS OF AN UNDAMPED SYSTEM BY PRINCIPAL COORDINATES

In Art. 2.3 (and Exercise 2.4) we have sketched a procedure whereby the set of homogeneous differential equations (1) may be transformed, through a linear transformation of coordinates, into another set of the form (10). Such transformation is also possible for equations in the general form (13) and for nonhomogeneous equations

$$\begin{aligned} a_{11}\ddot{q}_1 + c_{11}q_1 + a_{12}\ddot{q}_2 + c_{12}q_2 &= Q_1(t) \\ a_{12}\ddot{q}_1 + c_{12}q_1 + a_{22}\ddot{q}_2 + c_{22}q_2 &= Q_2(t) \end{aligned} \tag{44}$$

Without the use of matrix algebra, the steps involved become very tedious. Since the subject is discussed more fully in Chapter 3, we give only the final results here. If, as in (8), we let

$$\begin{aligned} q_1 &= p' + p'' \\ q_2 &= \mu'p' + \mu''p'' \end{aligned} \tag{45}$$

the set of differential equations (44) can be transformed into

$$\begin{aligned} \ddot{p}' + \omega'^2 p' &= F'(t) \\ \ddot{p}'' + \omega''^2 p'' &= F''(t) \end{aligned} \tag{46}$$

where

$$\begin{aligned} F'(t) &= \frac{(\mu''a_{22} + a_{12})Q_1(t) - (\mu''a_{12} + a_{11})Q_2(t)}{(a_{11}a_{22} - a_{12}^2)(\mu'' - \mu')} \\ F''(t) &= \frac{-(\mu'a_{22} + a_{12})Q_1(t) + (\mu'a_{12} + a_{11})Q_2(t)}{(a_{11}a_{22} - a_{12}^2)(\mu'' - \mu')} \end{aligned} \tag{47}$$

Since the variables are separated in (46), the solutions for p' and p'' can be obtained by methods discussed in Chapter 1. The initial conditions of p' and p'' are determined by those for q_1 and q_2 through (45). Similarly, the solutions for q_1 and q_2 are obtained by substituting the solutions for p' and p'' into (45).

Of particular interest are cases in which there is no inertia coupling between the coordinates. For such systems $a_{11} = m_{11}$, $a_{12} = 0$, $a_{22} = m_{22}$, and, according to (19),

$$\mu'\mu'' + \frac{m_{11}}{m_{22}} = 0$$

The expressions of F' and F'' can then be simplified to read

$$\begin{aligned} F'(t) &= \frac{\mu''}{m_{11}(\mu'' - \mu')} Q_1(t) + \mu' Q_2(t) \\ F''(t) &= \frac{\mu'}{m_{11}(\mu' - \mu'')} Q_1(t) + \mu'' Q_2(t) \end{aligned} \tag{48}$$

or

$$\begin{aligned} m_{11}(\mu'' - \mu')(\ddot{p}' + \omega'^2 p') &= \mu'' Q_1(t) + \mu'\mu'' Q_2(t) \\ m_{11}(\mu' - \mu'')(\ddot{p}'' + \omega''^2 p'') &= \mu' Q_1(t) + \mu'\mu'' Q_2(t) \end{aligned} \tag{49}$$

According to the principle of superposition discussed in Art. 1.11, the solutions to (46) or (49) can be obtained by substituting the appropriate parameters of these equations into (66), (74), and (76) of Chapter 1. This method is particularly advantageous when transient solutions are desired.

(C) INDICIAL RESPONSE FOR DAMPED SYSTEMS

When the system is damped, separation of variables by linear transform is possible but not practical. Nonperiodic motion of a damped system produced by external forces is of great interest in the study of control systems. The problem is best treated by methods in operational calculus, which is a subject by itself and cannot be included here. On the other hand, the same problem is only of passing interest in theory of mechanical vibration because complex systems with many damping forces are rare. The simpler practical problems can usually be solved by more elementary methods without too much extra labor.

If a transient problem is to be solved, the method discussed in Art. 1.11(D) may be used. First we obtain the transfer function in steady-state analysis. For instance, according to (42), the transfer function from Q_1 to q_1 or the frequency response of q_1 to Q_1 in (38) is

$$T_{11}(s) = \frac{a_{22}s^2 + b_{22}s + c_{22}}{D(s)} \tag{50}$$

where $D(s)$ may be factored into

$$D(s) = a(s - s_1)(s - s_2)(s - s_3)(s - s_4) \tag{51}$$

in which $a = a_{11}a_{22} - a_{12}^2$, and s_1, s_2, s_3, and s_4 are the roots of (34). If none of these roots is pure imaginary, the impulse response is then

$$u_{11}'(t) = \frac{1}{2\pi i}\int_{-i\infty}^{i\infty} \frac{a_{22}s^2 + b_{22}s + c_{22}}{D(s)} e^{st}\, ds \tag{52}$$

and the response $q_{11}(t)$, due to an arbitrary $Q_1(t)$ applied at $t = 0$ when the system is at rest and in equilibrium, becomes

$$q_{11}(t) = \frac{1}{2\pi i}\int_0^t \left(\int_{-i\infty}^{i\infty} \frac{a_{22}s^2 + b_{22}s + c_{22}}{D(s)} e^{s(t-\tau)}\, ds\right) Q_1(\tau)\, d\tau$$

Should $D(s)$ vanish for some pure imaginary values of s, a real positive constant c must be added to the limits of the integral with respect to s. The impulse response function can be evaluated by the results in Exercise 1.35 after the numerator and denominator of the transfer function $T(s)$ are factored and the fraction is broken into partial fractions.

2.9 Degenerated Cases

(A) THE CASE OF ZERO NATURAL FREQUENCY-SEMIDEFINITE SYSTEM

In most vibratory systems the vibrating masses are connected with a stationary frame by elastic and constraining forces in such a way that the equilibrium configuration of the system is uniquely determined and the system can remain at this configuration only when there is no motion. There is, however, a class of systems to which this does not apply. The inertia elements in these systems may move as a rigid-body ensemble without disturbing the equilibrium of the forces acting upon them. Such systems are said to be *semidefinite*. A simple example of a semidefinite system is the one obtained by removing the two outer springs k_{11} and k_{22} in Fig. 44. This system may be considered as a model of such practical things as two railroad cars elastically coupled or two pulleys mounted on a rotating shaft.

To analyze the vibration of a semidefinite system, two approaches are possible. We can treat it like any other vibratory system by writing down the differential equations of motion and obtaining the frequency equation. In the process of doing so we will find two peculiarities; the first is that the influence coefficients of a semidefinite system are not all defined, and the second is that the frequency equation will have a zero root, or roots, which corresponds to the possible rigid-body motions. The difficulties introduced by these peculiarities are discussed more fully in Chapter 3. The other way of analyzing a semidefinite system is by eliminating the rigid-body motions with the assumption that the total momentum vectors (linear or angular) associated with these rigid-body motions are identically zero. This is equivalent to introducing constraints into the system and thereby reducing the number of degrees of freedom. For instance, in Fig. 50 a rotating shaft carrying three disks, representing a driving pulley, a driven pulley, and a

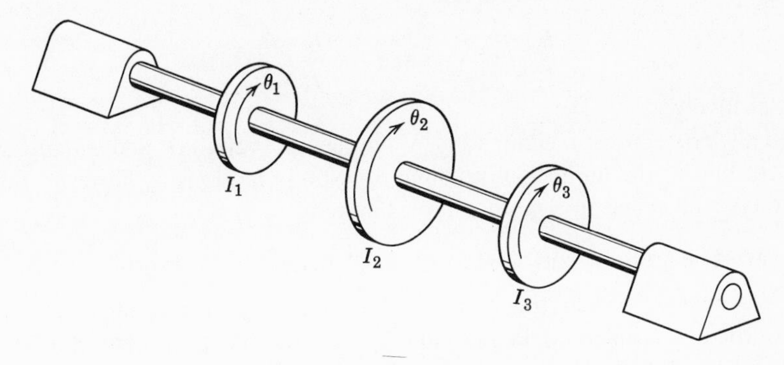

Figure 50

flywheel, has three degrees of freedom. One of the three is a rigid-body rotation, which is of no interest to vibration study. The set of differential equations is originally

$$\begin{aligned} I_1\ddot{\theta}_1 + k_{12}(\theta_1 - \theta_2) &= 0 \\ I_2\ddot{\theta}_2 + k_{12}(\theta_2 - \theta_1) + k_{23}(\theta_2 - \theta_3) &= 0 \\ I_3\ddot{\theta}_3 + k_{23}(\theta_3 - \theta_2) &= 0 \end{aligned} \tag{53}$$

Adding the three equations together, we have

$$I_1\ddot{\theta}_1 + I_2\ddot{\theta}_2 + I_3\ddot{\theta}_3 = 0$$

or

$$I_1\dot{\theta}_1 + I_2\dot{\theta}_2 + I_3\dot{\theta}_3 = \text{constant}$$

By assuming that there is no rigid-body motion, this constant becomes zero, or

$$I_1\theta_1 + I_2\theta_2 + I_3\theta_3 = \text{constant} = 0$$

This last constant can also be set equal to zero as the θ's are taken to be zero when the shaft is untwisted. By substituting

$$\theta_2 = -\frac{I_1\theta_1 + I_3\theta_3}{I_2}$$

into the first and third equations of (53), we have

$$I_1\ddot{\theta}_1 + k_{12}\left(\theta_1 + \frac{I_1\theta_1 + I_3\theta_3}{I_2}\right) = 0$$

$$I_3\ddot{\theta}_3 + k_{23}\left(\theta_3 + \frac{I_1\theta_1 + I_3\theta_3}{I_2}\right) = 0$$

This set of equations can be reduced to the standard form of (13) by multiplying them with the factors

$$\frac{I_2}{I_3}\sqrt{\frac{k_{23}}{k_{12}}} \quad \text{and} \quad \frac{I_2}{I_1}\sqrt{\frac{k_{12}}{k_{23}}}$$

respectively.

This procedure of eliminating a number of variables and equations according to the number of possible rigid-body motions is, however, not always convenient in a more complex system.

(B) THE CASE OF ZERO MASS—"HALF" DEGREE OF FREEDOM

We have seen that the motion of a single-degree-freedom system is governed by a differential equation of the second order and that of a two-degree-freedom system is governed by two differential equations of the second order, which are equivalent to one differential equation of the fourth order. If, however, the inertia forces in one of the two degrees of freedom are zero or negligible, the resulting differential equation of motion becomes a third-order one. Consider the system shown in Fig. 51, which has a single rigid body constrained to translate along a straight line. In a sense this system has only one degree of freedom, since the displacement function $X(t)$ specifies the location of all mass particles in the system. However, when the system is in motion, the value of $X(t)$ does not specify the location of the point P, whose motion must be considered as another independent unknown. This system is in reality the degenerated case of a two-degree-freedom system, which is obtained by first putting a mass m at P and then letting this mass become zero. The differential equations of motion degenerate into

$$M\ddot{X} + KX + k(X - x) = 0$$

$$c\dot{x} + k(x - X) = 0$$

By differentiating the first equation to obtain the additional equation

$$M\dddot{X} + K\dot{X} + k\dot{X} - k\dot{x} = 0$$

and by eliminating x and $\dot{x}$ from the three equations, we have

$$\frac{cM}{k}\dddot{X} + M\ddot{X} + \left(1 + \frac{K}{k}\right)c\dot{X} + KX = 0$$

This is a third-order differential equation whose characteristic equation is

$$\frac{cM}{k}s^3 + Ms^2 + \left(1 + \frac{K}{k}\right)cs + K = 0$$

This is a special case of the more general equation obtained by letting $a_{12} = a_{22} = 0$ in (34). Although the term makes very little physical

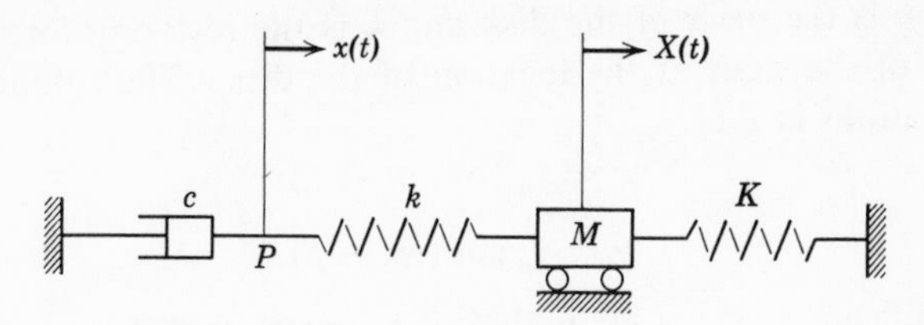

Figure 51

sense, we may conveniently think of such a system as having one and one half degrees of freedom. It is interesting to note that since a cubic equation with real positive coefficients has at least one real negative root at least one mode of the motion is an exponential decay.

$$X(t) = Ae^{-st}$$

2.10 Repeated Roots in Frequency Equations—Transverse Vibration of Rotating Shafts

When the frequency equation (14) has two equal roots, the two modes of vibration have the same frequency, and Mohr's circle, shown in Fig. 46, degenerates into a point. The physical implication of this condition is that any set of coordinates chosen to describe the two degrees of freedom can be considered as principal coordinates in the sense that there are no couplings between them. Consequently, such orthogonality relationship, as described by (19), may or may not exist.

The analytical peculiarities introduced by the existence of repeated roots in frequency equations are discussed in Chapter 3. At present, we shall study a practical problem related to this subject.

Take the simple case of a circular shaft carrying a heavy disk in the center and supported by bearings at the ends. Disregarding the rotational freedom of the shaft for the moment, we note that the system has two degrees of freedom which can be described by the displacement vector of the disk center from its equilibrium position. Evidently the disk can be set into a simple harmonic motion along any direction perpendicular to the axis of the shaft. Hence any such vibration is a principal mode of vibration.

For convenience, let us take the displacement components along two mutually perpendicular directions as the coordinates of the system. The differential equations for free vibrations are

$$m\ddot{x} + kx = 0$$
$$m\ddot{y} + ky = 0 \tag{54}$$

in which m is the mass of the disk and k is the restoring force per unit deflection of the shaft at the location of the disk. The solution to this set of equations is

$$x = x_0 \cos(\omega t - \alpha)$$
$$y = y_0 \cos(\omega t - \beta)$$

It is not difficult to show by analytical geometry that if ωt is eliminated between the two equations the resulting relationship between x and y represents an ellipse. In other words, the path traced by the disk center is, in general, an ellipse. For the particular case in which $x_0 = y_0$ and $\alpha - \beta = \pm\pi/2$, the path becomes a circle. The motion of the disk as a whole is a translation. That is to say, the paths traced by all points of the disk are congruent to one another, whether they are ellipses or circles. For the sake of clarity in later discussions, let us coin the term *whirling*[16] to denote the translation of the disk along a circular path. This whirling motion may be excited by a force which is constant in magnitude but which rotates with a uniform angular velocity ω_f. Let the force be in the x direction at $t = 0$ and have a constant magnitude F_0. Its x- and y-components at any time t are then $F_0 \cos \omega_f t$ and $F_0 \sin \omega_f t$, respectively. When this force is applied at the center of the disk, the differential equations of motion are

$$m\ddot{x} + kx = F_0 \cos \omega_f t$$
$$m\ddot{y} + ky = F_0 \sin \omega_f t \tag{55}$$

According to Art. 1.6, for $\omega_f \neq \omega$, the steady-state solution of (56) is

$$x = \frac{F_0}{k} \frac{1}{[1 - (\omega_f^2/\omega^2)]} \cos \omega_f t$$
$$y = \frac{F_0}{k} \frac{1}{[1 - (\omega_f^2/\omega^2)]} \sin \omega_f t \tag{56}$$

This solution represents a whirling motion. Let us observe that in this motion the displacement of the disk center is always colinear with the

[16] There is no standardized terminology for this motion. Some authors use the term revolving or revolution for this purpose.

force and that the two vectors are in the same or the opposite direction according to whether ω_f is less or greater than ω.

A rotating force such as the one described is realized physically when the disk has an eccentricity and rotates with the shaft at the speed ω_f. Intuitively, it is reasonable to suggest that the rotation and the eccentricity together produce a centrifugal force that is entirely equivalent to an

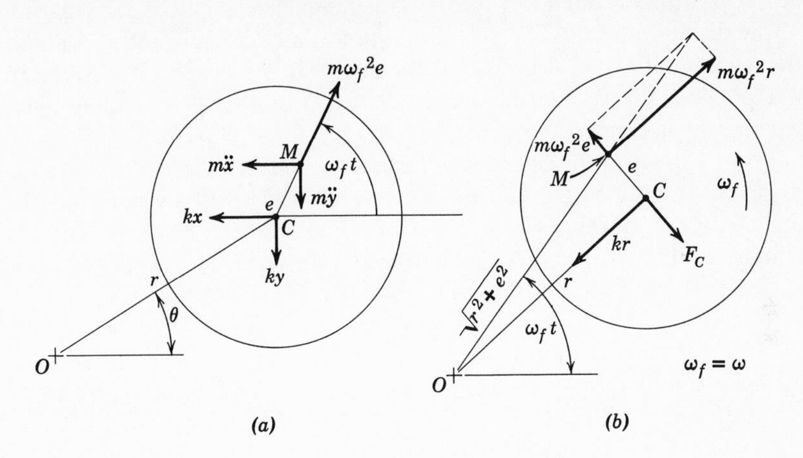

Figure 52

externally applied rotation force. To analyze the situation properly, let us refer to Fig. 52. In this figure O is the position occupied by the center of the shaft when the shaft is undeformed, C is the displaced location of the shaft center, and M is the location of the center of mass of the disk. The vector OC represents the translation of the disk and the rotation of the vector CM, which has a fixed length equal to the eccentricity e, represents the rotation of the disk. The acceleration of the mass center M can be resolved into the relative acceleration of M with respect to C and the acceleration of C with respect to O, which is fixed. The corresponding inertia forces are shown in Fig. 52*a*. In addition to these forces, there is an elastic restoring force exerted by the shaft on the disk at C. Assuming that at $t = 0$, CM is parallel to the x-direction, we have

$$\begin{aligned} m\ddot{x} + kx &= m\omega_f^2 e \cos \omega_f t \\ m\ddot{y} + ky &= m\omega_f^2 e \sin \omega_f t \end{aligned} \tag{57}$$

A comparison with (55) and (56) reveals that the displacement of the disk center C is given by

$$x = r \cos \omega_f t \qquad y = r \sin \omega_f t$$

where

$$r = \frac{m\omega_f^2 e}{k[1 - (\omega_f^2/\omega^2)]} = \frac{\omega_f^2 e}{\omega^2 - \omega_f^2} \tag{58}$$

and $\omega_f \neq \omega$.

The disk therefore whirls and rotates at the same time. The shaft center C whirls around O with the same angular velocity as the rotation of the disk around C. The over-all motion is a rotation of the disk about the fixed point O. In other words the angle OCM is fixed. According to our previous discussion, this angle is either 0 or 180°,[17] depending upon whether ω_f is greater or less than ω.

From a practical point of view, for any ω_f that is different from ω, the displacement vector OC can be made arbitrarily small by reducing the eccentricity e. In other words, the whirling motion can be almost entirely eliminated if the disk is very well balanced. However, as ω_f approaches ω, a very small eccentricity can still produce a large whirling motion if ω_f is sufficiently close to ω. This speed ω is therefore called the *critical speed.* The phenomenon is merely a special case of forced vibration at resonance, and the critical speed corresponds to the natural frequency of the system.

In engineering applications the rotating speed of a shaft is always kept apart from its critical speed to avoid excessive vibration. In many high-speed devices the operating speed is above the critical speed. To reach that operating speed, it is necessary during starting to pass through the critical speed quickly. The behavior of the system near its resonance condition is therefore also of practical interest. In Art. 1.6 it was pointed out that if there is no damping steady-state oscillation is not possible at $\omega_f = \omega$. Instead, the amplitude tends to build up as shown in Fig. 12. In an actual case there is always some damping, and the amplitude eventually becomes constant at some large but finite value. We also know that regardless of whether or not a steady-state condition is reached the excitation force leads the displacement by 90° at $\omega_f = \omega$, so that the relative location of O, C, and M is as shown in Fig. 52. Thus the centrifugal force of whirling motion, $m\omega^2 r$, and that of rotation, $m\omega^2 e$, are perpendicular to each other. In addition, there is the elastic restoring force kr along OC and another force F_c along CM. This force F_c may be interpreted in two different ways.

First, let us assume that whirling has just started and that the damping force is negligible, so that the amplitude, or r in this case, begins to grow.

---

[17] If this fact is taken for granted beforehand, (58) can be derived by simple equilibrium consideration, as it is done in most textbooks.

This means that the angular momentum about 0 increases; hence there is an inertia force due to Coriolis acceleration.

$$F_c r = \frac{d}{dt}[m\omega(r^2 + e^2)] = 2m\omega r \frac{dr}{dt}$$

According to discussions in Arts. 1.6 and 1.9, dr/dt = constant. Utilizing (35) of Chapter 1, we have

$$\frac{dr}{dt} = \frac{\delta_{st}}{2}\omega = \frac{m\omega^2 e}{2k}\omega = \frac{\omega e}{2}$$

Hence

$$F_c = m\omega^2 e = ke$$

Or we can assume that the steady-state condition is reached by having an amplitude large enough to produce a damping force

$$F_c = c\omega r = m\omega^2 e = ke$$

Between these two extreme cases both types of forces exist, but they will not be at their maximum values. Since the forces shown in Fig. 52*b* are the only forces on the disk. Newton's second law demands that

$$F_c = ke = c\omega r + 2m\omega\dot{r}r$$

These forces, however, do form a pure moment that must be balanced by an external driving torque on the disk in order to maintain the condition $\omega_f = \omega$. This torque is

$$M_t = F_c r = ker$$

Now if we want to speed up the shaft quickly, we must have a driving torque that is substantially greater than M_t. This is, of course, not a quantitatively useful statement, since e is usually unknown and r varies with t before the steady-state condition is achieved, But it does point out the importance of having sufficient driving torque to speed up the rotation quickly before large amplitudes can be built up to make the torque needed for acceleration still larger.

In the foregoing analysis we assume that the only inertia force is that due to a concentrated mass. This assumption is made merely to simplify the illustration of the principle that the critical speeds of rotating shafts are the same as their natural frequencies in transverse vibrations. If a shaft carries several masses, it will have several critical speeds, which are to be found by the method discussed in Chapter 3. If the mass of the shaft itself is not negligible, its critical speeds are to be determined by methods discussed in Chapter 4. If the location of the disk on the shaft is such that during vibration the disk also rotates about a diameter perpendicular to the plane of the shaft deflection, then the rotatory inertia of the disk about its diameter must also be taken into account. This effect is discussed in Art. 2.14.

In short, if the entire system—the disks, the shaft, and the bearing supports—has an axial symmetry, a rotating force can excite two transverse vibrations that are 90° out of phase and along two perpendicular planes. The rotation of the shaft merely furnishes the excitation needed without altering the vibrational characteristics of the system in other ways. In other words, if the shaft is prevented from rotating while the disks are allowed to rotate on the shaft, the result is assumed to be the same. There are, however, circumstances in which the rotation produces excitation other than a centrifugal force that rotates with the speed of the shaft. These are discussed in Art. 2.14.

SECTION B. METHODS AND APPLICATIONS

2.11 Illustrative Examples

In most cases the differential equations of motion for a vibratory system can be written down without much preliminary analysis. But when there are forces of constraint, which must be eliminated, the preliminary analysis may become somewhat involved. In this article we illustrate the procedure by analyzing two examples. The systems chosen have no practical utility, but they serve our purpose well.

Consider first the system shown in Fig. 53. It consists of a wedge of mass M sliding on a smooth table and a small block of mass m sliding on the wedge. Two linear springs of constants k and K couple the two masses together and to a stationary frame. Evidently this system has two degrees of freedom, and a convenient choice of coordinates consists of the horizontal displacement of M and the relative displacement of m on M. Let us call these displacements x_1 and x_2, respectively, and assign them the value zero when the gravity forces are in equilibrium with spring forces and forces between contacting surfaces. In this problem, the effect of gravity does not change with x_1 and x_2, and we need to consider only the variations in these forces from their values at equilibrium configuration when we analyze the motion of the system. With this simplification, the free-body diagrams of the two rigid bodies of the system are as shown. The assumption is also made that these variations are small, so that the string will remain taut and the block will remain on the incline. The pertinent equilibrium equations are

$$\Sigma F_{x_2} = 0 \qquad K(x_1 - x_2) - kx_2 = m\ddot{x}_2 - m\ddot{x}_1 \cos\theta$$

$$\Sigma F_N = 0 \qquad m\ddot{x}_1 \sin\theta = N$$

$$\Sigma F_{x_1} = 0 \qquad K(x_1 - x_2) + M\ddot{x}_1 - [K(x_1 - x_2) - kx_2]\cos\theta + N\sin\theta = 0$$

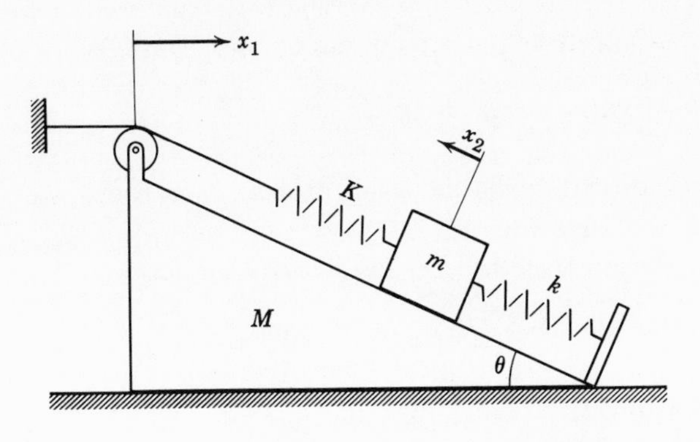

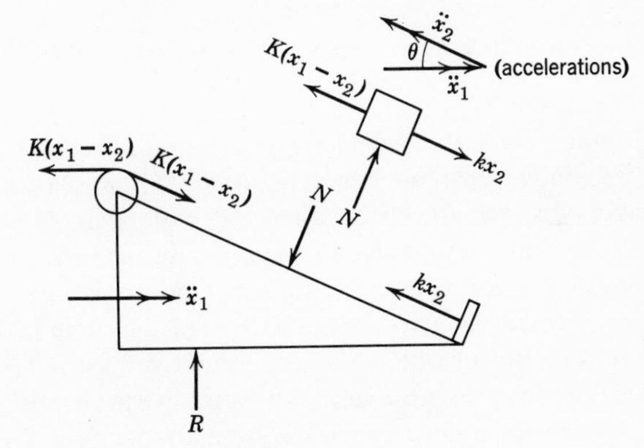

Figure 53

By substituting the first two equations into the third, we obtain

$$K(x_1 - x_2) + M\ddot{x}_1 - m\ddot{x}_2 \cos\theta + m\ddot{x}_1 = 0$$

A rearrangement of the first and the last of the foregoing equations yields

$$(M + m)\ddot{x}_1 + Kx_1 - m\cos\theta\ddot{x}_2 - Kx_2 = 0$$

$$-m\cos\theta\ddot{x}_1 - Kx_1 + m\ddot{x}_2 + (K + k)x_2 = 0$$

This rearrangement reduces the equations to the standard form[18] of (13). There are both inertia coupling and elastic coupling between the coordinates represented by the coefficients ($-m \cos \theta$) and ($-K$), respectively.

Next we want to show how the same set of equations can be obtained with much less labor and thought. It can easily be seen that the kinetic energy and potential energy expressions of the system are

$$T = \tfrac{1}{2}M\dot{x}_1^2 + \tfrac{1}{2}m[(\dot{x}_1 - \dot{x}_2 \cos \theta)^2 + \dot{x}_2^2 \sin^2 \theta]$$

$$V = \tfrac{1}{2}K(x_1 - x_2)^2 + \tfrac{1}{2}kx_2^2$$

By simplifying and rearranging the terms in these expressions, we have

$$T = \tfrac{1}{2}[(M + m)\dot{x}_1^2 - 2m \cos \theta \dot{x}_1\dot{x}_1 + m\dot{x}_2^2]$$

$$V = \tfrac{1}{2}[Kx_1^2 - 2Kx_1x_2 + (K + k)x_2^2]$$

A comparison with (11) reveals that

$$a_{11} = M + m \qquad a_{12} = -m \cos \theta \qquad a_{22} = m$$

$$c_{11} = K \qquad c_{12} = -K \qquad c_{22} = K + k$$

By putting these constants into (13) and (14), we can write down the equilibrium equation and the frequency equations immediately.

For our second example let us consider the system shown in Fig. 54. A disk of mass M, moment of inertia I, and radius R rolls without slipping inside a cylindrical surface of radius $3R$. The disk is in vertical plane and has a diametric slot in which a spring-mounted mass m can slide without friction. This slot is at a horizontal position when the disk is at its lowest point. The springs connected with m have an over-all constant k, and the neutral position of the mass is at the center.

This system contains many constraining forces in which we are not primarily interested. Analysis by energy consideration will relieve us of the necessity of dealing with these forces. Let us choose as the coordinates for this system the angle θ and the distance r, as indicated.

---

[18] When the equations are obtained by equilibrium consideration, they are not always in the standard form, but they can always be reduced to such form by simple algebraic operations. It is most convenient to have the equations in the standard form because their solutions can then be written down by direct substitution of constants into the standard solution.

In terms of these coordinates, we have

$$
\begin{aligned}
v_0 &= \text{velocity of the center of the disk} = 2R\dot{\theta} \\
\Omega &= \text{angular velocity of the disk} = 2\dot{\theta} \\
v_m^{\,2} &= \text{velocity of } m \text{ squared} \\
&= (v_0 \cos 3\theta + \dot{r})^2 + (v_0 \sin 3\theta - r\Omega)^2 \\
&= v_0^{\,2} + \dot{r}^2 + r^2\Omega^2 + 2v_0\dot{r}\cos 3\theta - 2v_0 r\,\Omega \sin 3\theta
\end{aligned}
$$

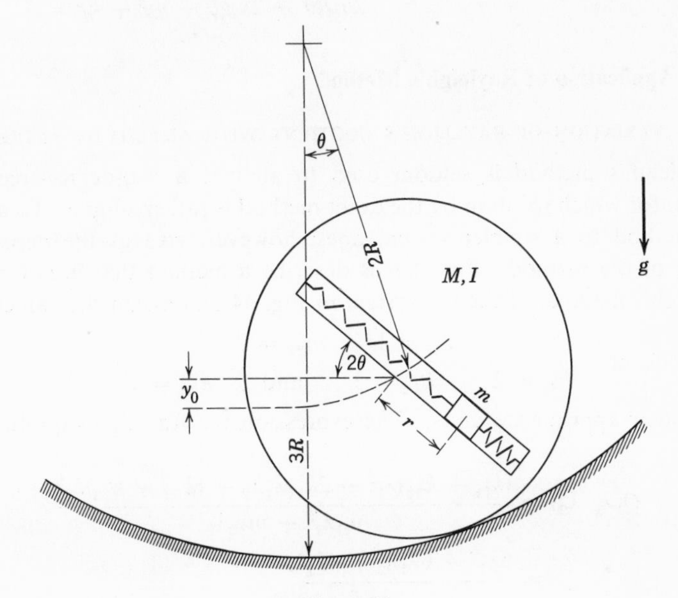

Figure 54

For small oscillations both r/R and θ are small, so that the third and the last terms can be neglected. After eliminating v_0, we have

$$v_m^{\,2} \doteq 4R^2\dot{\theta}^2 + \dot{r}^2 + 4R\dot{r}\dot{\theta}$$

The kinetic energy of the system is then

$$
\begin{aligned}
T &= \tfrac{1}{2}Mv_0^{\,2} + \tfrac{1}{2}I\Omega^2 + \tfrac{1}{2}mv_m^{\,2} \\
&= \tfrac{1}{2}[4(MR^2 + mR^2 + I)\dot{\theta}^2 + 4mR\dot{r}\dot{\theta} + m\dot{r}^2]
\end{aligned}
$$

Now let

$$
\begin{aligned}
y_0 &= \text{the rise of the center of the disk} = 2R(1 - \cos\theta) \\
&\doteq R\theta^2 \\
y_m &= \text{the rise of } m = y_0 - r\sin 2\theta \\
&\doteq R\theta^2 - 2r\theta
\end{aligned}
$$

The potential energy is then

$$V = Mgy_0 + mgy_m + \tfrac{1}{2}kr^2$$
$$= \tfrac{1}{2}[(M + m)Rg\theta^2 - 4mgr\theta + kr^2]$$

From these energy expressions it follows that the differential equations of motion are

$$4(MR^2 + mr^2 + I)\ddot{\theta} + 2(M + m)g\theta + 2mR\ddot{r} - 2mgr = 0$$
$$2mR\ddot{\theta} - 2mg\theta + m\ddot{r} + kr = 0$$

2.12 Application of Rayleigh's Method

(A) VARIATION OF RAYLEIGH'S QUOTIENT WITH AMPLITUDE RATIO

Rayleigh's method is seldom used to analyze a two-degree-freedom system, for which solution by the exact method is rather simple. To apply this method to a simpler system does, however, give us the necessary feeling of the method. First let us describe a method that is not really Rayleigh's method. Take the system in Fig. 44 and assign the values

$$m_{11} = 1 \qquad m_{22} = 3$$
$$k_{11} = 2 \qquad k_{12} = 3 \qquad \text{and} \qquad k_{22} = 1$$

all in their appropriate units. The expression for Rayleigh's quotient is then

$$Q(\lambda_1, \lambda_2) = \frac{(k_{11} + k_{12})\lambda_1^2 - 2k_{12}\lambda_1\lambda_2 + (k_{22} + k_{12})\lambda_2^2}{m_{11}\lambda_1^2 + m_{22}\lambda_2^2}$$
$$= \frac{5\lambda_1^2 - 6\lambda_1\lambda_2 + 4\lambda_2^2}{\lambda_1^2 + 3\lambda_2^2}$$

As a first trial, let $\lambda_1 = \lambda_2 = 1$.

$$Q(1, 1) = \frac{5 - 6 + 4}{1 + 3} = 0.75$$

By substituting $\omega^2 = 0.75$ into either of the equations in (3) or (5), we get some idea about how good our starting assumption is. In this case we get

$$\frac{-m_{11}\omega^2 + k_{11} + k_{12}}{k_{12}} = \frac{4.25}{3} = 1.42$$

The ratio $\lambda_2/\lambda_1 = 1.42$ is most likely a better approximation. Rayleigh's quotient for this ratio is

$$Q(1, 1.42) = \frac{5 - 6 \cdot 1.42 + 4 \cdot 1.42^2}{1 + 3 \cdot 1.42^2} = 0.640$$

If we take this value to be ω^2, we have $\omega = 0.800$.

The correct solution to three significant figures is $\omega = 0.800$ and $\lambda_2/\lambda_1 = 1.45$. To show how close Rayleigh's quotient gives the square of the natural frequency when the assumed amplitude ratio is reasonably correct, let us observe that

$$Q(1, 1.3) = 0.652 \qquad \omega = 0.810$$

$$Q(1, 1.6) = 0.651 \qquad \omega = 0.809$$

In other words, 10 per cent error in amplitude ratio produces about 1 per cent error in frequency.

The other natural frequency can be obtained in a similar way. First we know that $\omega''^2 > \omega_{11}{}^2 = 5$. If we assume that $\omega^2 = 5$, the second equation of (3) gives $\lambda_1/\lambda_2 = -11/3$. (The first equation is too sensitive to changes of ω^2 when it is around 5.) Next we find $Q(-11, 3) = 5.67$. Repeating the process once, we find $\lambda_1/\lambda_2 = -4.34$ and $\omega^2 = 5.69$. These values are nearly the correct answers.

In concluding this example, let us mention that the procedure demonstrated unfortunately cannot be adapted in a practical way to systems with more degrees of freedom. The purpose of this example is to show that when the amplitude ratio of a given mode of vibration is known approximately Rayleigh's quotient provides the corresponding natural frequency accurately.

(B) RAYLEIGH'S METHOD FOR SYSTEMS WITH KNOWN INFLUENCE COEFFICIENTS

In contrast to the example just given, the following illustration has practical utility because it can be immediately adapted to systems with more degrees of freedom. The method to be discussed deals with systems in which the influence coefficients instead of the elastic constants are known. To apply the procedure previously shown, it would be necessary to find the elastic constants according to relationships such as (22). This is very inconvenient, especially for systems with many degrees of freedom. A modification of the procedure is therefore needed.

Consider the transverse vibration of a beam supported at the ends and carrying two concentrated masses weighing W_{11} and W_{22}, respectively, as shown in Fig. 48. As usual, we start with the first trial.

$$\lambda_1 = \lambda_2$$

In the previous example we determined ω^2 by Rayleigh's quotient corresponding to the $\lambda_1 = \lambda_2$ and then obtained a better estimate of the amplitude ratio by the equilibrium equations (3). From the revised amplitude ratio the frequency is then obtained from Rayleigh's quotient to a close degree of approximation. We now show that a revised amplitude ratio can actually be obtained directly without computing Rayleigh's quotient first. Let us write (24) as

$$\begin{aligned} \lambda_1 &= (W_{11}\gamma_{11}\lambda_1 + W_{22}\gamma_{12}\lambda_2)\omega^2/g \\ \lambda_2 &= (W_{11}\gamma_{12}\lambda_1 + W_{22}\gamma_{22}\lambda_2)\omega^2/g \end{aligned} \tag{i}$$

or

$$\frac{\lambda_1}{\lambda_2} = \frac{W_{11}\gamma_{11}\lambda_1 + W_{22}\gamma_{12}\lambda_2}{W_{11}\gamma_{12}\lambda_1 + W_{22}\gamma_{22}\lambda_2} \tag{ii}$$

An iteration process can then be instituted by putting the estimated ratio into the right-hand side of the equation and obtaining a revised ratio from the left-hand side. If our assumed first-trial ratio is $(\lambda_1/\lambda_2)_1 = 1$, the revised ratio is

$$\left(\frac{\lambda_1}{\lambda_2}\right)_2 = \frac{W_{11}\gamma_{11} + W_{22}\gamma_{22}}{W_{11}\gamma_{12} + W_{22}\gamma_{22}} = \frac{\delta_1}{\delta_2} \tag{iii}$$

in which δ_1 and δ_2 are the static deflections of the shaft that would be produced by the gravity forces on the weights if the beam were in a horizontal position. Now we can compute Rayleigh's quotient corresponding to the revised ratio by letting $\lambda_1 = \delta_1$ and $\lambda_2 = \delta_2$. The potential energy of the elastic forces corresponding to these deflections will simply be

$$V_m = \tfrac{1}{2}(W_{11}\delta_1 + W_{22}\delta_2) \tag{iv}$$

and the value of V_m is thus obtained without the need of converting the influence coefficient into the elastic constants. Finally

$$Q(\delta_1, \delta_2) = \frac{(W_{11}\delta_1 + W_{22}\delta_2)g}{W_{11}\delta_1^2 + W_{22}\delta_2^2} \tag{v}$$

If $\lambda_1 = \lambda_2$ is anywhere near being a reasonable first-trial ratio, $(\lambda_1/\lambda_2)_2 = \delta_1/\delta_2$ will represent an improved estimate, and Rayleigh's quotient above should yield the natural frequency very closely. It must be realized that there is no inherent reason for $\lambda_1/\lambda_2 = \delta_1/\delta_2$ always to be a good estimate. For example, if the beam in Fig. 48 had a third pivot support between the masses, the free vibration with the lower frequency would be such that the masses would move in the opposite directions. If static deflections δ_1 and δ_2 are to be taken as the amplitudes, it is more reasonable to compute them as if the gravity forces acting on the masses were in the opposite directions. The results obtained when such artifice is needed are not generally so reliable.

Generalization of the expression (v) to cover systems with more than two masses is immediate.

$$\omega^2_{\text{approx}} = \frac{g(W_{11}\delta_1 + W_{22}\delta_2 \cdots W_{nn}\delta_n)}{W_{11}\delta_1^2 + W_{22}\delta_2^2 \cdots W_{nn}\delta_n^2} \tag{vi}$$

Usually this approximation is good only for the vibration mode with the lowest frequency, in which the static deflections more closely approximate the amplitudes.

The appearance of the constant g in (ii) and (vi) does not mean that the gravitational force has an effect on the natural frequency. If we were to perform our measurements on the moon, where g is much smaller, the δ's would also be proportionally smaller. The resulting value of ω^2 would still be the same.

2.13 Some Principles in Vibration Control

Methods and techniques in vibration control and isolation are matters in art as much as in science. As pointed out by Macduff and Curreri,[19] the problems involved are psychological, economical, and analytical, and their degrees of difficulty are usually in that order. Within the scope of this book only the basic principles concerning theory of vibration can be discussed. From these principles successful solutions of practical problems may be carried out if one also possesses experience, ingenuity, and persuasiveness. The last quality is needed by the consulting engineer to convince the client that the methods proposed are proper or the results achieved are satisfactory.

(A) REMOVAL OR MINIMIZATION OF EXCITATION FORCES

Ideally, the way of removing vibrations in machines is to eliminate or minimize the sources of excitation. In practice, this is not always feasible. Much can be accomplished sometimes in the design stage of certain types of equipment. Others, such as punch presses, high-speed card printers, and riveting machines, have excitation sources that are inherent to their functioning. In an existing machine, if avoidable and excessive sources of excitation are suspected, measurements of the objectionable vibration should be taken and analyzed. If the vibratory motion is found to be clearly periodic, with a fundamental frequency forming a simple ratio[20] with the rotating speed or reciprocating frequency of certain parts of the equipment, the source or sources of the excitation may be located and sometimes removed by proper balancing and replacement of faulty parts. When possible, efforts should also be made to vary the running speed and to observe whether amplitude "peaks" at a certain particular speed.

[19] See Macduff and Curreri, *Vibration Control*, McGraw-Hill, New York, 1958, p. 117.

[20] The resulting vibration can be the harmonics or the subharmonics of the excitation. Subharmonics are produced by the nonlinearity in the system and have frequencies lower than that of excitation.

Should that be the case, the trouble lies with resonance, not with large unbalanced disturbances. The corrective measure is then to separate the resonant frequency from that of disturbing forces. The kinds of objectionable but avoidable vibrations described in this paragraph need not happen if proper design and manufacturing procedures are employed; but they do happen just the same.

(B) THE LOWERING OF NATURAL FREQUENCIES AND THE EFFECT OF COUPLINGS

A cardinal principle of vibration control demands that the frequency of excitation be kept away from any of the natural frequencies of the system in which vibration is to be minimized. In most practical cases this principle also demands that the natural frequencies be kept low. In spring-mounted machinery springs with low stiffness will have to be used to keep the natural frequencies low. Soft springs, however, pose practical problems of their own. For instance, helical compression springs of low stiffness may be too unstable without lateral guides. Also, the large static deflections associated with soft springs may also become undesirable when the total weight of the mounted system is a variable. For example, if the suspension of an automobile is too soft, the road clearance may change drastically as passengers enter.[21] Apart from the stiffness of the springs used in mounting, their placement may also affect the natural frequencies. Consider the system shown in Fig. 55, which may be taken as a simplified representation of a long narrow machine mounted on springs. Let us assume that the springs are guided so that the possible motion consists of a vertical displacement of the center of gravity y and an angular displacement θ. For small oscillations the energy expressions for the system are

$$
\begin{aligned}
T &= \tfrac{1}{2}(M\dot{y}^2 + I\dot{\theta}^2) \\
V &= \tfrac{1}{2}[k(y - a\theta)^2 + k(y + b\theta)^2] \\
&= \tfrac{1}{2}[2ky^2 + 2k(b - a)y\theta + k(a^2 + b^2)\theta^2]
\end{aligned}
$$

Using the notations in (17), we have

$$
\omega_{11}^2 = \frac{2k}{M} \qquad \omega_{22}^2 = \frac{k(a^2 + b^2)}{I}
$$

$$
\omega_{12}^2 = \frac{k(b - a)}{\sqrt{MI}}
$$

Evidently, if the springs are located so that $a = b$, there will be no coupling

[21] A desirable feature of torsion bar springs and of air springs is that the road clearance can be readjusted by an automatic device after the loading or unloading of the vehicle.

between the coordinates, and the natural frequencies are ω_{11} and ω_{22}. The difference between a and b creates a coupling, and, according to (16), this coupling has the effect of separating the two frequencies and making the higher of the two still higher. Also, for a given distance between the springs an increase in the difference $a - b$ tends to make ω_{22} higher, since

$$2(a^2 + b^2) = (a + b)^2 + (a - b)^2$$

The existence of couplings between coordinates is therefore undesirable in our effort to keep all of the natural frequencies low.

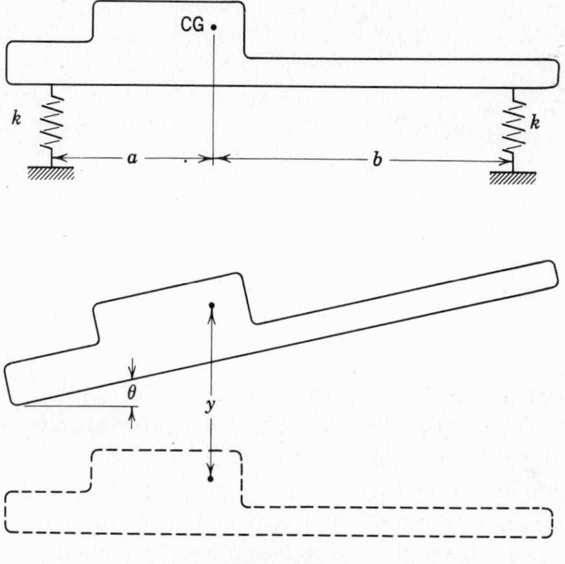

Figure 55

In discussing the effect of couplings on the natural frequencies, a conceptual point must be cleared up. In Art. 2.4 it was pointed out that for a given system the existence and the nature of coupling are matters dependent upon the choice of coordinates, whereas the natural frequencies are properties independent of the choice of coordinate system. For instance, in the system just studied, if y denotes the displacement of a point midway between the springs instead of the center of mass, we will find inertia coupling instead of elastic coupling. In the context of our present discussion, when we speak of the effect of couplings upon the natural frequencies we mean the effect of physical rearrangements that cause changes in the coupling constants a_{12} and c_{12} *between a given pair of coordinates.*

Generally speaking, the presence of symmetry favors the elimination of coupling forces. When a piece of equipment is spring-mounted at the base, it is usually possible to place the springs so that the vertical motion is a principal mode. On the other hand, as long as the center of mass is above the base support, any possible horizontal translation will be coupled to rotary motions. (See Fig. 56.)

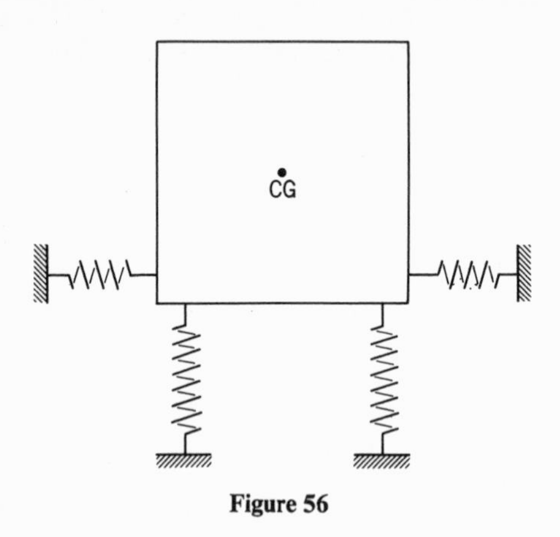

Figure 56

Aside from its effect on natural frequencies, a coupling between the coordinates also couples the effect of external disturbances. In Fig. 55 an up-and-down force acting on the center of mass will also produce a rotary motion unless the two springs are properly located. If the natural frequency of the rotary motion is near to that of the force, decoupling them from each other will also produce a beneficial effect.

(c) DYNAMIC VIBRATION ABSORBERS

A dynamic vibration absorber is a small vibratory system coupled to a machine or structure to control its vibrations. The absorber is designed so that when the machine is subjected to a periodic excitation the resulting vibration of the absorber produces a coupling force that tends to cancel out the excitation force.

A simple form of this arrangement is shown in Fig. 57, where M is a mass simulating a machine and K is its mounting spring. The small mass m and the coupling spring k constitute the absorber system. A damper c may or may not be present. Assume that all motions are confined in the vertical direction. Let Y be the displacement of M and y, the relative displacement of m with respect to M. The energy expressions in terms of these coordinates are

$$T = \tfrac{1}{2}M\dot{Y}^2 + \tfrac{1}{2}m(\dot{Y} + \dot{y})^2$$
$$= \tfrac{1}{2}[(M + m)\dot{Y}^2 + 2m\dot{Y}\dot{y} + m\dot{y}^2]$$
$$V = \tfrac{1}{2}KY^2 + \tfrac{1}{2}ky^2$$

The power dissipation in the damper P is

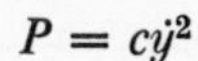

$$P = c\dot{y}^2$$

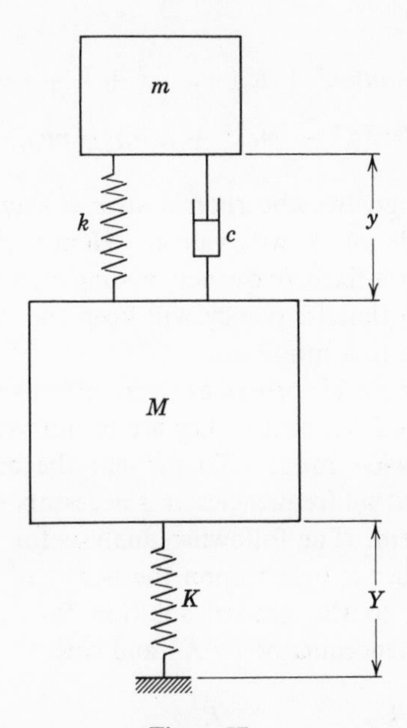

Figure 57

Let $Q(t)$ be a force acting on M; the energy equation for the system is evidently

$$\frac{d}{dt}(T + V) + P = Q\dot{Y}$$

From this equation and the energy expressions we obtain the differential equations of motion:

$$(M + m)\ddot{Y} + KY + m\ddot{y} = Q(t)$$
$$m\ddot{Y} + m\ddot{y} + c\dot{y} + ky = 0$$

This set of differential equations can also be obtained from equilibrium considerations.

Suppose that Q is a sinusoidal force and that we are interested in the steady-state response of Y. Let

$$Q(t) = Fe^{i\omega_f t} \qquad \text{and} \qquad Y = \lambda e^{i\omega_f t}$$

According to (42) and (43),

$$\lambda = \frac{F(-m\omega_f^2 + ic\omega_f + k)}{D}$$

$$\begin{aligned} D &= [-(M+m)\omega_f^2 + K](-m\omega_f^2 + k + ic\omega_f) - (m\omega_f^2)^2 \\ &= (K - M\omega_f^2)(k - m\omega_f^2 + ic\omega_f) - m\omega_f^2(k + ic\omega_f) \end{aligned}$$

Evidently, if we design the absorber in such a way that $k/m = \omega_f^2$ and $c = 0$, the amplitude of Y will vanish. Hence, if the excitation is a sinusoidal force with a fixed frequency, a simple and undamped dynamic absorber "tuned" to that frequency will keep the vibration of the main structure or machine to a minimum.

Although such simple absorbers are very effective when the excitation force is at the designed frequency, they are of little value if ω_f is subjected to variations in a wide range. To prevent the amplitude of Y from becoming excessive at all frequencies, it is necessary to introduce damping in the absorber system. The following analysis for the optimum design of a dynamic absorber is based upon the works of a number of investigators.[22] Returning to the general solution for λ, we divide both the numerator and the denominator by Kk and call

$$\frac{F}{K} = \delta_{st} \qquad \frac{k}{m} = \omega^2 \qquad \frac{K}{M} = \Omega^2 \qquad \text{and} \qquad \frac{c\omega_f}{k} = \eta$$

The nondimensional equation obtained is

$$\frac{\lambda}{\delta_{st}} = \frac{1 - \left(\dfrac{\omega_f}{\omega}\right)^2 + i\eta}{\left[1 - \left(\dfrac{\omega_f}{\Omega}\right)^2\right]\left[1 - \left(\dfrac{\omega_f}{\omega}\right)^2 + i\eta\right] - \dfrac{m}{M}\left(\dfrac{\omega_f}{\Omega}\right)^2(1 + i\eta)}$$

[22] See Timoshenko, *Vibration Problems in Engineering*, Van Nostrand, Princeton, N.J., 3rd edition, pp. 213–220, and Den Hartog, *Mechanical Vibration*, McGraw-Hill, New York, 1956, 4th edition pp. 93–106.

To simplify the expression, set

$$1 - \left(\frac{\omega_f}{\omega}\right)^2 = \alpha \qquad 1 - \left(\frac{\omega_f}{\Omega}\right)^2 = \beta$$

$$\frac{m}{M} = \gamma \qquad \text{and} \qquad \frac{\lambda}{\delta_{st}} = T(i\omega_f) \qquad \text{(footnote 23)}$$

$$T = \frac{\lambda}{\delta_{st}} = \frac{\alpha + i\eta}{\beta(\alpha + i\eta) - \gamma(1 - \beta)(1 + i\eta)}$$

$$= \frac{\alpha + i\eta}{(\alpha\beta - \gamma + \gamma\beta) + i(\beta - \gamma + \gamma\beta)\eta}$$

$$|T|^2 = \frac{\alpha^2 + \eta^2}{(\alpha\beta - \gamma + \gamma\beta)^2 + (\beta - \gamma + \gamma\beta)^2\eta^2} \qquad \text{(i)}$$

The object is now to design a system so that $|T|$ will be kept low for a wide range of ω_f. Let us observe that, of all the parameters determining $|T|$, η is the only one containing the damping constant c, and that when

$$\alpha = \pm\left(\frac{\alpha\beta - \gamma + \gamma\beta}{\beta - \gamma + \gamma\beta}\right) \qquad \text{(ii)}$$

$|T|$ is independent of η. Physically, this means that for certain combinations of m, k, M, K, and ω_f the amplitude of vibration of M may be made independent of the damping constant c. To determine such combinations more specifically, we find that

$$\alpha = +\frac{\alpha\beta - \gamma + \gamma\beta}{\beta - \gamma + \gamma\beta}$$

is satisfied by $\alpha = 1$, $\beta = 1$, or $\gamma = 0$. These values imply the trivial conditions $m = 0$ or $\omega_f = 0$. The other possibility

$$\alpha = -\frac{\alpha\beta - \gamma + \gamma\beta}{\beta - \gamma + \gamma\beta} \qquad \text{(iii)}$$

leads to

$$(2 + \gamma)\alpha\beta - (\alpha - \beta + 1)\gamma = 0$$

which expands into

$$\left(1 + \frac{\gamma}{2}\right)\omega_f^4 - (\Omega^2 + \omega^2 + \gamma\omega^2)\omega_f^2 + \omega^2\Omega^2 = 0 \qquad \text{(iv)}$$

This is a quadratic equation of ω_f^2. It can be shown that the discriminant of this equation is

$$(\Omega^2 - \omega^2)^2 + \gamma\omega^4(2 + \gamma) > 0$$

[23] There is no danger of confusing the symbol for transfer function with that for the kinetic energy of the system. So we use T for both.

and the equation has two positive roots for ω_f^2. In other words, if a family of frequency response curves ($|T|$ versus ω_f) is plotted with damping constant c as a parameter, all the curves will have two points in common, as shown in Fig. 58.

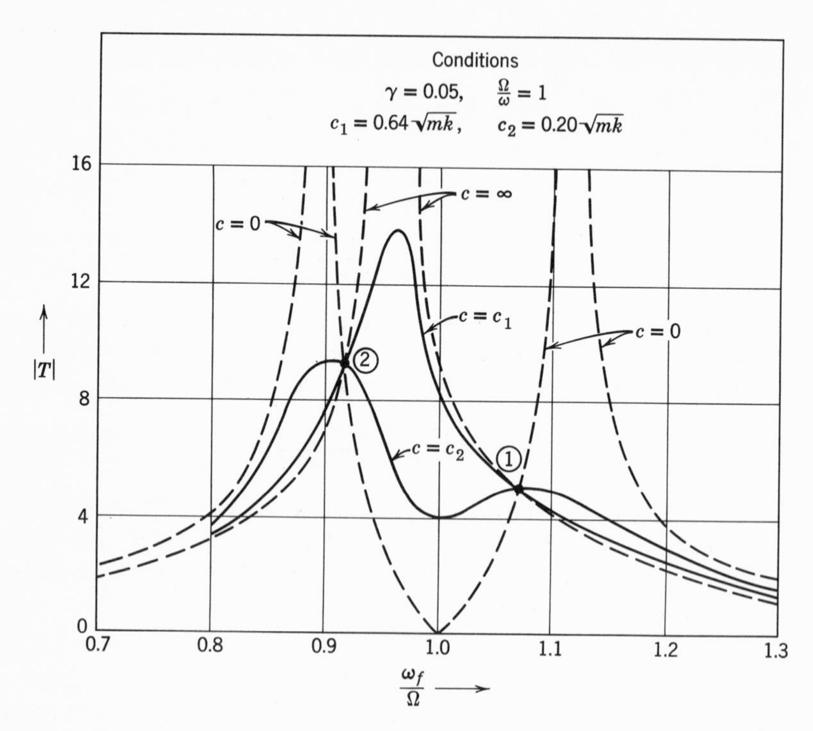

Figure 58

The abscissae of these two points, ω_1 and ω_2, are determined by (iv), and the corresponding ordinates $|T_1|$ and $|T_2|$ are determined by (i) and (iii). They are

$$|T_1| = \frac{1}{\pm(\beta_1 - \gamma + \gamma\beta_1)} \quad \text{and} \quad |T_2| = \frac{1}{\mp(\beta_2 - \gamma + \gamma\beta_2)} \tag{v}$$

where

$$\beta_1 = 1 - \left(\frac{\omega_1}{\Omega}\right)^2 \quad \text{and} \quad \beta_2 = 1 - \left(\frac{\omega_2}{\Omega}\right)^2$$

The signs to choose are the ones that make $|T|$'s positive. It can be shown that the correct signs are such that one is positive while the other is negative.

To achieve an optimum design of the vibration-absorber system our approach is now as follows. We consider M and K as being fixed because they belong to the system whose vibration is to be controlled. *Tentatively*, we try to utilize the freedom we have in choosing three parameters, m, k, and c, to achieve the following three things. One is to make $|T_1| = |T_2|$, and the other two are to make $|T_1|$ and $|T_2|$ the maxima of the frequency response curve. It is reasonable to expect that an optimum design would be achieved when the ordinates of the two points, through which all curves must pass, are made to be the two maxima having equal values. Upon setting

$$|T_1| = |T_2|$$

we have

$$(\beta_1 - \gamma + \gamma\beta_1) = -(\beta_2 - \gamma + \gamma\beta_2)$$

Substitute in the expression for β_1 and β_2 and simplify.

$$\omega_1{}^2 + \omega_2{}^2 = \frac{2\Omega^2}{1 + \gamma} \tag{vi}$$

Since $\omega_1{}^2$ and $\omega_2{}^2$ are roots of (iv), their sum is

$$\frac{2\Omega^2}{1 + \gamma} = \frac{2(\Omega^2 + \omega^2 + \gamma\omega^2)}{2 + \gamma} \tag{vii}$$

This simplifies into

$$\frac{\Omega}{\omega} = 1 + \gamma \tag{viii}$$

Or

$$\frac{mK}{Mk} = \left(1 + \frac{m}{M}\right)^2$$

This is one relationship that must be satisfied in an optimum design. The corresponding value of $|T|$ is then

$$|T| = |T_1| = |T_2| = \tfrac{1}{2}(|T_1| + |T_2|)$$

Substituting (v) into the above, we obtain through simplification

$$|T_1| = |T_2| = \frac{2\omega\Omega}{(\omega_1{}^2 - \omega_2{}^2)} \qquad \text{if} \qquad \omega_1 > \omega_2$$

This expression evidently has to do with the difference between the roots of the quadratic equation (iv), which may be written as

$$\left(\frac{\omega_f{}^2}{\omega\Omega}\right)^2 - \frac{2[\Omega^2 + \omega^2(1 + \gamma)]}{(2 + \gamma)\omega\Omega}\left(\frac{\omega_f{}^2}{\omega\Omega}\right) + \frac{2}{2 + \gamma} = 0$$

By utilizing (viii), we have

$$\left(\frac{\omega_f{}^2}{\omega\Omega}\right)^2 - 2\left(\frac{\omega_f{}^2}{\omega\Omega}\right) + \frac{2}{2 + \gamma} = 0 \tag{ix}$$

Treated as an equation in $\omega_f^2/\omega\Omega$, the difference between its roots is

$$\sqrt{2^2 - 4\frac{2}{2+\gamma}} = 2\sqrt{\frac{2}{2+\gamma}}$$

Hence

$$|T| = \sqrt{\frac{\gamma+2}{\gamma}} = \sqrt{1 + \frac{2M}{m}} \tag{x}$$

and

$$\frac{\omega_f^2}{\omega\Omega} = 1 \pm \frac{1}{|T|}$$

To make $|T|$ a maximum at $\omega_f = \omega_1$ and $\omega_f = \omega_2$, we demand, *if possible*, at $\omega_f = \omega_1$ and $\omega_f = \omega_2$

$$\frac{d|T|^2}{d(\omega_f^2)} = 0 \tag{xi}$$

For simplicity let us write (i) as

$$|T|^2(A^2 + B^2\eta^2) = \alpha^2 + \eta^2$$

in which $A = \alpha\beta - \gamma + \gamma\beta$ and $B = \beta - \gamma + \gamma\beta$, and use the symbol prime (′) to denote differentiation with respect to ω_f^2. The condition (xi) leads to

$$|T|^2(AA' + BB'\eta^2 + B^2\eta\eta') = \alpha\alpha' + \eta\eta'$$

According to (v) and (iii), at ω_1 and ω_2

$$|T|^2B^2 = 1 \qquad \text{and} \qquad \frac{A}{B} = \alpha$$

Hence

$$B'\eta^2 = B\alpha\alpha' + \alpha A'$$

By utilizing the definitions of A and B and the relation

$$\frac{\alpha'}{\beta'} = \frac{\Omega^2}{\omega^2} = (1+\gamma)^2$$

we obtain through some simplification

$$(1+\gamma)\eta^2 = \alpha[(1-\gamma)(B+\beta) + \alpha + \gamma] \tag{xii}$$

Now the solution of (ix), together with (v), (viii), and (x), gives

$$\begin{aligned} &\frac{\omega_f^2}{\omega\Omega} = (1 - B) \qquad \frac{\omega_f^2}{\omega^2} = (1-B)(1+\gamma) \\ &\frac{\omega_f^2}{\Omega^2} = \frac{(1-B)}{(1+\gamma)} \qquad \text{and} \qquad B = \pm\sqrt{\frac{\gamma}{\gamma+2}} \end{aligned} \tag{xiii}$$

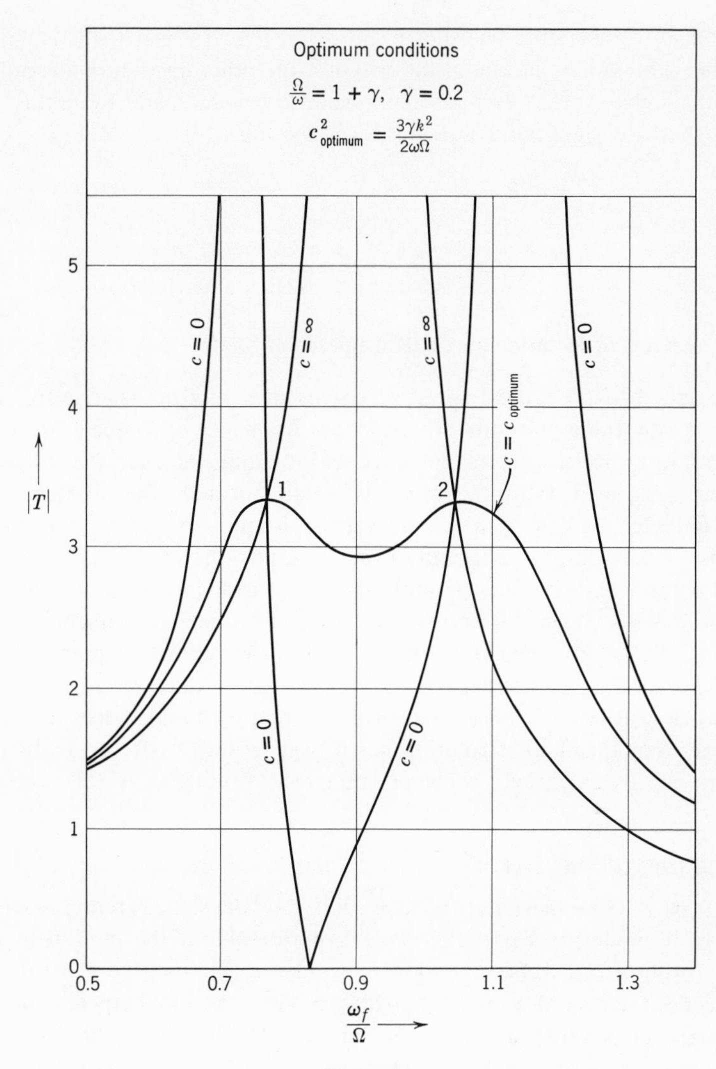

Figure 59

Elimination of α, β, B, and η in (xii) by the use of (xiii) produces the final result

$$\left(\frac{c}{k}\right)^2 \omega\Omega = \frac{3\gamma \pm \gamma\sqrt{\gamma/(2 + \gamma)}}{2} \tag{xiv}$$

in which the "+" sign is for $\omega_f = \omega_1$ and the "−" sign for $\omega_f = \omega_2$ with $\omega_1 > \omega_2$. Since $\gamma \neq 0$, it is not possible to make $|T|$ a maximum at both

ω_1 and ω_2. Experience has shown, however, that if T versus the ω_f curve reaches a maximum at one of the two ω's, the other maximum has only a slightly higher value. Hence a compromise can be made by taking the average of the right-hand side in (xiv). (See Fig. 59.)

$$\left(\frac{c}{k}\right)^2 \omega\Omega = \frac{3\gamma}{2}$$

$$c^2 = \frac{3}{2}\frac{mk^2}{M\omega\Omega} = \frac{3}{2}\frac{m^2k\omega}{M\Omega} = \frac{3}{2}\frac{m^2k}{m + M}$$

2.14 Effects of Rotation on Critical Speeds of Shafts

In Art. 2.10 the critical speed or speeds of a rotating shaft were considered as nothing more than the resonant frequency or frequencies of the system in transverse vibrations. It was maintained that the rotation merely furnished the necessary excitation through the existence of unavoidable eccentricity in the mass distribution of the system. In other words, if we want to determine experimentally the critical speeds of a certain shaft carrying one or more disks, we can, instead of rotating it, excite it with sinusoidal transverse forces of different frequencies and observe the speeds when resonant transverse vibrations take place.

The situation represented is a simplification that serves practical purposes well in most cases. However, there are circumstances in which the fact that the shaft is rotating has a bearing on the problem. In this article we discuss briefly some of the effects produced by the rotation itself.

(A) GYROSCOPIC EFFECT

In Art. 2.10 the inertia of the disk carried by the shaft is represented by that of a single mass particle. This is permissible if the motion of the disk during a transverse vibration is a pure translation. In general, the motion of the disk also includes a rotation about an axis perpendicular to the plane of bending, as shown in Fig. 60. The inertia of the disk thus exerts a moment on the shaft when the system is in simple transverse vibration. If the shaft is also rotating about its own axis, there is an additional gyroscopic moment as the rotating disk changes its spatial attitude.

Let us first investigate the case of a nonrotating shaft. Assume that the system vibrates in the xy-plane. Let y and θ denote, respectively, the deflection and the rotation of the cross section of the shaft where the disk is located. During a transverse vibration in the xy-plane the disk exerts on the shaft a force $m\ddot{y}$ and a moment $I_z\ddot{\theta}$. When the system is in simple harmonic vibration, y and θ may be represented by

$$y = \lambda \cos \omega t \qquad \theta = \beta \cos \omega t$$

At the extreme position of the disk, the inertia force and moment are as shown in Fig. 60.

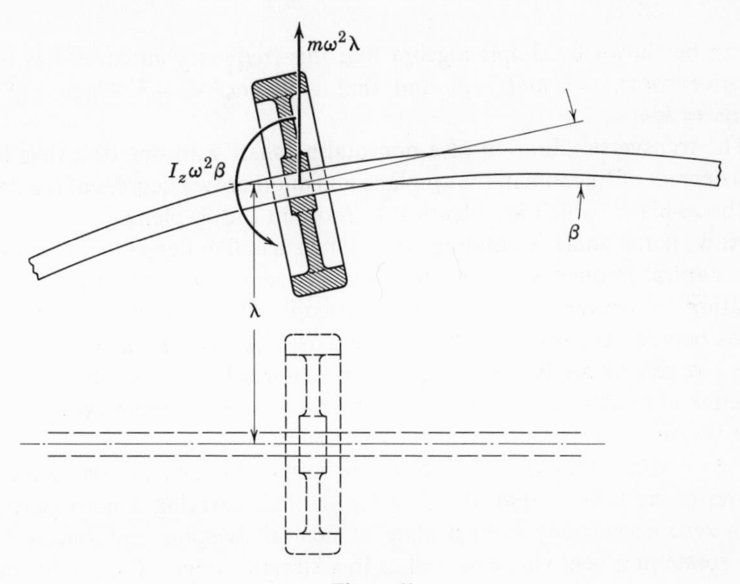

Figure 60

We now define the influence coefficients:

γ_f = deflection of a cross section per unit force applied at the cross section

γ_m = deflection of a cross section per unit moment applied at the cross section

ϕ_f = rotation of a cross section per unit force applied at the cross section

ϕ_m = rotation of a cross section per unit moment applied at the cross section

Maxwell's reciprocal relation is also valid here, so that $\gamma_m = \phi_f$. With the help of these coefficients, we can relate the deformation of the shaft with the force and moment produced by the inertia of the disk:

$$\begin{aligned} \lambda &= m\omega^2\lambda\gamma_f + I_z\omega^2\beta\gamma_m \\ \beta &= m\omega^2\lambda\phi_f + I_z\omega^2\beta\phi_m \end{aligned} \qquad \text{(i)}$$

This set of equations is evidently in the standard form of (24). The natural frequency of the system is thus given by

$$\begin{vmatrix} m\gamma_f - \dfrac{1}{\omega^2} & I_z\gamma_m \\ m\gamma_m & I_z\phi_m - \dfrac{1}{\omega^2} \end{vmatrix} = 0 \qquad \text{(ii)}$$

It can be shown by simple algebra that this frequency equation has two positive roots, ω_1^2 and ω_2^2, and that $\omega_1^2 < \omega_0^2 < \omega_2^2$ where $\omega_0^2 = 1/m\gamma_f = k/m$.

The transverse vibration of a nonrotating shaft with one disk thus has two degrees of freedom in the xy-plane and another two degrees of freedom in the xz-plane, which are identical to those in the xy-plane.

Now, if the shaft is rotating, the system has five degrees of freedom. The natural frequency in the fifth degree is zero, since it is a rigid-body rotation. However, because of the gyroscopic effect a nonlinear coupling exists between the rotation about the x-axis with that about the y- and z-axes. A general analysis of the problem requires Euler's equation for the rotation of rigid bodies. There is, however, a simple and practical situation that we can analyze with elementary considerations.

Let us recall that the essence of the result obtained in Art. 2.10, as expressed by (58), is that at $\omega_f^2 = k/m$ a shaft carrying a mass particle with zero eccentricity is in a state of neutral dynamic equilibrium. It can rotate in a bent shape as well as in a straight shape. For a real shaft with a small but unavoidable eccentricity this speed marks a condition of instability. The question is now whether the situation is still the same when the mass carried by the shaft is in the form of a disk. Let us suppose that the shaft and the disk rotate together around the x-axis in a bent shape, as shown in Fig. 61. The centrifugal force acting on each mass element of the disk is proportional to the displacement of that element from the x-axis. This distributed centrifugal force produces a resultant force perpendicular to the x-axis and a resultant moment which tends to restore the disk to its neutral position. A comparison of Fig. 61 with Fig. 60 reveals that the moments of the inertia forces have opposite directions when the system is in transverse vibration and when it is rotating around the x-axis in a bent shape.

To determine the force F and the moment M in Fig. 61, we can integrate the contributions of each mass element of the disk with the help of an appropriate coordinate system. The procedure is routine but a little tedious; therefore we shall analyze the problem by a different approach.

The motion of the disk is assumed to be made up of a whirling motion, which is a translation, and a rotation about an axis parallel to the x-axis. The translation produces a linear momentum whose time rate of change results in a centrifugal force F given by

$$F = m\omega_f^2\lambda$$

The rotation produces a moment of momentum L whose time rate of change results in a moment M to be found as follows. Let us first observe

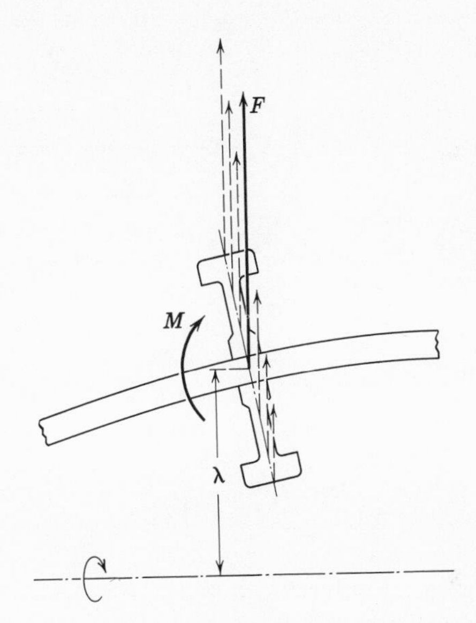

Figure 61

that the angular velocity vector ω_f, being along the x-axis, does not coincide with any of the axes of principal moment of inertia of the disk. Therefore the moment of momentum vector L is not in the direction of ω_f. (See Fig. 62.) Let I_1 denote the principal moment of inertia of the disk about its centroidal axis perpendicular to the plane of the disk. This axis is also tangent to the deflection curve of the shaft. The component of L along this axis, called L_1, is

$$L_1 = I_1(\omega_f \cos \beta)$$

Let I_2 denote the principal moment of inertia of the disk about the diametrical axis that lies in the plane of bending. The component of L along this axis is

$$L_2 = I_2(\omega_f \sin \beta)$$

The x-component of L is therefore

$$\begin{aligned} L_x &= L_1 \cos \beta + L_2 \sin \beta \\ &= (I_1 \cos^2 \beta + I_2 \sin^2 \beta)\omega_f \\ &= \left(\frac{I_1 + I_2}{2} + \frac{I_1 - I_2}{2} \cos 2\beta\right) \omega_f = I_x \omega_f \end{aligned}$$

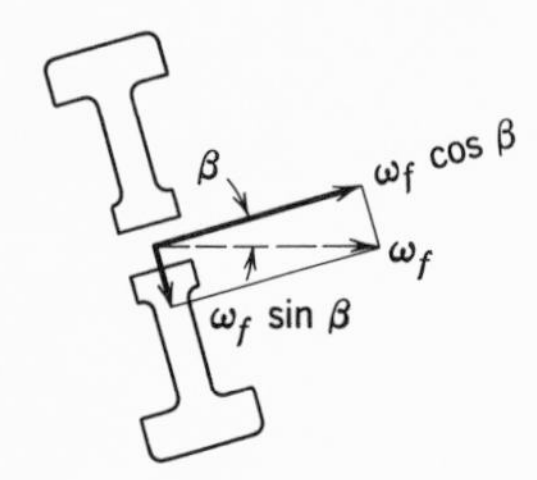

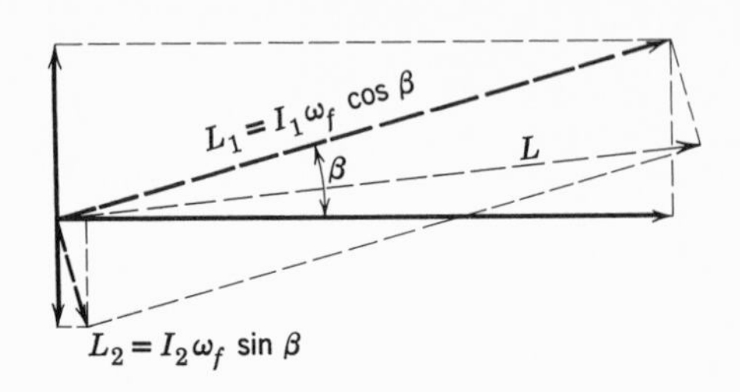

Figure 62

and the y-component of L is

$$\begin{aligned} L_y &= L_1 \sin \beta - L_2 \cos \beta \\ &= \left(\frac{I_1 - I_2}{2} \sin 2\beta\right) \omega_f = I_{xy} \omega_f \end{aligned}$$

in which I_x is the moment of inertia about the x-axis and I_{xy} is the product of inertia in the xy-plane.

The so-called y-component, however, has no fixed direction, since it always lies in the plane of bending and rotates with it. The time rate of change of L is the same as that of L_y and is represented by a vector in the z-direction of a magnitude given by

$$\frac{dL_y}{dt} = \omega_f L_y = I_{xy} \omega_f^2$$

According to d'Alembert's principle, the moment produced by this change is represented by a vector in the opposite direction, which gives the direction shown in Fig. 61 through the right-hand rule.

When β is small, this inertia moment becomes

$$M = -\frac{dL_y}{dt} = -I_{xy}\omega^2 = -(I_1 - I_2)\omega_f^2 \beta$$

The minus sign indicates the fact that M is opposite β. Using the influence coefficient previously defined, we have

$$\begin{aligned}\lambda &= m\omega_f^2\lambda\gamma_f - (I_1 - I_2)\omega_f^2\beta\gamma_m \\ \beta &= m\omega_f^2\lambda\gamma_m - (I_1 - I_2)\omega_f^2\beta\phi_m\end{aligned} \qquad \text{(iii)}$$

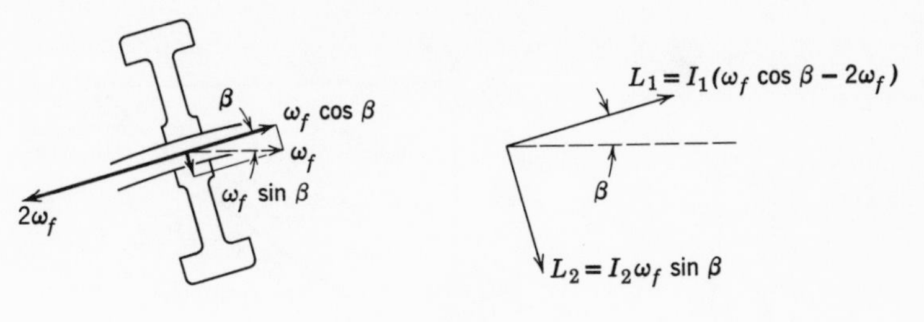

Figure 63

Since this is a set of linear homogeneous equations in λ and β, it admits nonzero solutions only if

$$\begin{vmatrix} m\gamma_f - \dfrac{1}{\omega_f^2} & -(I_1 - I_2)\gamma_m \\ m\gamma_m & -(I_1 - I_2)\phi_m - \dfrac{1}{\omega_f^2} \end{vmatrix} = 0 \qquad \text{(iv)}$$

For circular disks whose axial dimensions are small in comparison with radial dimensions, we have

$$I_1 - I_2 = I_z \qquad \text{and} \qquad I_2 = I_z$$

and

$$\begin{vmatrix} m\gamma_f - \dfrac{1}{\omega_f^2} & -I_z\gamma_m \\ m\gamma_m & -I_z\phi_m - \dfrac{1}{\omega_f^2} \end{vmatrix} = 0 \qquad \text{(v)}$$

In comparing (v) with (ii), we see that the terms containing I_z have different signs. As a result, there are two positive roots for (ii) but only one such root for (v). Hence for a shaft carrying a single disk there is only one critical speed at which the system is in a state of neutral dynamic equilibrium. (See Exercise 2.13.)

It has been observed in practice that sometimes the gyroscopic effect can cause large vibrations in a rotating shaft at another speed, at which the shaft whirls in one direction while the disk rotates in the opposite direction at the same speed. A little reflection will reveal that the rotary motion of the disk in this case can be represented by the sum of the two angular velocity vectors, shown in Fig. 63. The y-component of the moment of momentum vector is then

$$L_y = I_1(-2\omega_f + \omega_f \cos\beta)\sin\beta - I_2\omega_f \sin\beta\cos\beta$$

and for small β

$$L_y = -(I_1 + I_2)\omega_f\beta$$

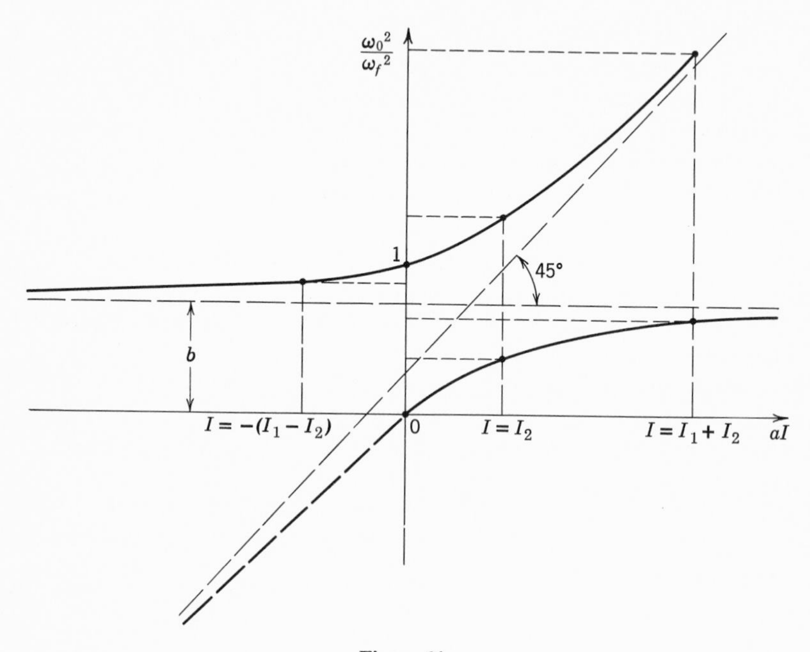

Figure 64

The moment due to the inertia force is thus

$$M = (I_1 + I_2)\beta\omega_f^2$$

This time the moment is in the same direction as β. The rest of the procedure is the same as before, and we obtain

$$\begin{vmatrix} m\gamma_f - \dfrac{1}{\omega_f^2} & (I_1 + I_2)\gamma_m \\ m\gamma_m & (I_1 + I_2)\phi_m - \dfrac{1}{\omega_f^2} \end{vmatrix} = 0 \tag{vi}$$

This equation has two positive roots for ω_f^2. The solutions to (iv) and (vi) can be put into a common nondimensional form:

$$\left(\frac{\omega_0}{\omega_f^2}\right)^2 = \frac{1}{2}[(1 + aI)^2 \pm \sqrt{(1 + aI)^2 + 4baI}] \tag{vii}$$

in which $\omega_0{}^2 = 1/mr_f$ is the critical speed ignoring the gyroscopic effect

$$a = \frac{\phi_m}{m\gamma_f} = \phi_m \omega_0{}^2$$

and

$$b = 1 - \frac{\gamma_m{}^2}{\gamma_f \phi_m} \qquad (0 \leq b \leq 1)$$

I is the appropriate moment of inertia appearing in (iv) or (vi). The hyperbola shown in Fig. 64 describes the relationship between ω_f and I. The relative magnitudes of the different roots of (iv) and (vi) are as indicated.

Let us call the velocity condition described by Fig. 62 a *forward whirling* and that by Fig. 63 a *backward whirling*. Figure 64 shows that forward whirling can take place only at one speed, whereas the backward whirling can take place at two speeds. It was assumed that in either forward whirling or backward whirling the whirling speed is numerically equal to the rotation speed. A question that may be asked is then, "Can the shaft whirl and rotate at two different speeds?" Reviewing the method of analysis employed, we see that given an arbitrary ratio of the whirling speed to the rotation speed we can find, at least theoretically, the speed or speeds of rotation at which the assumed ratio is realized. Since that is the case, we must ask, "Why are the speeds given by (iv) and (vi) called critical?" The answer to this question lies within the fact that all the motions postulated are free motions in the sense that there is no energy input. Because of the unavoidable dissipative forces in real systems, such motions cannot be sustained without some kind of suitable excitation. In the case of forward whirling at the speed of rotation the needed excitation is immediately available in the form of a centrifugal force produced by the unavoidable eccentricity. The critical speed given by (iv) is therefore always observable in practice, and it may be considered as the *true critical speed*. The backward whirling cannot be excited as effectively by the eccentricity, but a real shaft, which is a part of a piece of machinery, may be subjected to other suitable excitation created by the rotation. Backward whirling is therefore only occasionally observed.[24] Motions in which the whirling speed and rotation speed are entirely different do not usually have the necessary excitation to sustain them.

(B) EFFECTS OF GRAVITY FORCE

If a shaft carrying a disk is in a horizontal position, the gravity force will cause it to assume a bent shape even when it is at rest. But aside from

[24] See Den Hartog, *op cit.*, p. 265.

producing this change in the equilibrium configuration of the system, the gravity force has no effect on the frequency of the free vibrations of a nonrotating shaft. The situation, however, is different when the shaft rotates in a horizontal position.

Consider the simple case in which the gyroscopic effect is not present. During rotation there are three forces acting on the disk: a gravity force, an inertia force, and an elastic restoring force, as shown in Fig. 65. In

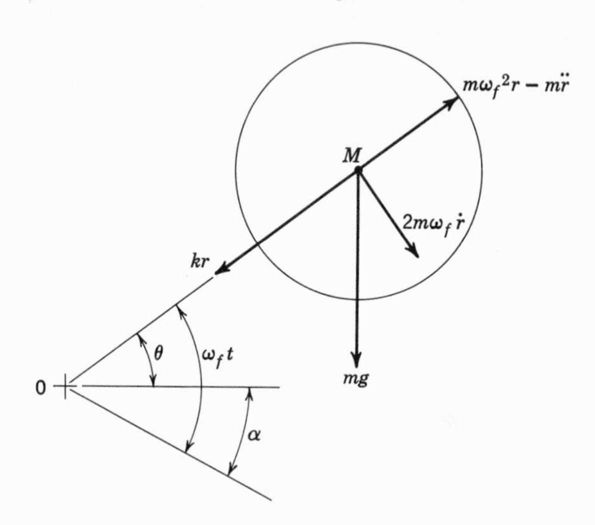

Figure 65

this figure 0 is the neutral position of the center of the shaft when it is straight and θ is the angle between the horizontal plane and the plane of bending of the shaft. A normal way of operation is obviously that in which the plane of bending remains vertical so that the gravity force balances the elastic force and there is no inertia force as the disk rotates about its lowered center M. The question to be asked now is, "Is it also possible to achieve a dynamic equilibrium with the plane of bending whirling around at a constant speed ω_f?" Assume that this is possible. Let us first resolve the inertia force into a radial component $m\omega_f^2 r - m\ddot{r}$ and a tangential component $2m\omega_f\dot{r}$, which is the Coriolis force. The whirling speed ω_f is assumed to be constant, and $\theta = (\omega_f t - \alpha)$. Hence

$$\begin{aligned} m\ddot{r} + (k - m\omega_f^2)r &= -mg \sin(\omega_f t - \alpha) \\ 2m\dot{r}\omega_f &= -mg \cos(\omega_f t - \alpha) \end{aligned} \qquad \text{(viii)}$$

Obviously, these equations are satisfied by $\omega_f = 0$, $\alpha = \pi/2$, and $r =$ constant $= mg/k$. Another way of satisfying (viii) is for ω_f to have the appropriate value so that

$$r = r_0 \sin (\omega_f t - \alpha) \tag{ix}$$

To see that this is true we substitute (ix) into (viii), and obtain

$$-m\omega_f^2 r_0 + (k - m\omega_f^2) r_0 = -mg$$

$$2m\omega_f^2 r_0 = -mg$$

or

$$(k - 4m\omega_f^2) r_0 = 0$$

$$\omega_f = \tfrac{1}{2}\sqrt{k/m} = \tfrac{1}{2}\omega_0$$

$$r_0 = \frac{-mg}{2m\omega_f^2} = \frac{-2mg}{k} = -2\delta_{st}$$

Since

$$x = r \cos \theta = r_0 \sin \theta \cos \theta = -\delta_{st} \sin 2\theta$$
$$y = r \sin \theta = r_0 \sin^2 \theta = -\delta_{st}(1 - \cos 2\theta)$$

where $\theta = \omega_f t - \alpha$, the path traced by M as the plane of bending whirls is a circle having radius δ_{st} and lying below but tangent to the horizontal plane containing 0.[25]

Theoretically, the motion described can take place regardless of the speed of rotation of the disk. But again without suitable excitation this motion cannot be sustained in real systems with the ever-present damping forces. In real shafts the unavoidable eccentricity causes a whirling motion at the speed of rotation. When this speed is $\omega_0/2$, the motion produced by the gravity force reinforces that produced by the eccentricity, and the resulting motion is represented by

$$r = r_0 \sin (\omega_f t - \alpha) + \frac{\omega_0^2 e}{\omega_0^2 - \omega_f^2}$$

$$= -\delta_{st} \sin \left(\frac{\omega_0 t}{2} - \alpha\right) + \frac{4e}{3}$$

With or without eccentricity, at the so-called *critical speed of the second order*, $\omega_f = \omega_0/2$, the vibrations produced have only finite amplitudes, which are of the order of δ_{st}. Sometimes vibrations at this speed are observed in practice with a substantially larger amplitude. Such vibrations are usually due to other causes, such as a difference in the rigidity of the shaft and its support in two different planes.

---

[25] This motion is the same as one of those described in Exercise 1.35. It is, however, instructive to compare the difference as well as the similarity between the system described in Exercise 1.35 and the one being studied.

(c) HYSTERESIS WHIRLING

It has been observed in practice that a shaft rotating above its critical speed may develop a whirling motion that is near its critical speed. This phenomenon is commonly attributed to the existence of a hysteresis loop in the shaft material. To explain such whirling motion on the basis of the hysteresis characteristic of the material, we begin with a simpler phenomenon with which the structural damping law of Kimball and Lovell, cited in Art. 1.18, was first deduced. Consider a rotating shaft supported between two bearings and subjected to an external lateral force P, which causes the shaft to bend as shown in Fig. 66. If the shaft material is perfectly elastic, the plane of bending will contain the force P, which

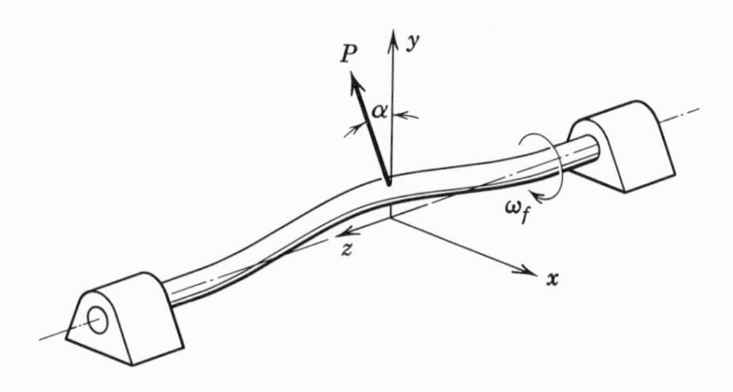

Figure 66

causes the bending. But if the shaft material has a hysteresis loop in its stress-strain relation, as shown in Fig. 67*a*, the plane of bending will not contain P. To arrive at this conclusion, let us assume that the plane of bending is the yz-plane in Fig. 66. Consider a cross section of the shaft, which is in the xy-plane. The fibers above the xz-plane, such as those represented by points A and B in Fig. 67*a*, are under tensile strains, whereas the fibers below (C and D) are under compressive strains. As the shaft rotates in the direction indicated, it is not difficult to see that A and C are being loaded, whereas B and D are being unloaded. Therefore, if Fig. 67*a* represents the stress-strain history of all the outer fibers of the rotating shaft, the stress-strain states of fibers A, B, C, and D are given by those correspondingly labeled points in Fig. 67*a*. Hence the tensile stress is higher at A than that at B, and the compressive stress is higher at C than at D. If we consider all the fibers in the shaft, the net result is an angle between the neutral axis of zero *strain* $x' - x$ and that of zero *stress* $n' - n$, as shown in Fig. 67*b*. Hence the external force P required to keep the plane of bending in the yz-plane must be making an angle α with the y-axis, as shown. Let the deflection of the shaft where P is applied be

$|\lambda|$. The x-component of the force P and those of the reactions at the bearing form a torque which must be balanced by an external driving torque in order to maintain the speed ω_f and the deflection $|\lambda|$. The energy input per revolution of the shaft is therefore

$$E_d = 2\pi P_x|\lambda| = 2\pi P \sin \alpha|\lambda| \tag{i}$$

This energy is dissipated by the hysteresis of the material.

As discussed in Art. 1.18, the experiments of Kimball and Lovell established that

$$E_d \propto |\lambda|^2$$

Hence $P \propto |\lambda|$, and the angle α is a measure of the structural or hysteresis

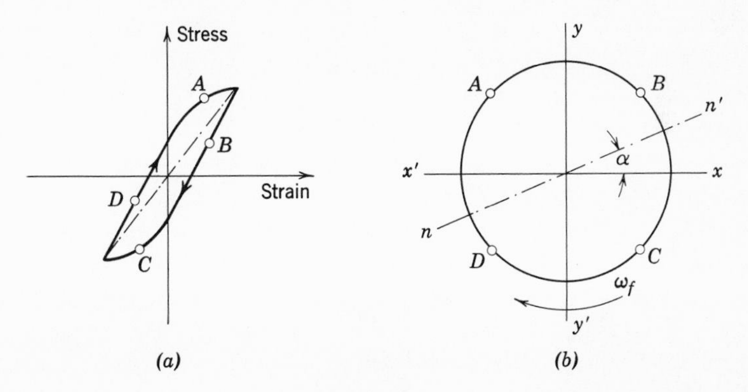

Figure 67

damping force in the system. To summarize, if a rotating shaft is deflected in a certain direction, it offers a resisting force which has two components. One component is due to the elasticity of the shaft, and it is proportional and opposite to the deflection. The other component is due to the hysteresis of the stress-strain cycling suffered by the material in a rotating shaft, and this component is proportional and perpendicular to the deflection. It is 90° from the elastic component measured *against the direction of the shaft rotation.*

As pointed out in Art. 1.18, strictly speaking, the description of the hysteresis force given above holds true only if the deflection of a rotating shaft is static. It is, however, reasonable to assume that this description also holds when the deflection varies slowly with respect to time; that is, the bending motion is slow in comparison with the rotation. Let us now consider a shaft carrying an inertia mass and rotating at a speed above its critical. In the absence of other forces the equilibrium configuration of the system is such that the shaft is straight. Suppose that a transient disturbance causes the mass to move away from the center-line of rotation. Now we want to study the motion that ensues. The restoring force and the inertia force on the mass are shown in Fig. 68. Let k and h be the constants of proportionality of the elastic force and the hysteresis force, respectively. The differential equations of motion are therefore

$$m\ddot{x} + kr\cos\theta - hr\sin\theta = 0$$
$$m\ddot{y} + kr\sin\theta + hr\cos\theta = 0$$

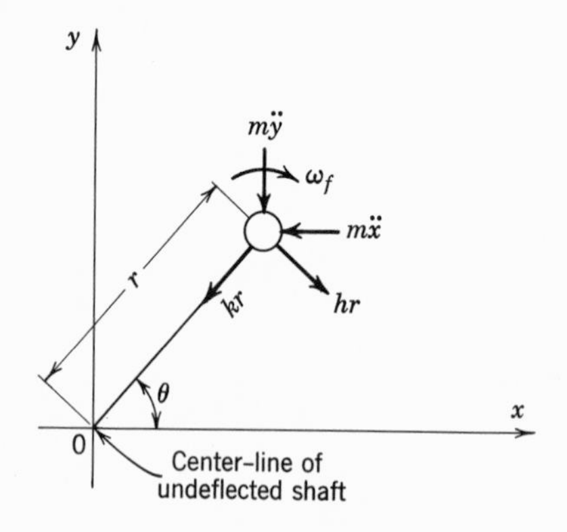

Figure 68

Since $r\cos\theta = x$ and $r\sin\theta = y$,

$$\begin{aligned} m\ddot{x} + kx - hy &= 0 \\ m\ddot{y} + ky + hx &= 0 \end{aligned} \tag{ii}$$

If we let $\zeta = x + iy$, the two equations can be combined to yield

$$m\ddot{\zeta} + (k + ih)\zeta = 0$$

In the Argand diagram the complex variable ζ *graphically describes* the location of the mass m. Defining as usual $h = \eta k$ with $\eta = \tan\alpha > 0$, we have finally

$$m\ddot{\zeta} + k(1 + i\eta)\zeta = 0$$

or

$$m\ddot{\zeta} + \kappa\zeta = 0 \tag{iii}$$

where $\kappa = k(1 + i\eta)$. The solution to (iii) is

$$\zeta = Ae^{s_1 t} + Be^{s_2 t} \tag{iv}$$

where

$$\begin{matrix} s_1 \\ s_2 \end{matrix} = \pm i\omega\sqrt{1 + i\eta} \tag{v}$$

and $\omega = \sqrt{k/m}$ = critical speed in the absence of hysteresis.

Through the usual complex number algorism, we obtain

$$\begin{matrix} s_1 \\ s_2 \end{matrix} = \left(\mp\sqrt{\frac{-1 + \sqrt{1 + \eta^2}}{2}} \pm \sqrt{\frac{1 + \sqrt{1 + \eta^2}}{2}}\, i\right)\omega$$

For small η or $\eta \ll 1$

$$\sqrt{1 + \eta^2} \doteq 1 + \tfrac{1}{2}\eta^2$$

and

$$\begin{matrix} s_1 \\ s_2 \end{matrix} \doteq \mp\frac{\eta\omega}{2} \pm i\omega$$

By substituting the expressions for s_1 and s_2 into (iv) and remembering that ζ describes graphically in Argand's diagram the location of the mass in the xy-plane, we conclude that the motion of m consists of a counterclockwise whirling ($+i\omega$) with decaying deflection ($-\eta\omega/2$) and a clockwise whirling ($-i\omega$) with increasing deflection ($+\eta\omega/2$). The latter motion represents an instability of the system. Since the rotation of the shaft viewed from the same plane is clockwise, the unstable whirling is with the rotation.

Returning to the physical picture, we observe that the foregoing conclusions are contingent upon these assumptions:

(1) $\omega_f \gg \omega$; otherwise the experimental law (i) cannot be used.

(2) There are external driving torques sufficient to maintain the speed of rotation ω_f.

(3) There are no other damping forces operating.

In an actual case a viscous force, such as air damping, will limit the whirling motion to small amplitudes.

To close this discussion, let us mention one mathematical observation. In Fig. 68, if we reverse the direction of rotation ω_f, the direction of the force hr will also be reversed. Consequently (ii) and (iii) will be modified into

$$m\ddot{x} + kx + hy = 0$$
$$m\ddot{y} + ky - hx = 0$$

and

$$m\ddot{\zeta} + \bar{\kappa}\zeta = 0 \tag{vi}$$

where $\bar{\kappa} = k(1 - i\eta)$ is the complex conjugate of κ. Since (vi) can be written as

$$m\ddot{\bar{\zeta}} + \kappa\bar{\zeta} = 0$$

Its solution is complex-conjugate to that of (iii). This time the unstable whirling is in the counterclockwise direction, which is still the direction of shaft rotation. Hence the physical picture remains the same. In other words, whether we call $\kappa = k(1 + i\eta)$ the complex stiffness or $\bar{\kappa} = k(1 - i\eta)$, the result is the same.

(D) OIL WHIP

When a shaft is supported by journal bearings with hydrodynamic lubrications, the lift force produced by the oil film may pulsate and interact with the elastic and inertia forces of the system to produce large vibration. A detailed analysis of the problem is quite complicated. As a first approximation, we may neglect the elastic effect and consider the shaft to be perfectly rigid and straight. We know from hydrodynamic theory of lubrication that in a journal bearing with a certain amount of clearance, the journal is displaced from the concentric position, a lift force is produced by the oil pressure distribution. This lift force is perpendicular in direction and proportional in magnitude to the displacement of the journal.[26] If a shaft is running with no transverse load and its journal is displaced from the concentric position by a transient disturbance, this lift force may cause the journal, hence the shaft, to whirl. The situation is similar to the hysteresis effect already discussed. The equation of motion may be written

$$m\ddot{x} + hy = 0$$
$$m\ddot{y} - hx = 0$$

where h is found by Robertson[27] to be

$$h = H(\omega_f - 2\dot{\theta})$$

with H a constant determined by the bearing dimensions and lubricant property, ω_f, the rotation speed, and θ, the angular velocity of whirling. This set of differential equations can be satisfied by

$$\dot{\theta} = \text{constant} = \omega_1$$

$$\left.\begin{matrix} x \\ y \end{matrix}\right\} = e^{\omega_1 t}\left\{\begin{matrix}\cos \\ \sin\end{matrix}\right. (\omega_1 t - \alpha)$$

and

$$2m\omega_1^2 - H(\omega_f - 2\omega_1) = 0$$

In bearings of usual design H is often a large number in comparison with

[26] If the displacement is small in comparison with the clearance. See Norton, *Lubrication*, McGraw-Hill, New York, 1942, pp. 106–113.

[27] "The Whirling of Shafts," by D. Robertson, *The Engineer*, Vol. 158, 1934.

$m\omega_1$, so that the whirling speed ω_1 is very nearly equal to one half the rotation speed ω_f:

$$\omega_1 \doteq \tfrac{1}{2}\omega_f$$

Again we have a situation in which the displacement tends to infinity if not checked by other forces unaccounted for here.

It may be noted that the two phenomena discussed in (C) and (D) do not by themselves favor a particular speed or speeds to take place. Based upon the much simplified analysis given, they will take place theoretically at all speeds. In practice, other contributing factors determine whether or not they will appear at all.

Exercises

2.1. Show that the solutions for ω^2 in (4) are always positive.

2.2. In Fig. 44, if we define x_1 as positive when m_{11} moves to the right and x_2 as positive when m_{22} moves to the left, what changes if any will we have to make in (1), (3), (4), and (5)? How will the values of ω and μ be affected by this change in sign convention?

2.3. In general, are $x_1(t)$ and $x_2(t)$, as described by (7), periodic functions? Under what condition will they be periodic?

2.4. Substitute (8) into (1), utilize (5), and compare the results with (10).

2.5. In Fig. 44 let m_{11} and m_{22} weigh 2 lb each, $k_{11} = 3$ lb per in., $k_{12} = 2$ lb per in., and $k_{22} = 1$ lb per in. Let the initial conditions of the masses be $x_1(0) = 2$ in., $x_2(0) = 0$, and $\dot{x}_1(0) = \dot{x}_2(0) = 0$. Find the motions of the two masses.

2.6. A mass particle constrained to move in the xy-plane is connected to a stationary frame by three springs of equal natural lengths as shown.

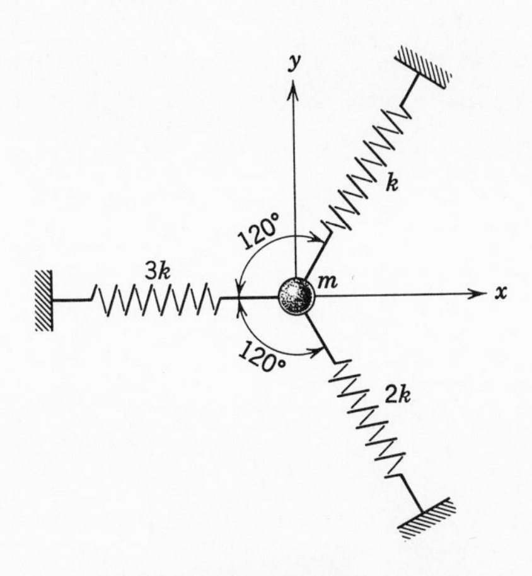

Exercise 2.6

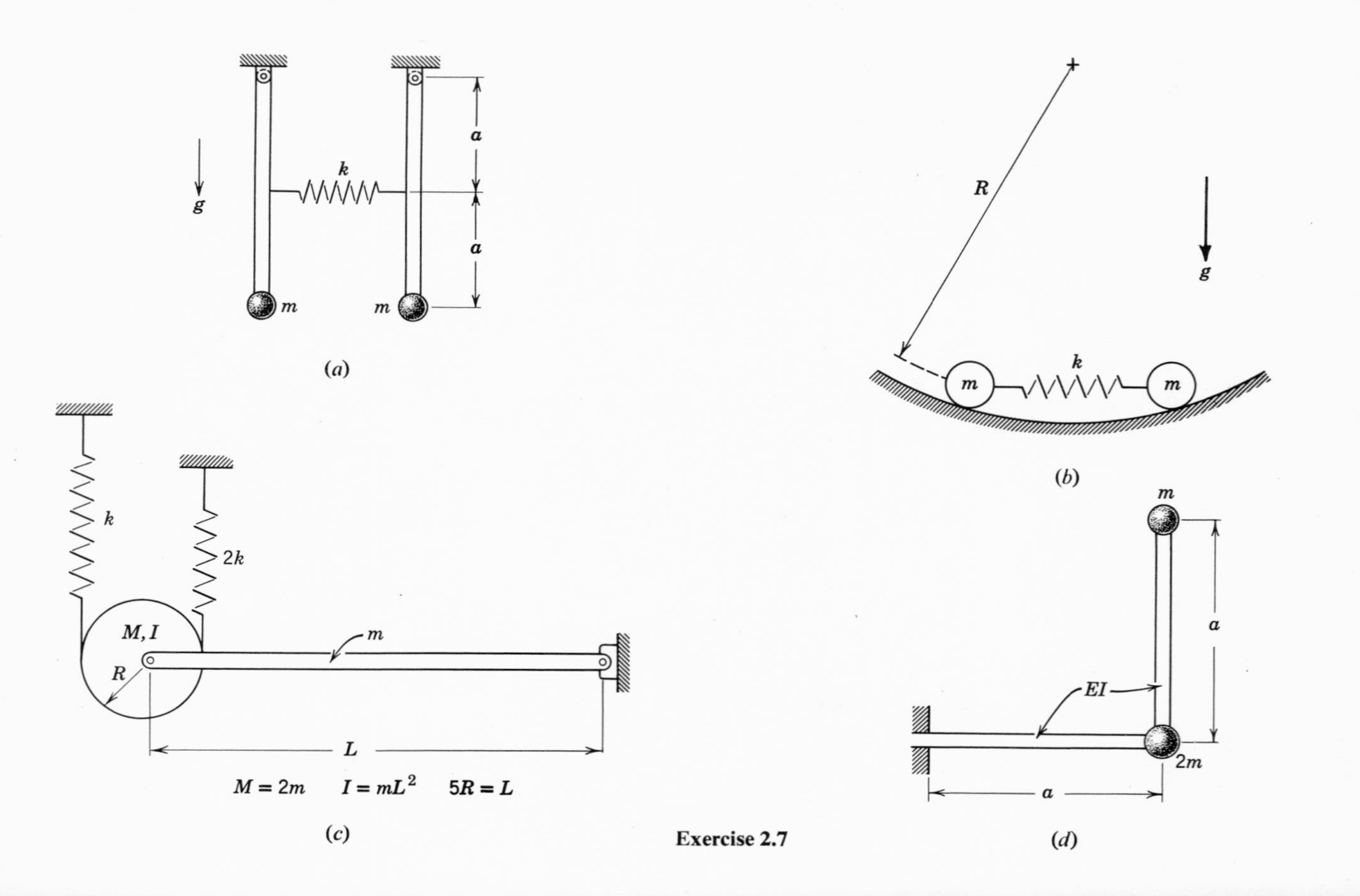

Exercise 2.7

(*a*) With x and y indicated in the figure as the coordinates, write the differential equations of motion for small oscillations of m and solve the frequency equation.

(*b*) Without solving the problem, we know the two principal modes of vibration are two mutually perpendicular rectilinear simple harmonic motions. How do we know this is the case?

(*c*) Find the directions of the two motions representing the principal modes.

(*d*) If we use Rayleigh's method to determine the frequencies, we shall need a reasonable estimate of these two directions. The mode having the lower frequency must favor the softer spring, and vice versa. So let us assume that the low-frequency mode is perpendicular to the spring $3k$. Find the frequency by Rayleigh's method and compare the result with those from (*a*).

2.7. Find the frequency equations for small oscillations of the systems shown.

2.8. Find by *Mohr circle construction* the natural frequencies and the corresponding amplitude ratios of the two modes of free vibration of the system shown in Fig. 53, if $\theta = 30°$, $Mg = 2mg = 10$ lb, $K = 3k = 15$ lb/in.

2.9. Find and solve the frequency equation for the transverse vibration of a cantilever beam carrying a mass m at its free end and another mass $2m$ at its midspan. The length of the beam is L, and its section stiffness is EI.

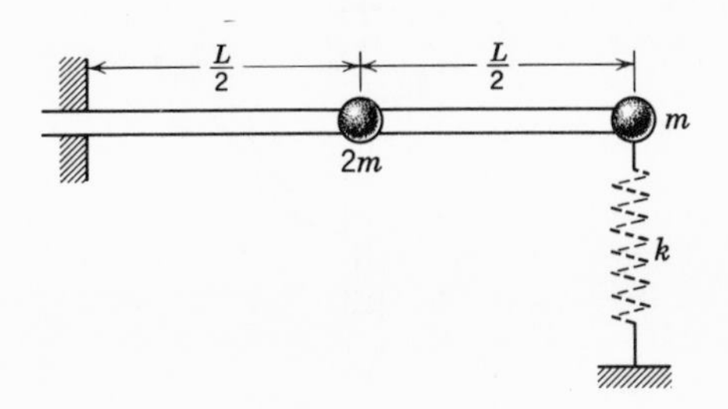

Exercise 2.9

2.10. If at the free end of the beam a spring of constant $k = EI/L^3$ is also attached, find its frequency equation.

2.11. Prove (22) by the following considerations:

$$V = \tfrac{1}{2}(P_1\delta_1 + P_2\delta_2)$$

$$V = \tfrac{1}{2}(c_{11}\delta_1^{\,2} + 2c_{12}\delta_1\delta_2 + c_{22}\delta_2^{\,2})$$

in which δ_1 and δ_2 are the deflections at two points of an elastic system produced by two loads P_1 and P_2. Or

$$\delta_1 = P_1\gamma_{11} + P_2\gamma_{12}$$

$$\delta_2 = P_1\gamma_{12} + P_2\gamma_{22}$$

2.12. Show that if the potential energy expression V is always positive for arbitrary δ_1 and δ_2, which do not vanish simultaneously, it is necessary that

$$c_{11} > 0 \qquad \text{and} \qquad c_{11}c_{22} > c_{12}^{\,2}$$

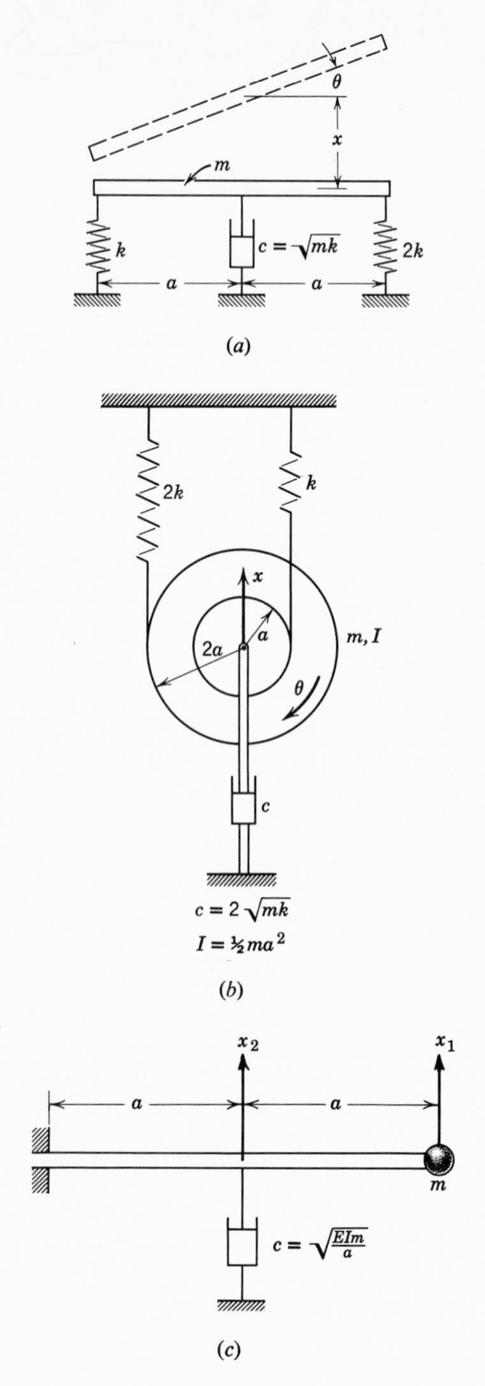

Exercise 2.14

Hint.

$$V = \tfrac{1}{2}[(\sqrt{c_{11}}\delta_1 \pm \sqrt{c_{22}}\delta_2)^2 \mp 2(\sqrt{c_{11}c_{22}} - c_{12})\delta_1\delta_2]$$

$$V > 0 \qquad \text{for } \delta_1 = 0$$

$$V > 0 \qquad \text{for } \delta_2 = 0$$

$$V > 0 \qquad \text{for } \sqrt{c_{11}}\delta_1 \pm \sqrt{c_{22}}\delta_2 = 0$$

2.13. Show that there is only one positive solution to (iv) and (v) of Art. 2.14, since $c_{11}c_{22} > c_{12}^2$ implies $\gamma_{11}\gamma_{22} > \gamma_{12}^2$.

2.14. Set up the differential equations of motion in terms of the coordinates indicated for the free vibrations of the damped systems shown and determine their characteristic equations.

2.15. In the accompanying figure M represents an instrument which is packed in a box B with springy padding having an equivalent spring constant K. Inside

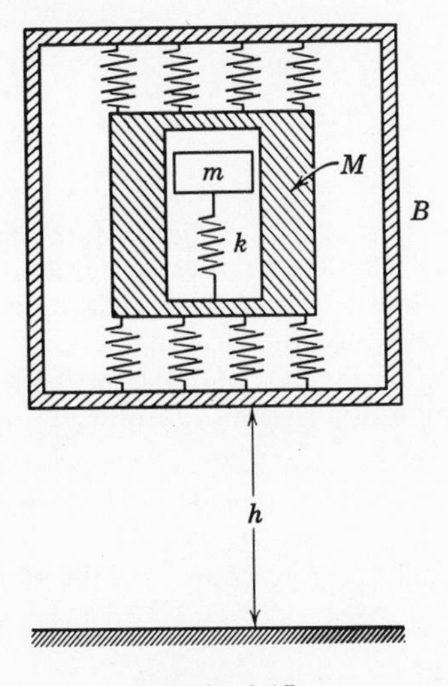

Exercise 2.15

the instrument is a small part m shock-mounted by spring k. The box with its content is dropped from a height h. If

$$M \text{ weighs 25 lb} \qquad 1/K = 0.02 \text{ in/lb}$$

$$m \text{ weighs 0.5 lb} \qquad 1/k = 0.5 \text{ in/lb}$$

$$h = 5 \text{ ft}$$

Find the maximum spring force in k.

2.16. An electric motor is mounted at the center of a horizontal beam that is supported at its ends by springs and dampers and is presented from sideways movement. An eccentric mass is attached to the rotor of the motor and is being turned around in a vertical plane with a constant speed ω_f. Let

m = the combined mass of the assembly consisting of the rotor and the mass attached
e = the eccentricity of the center of mass of the assembly
M = the combined mass of the assembly consisting of the beam and the stator
r = the radius of gyration of the assembly above

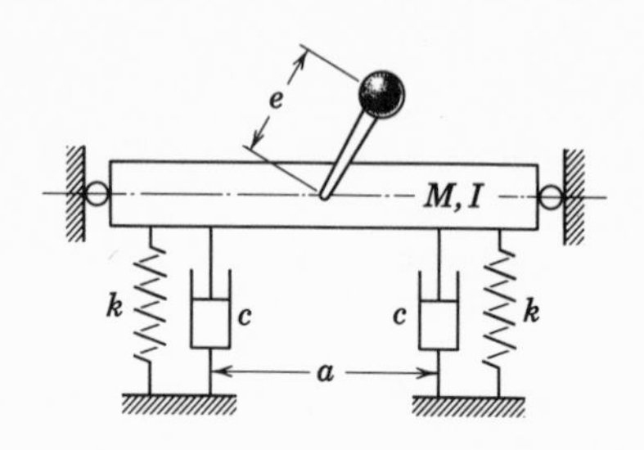

$M = 2m \quad I = Mr^2 \quad r = 4e \quad a = 2r$

Exercise 2.16

Write the differential equations of motion for the up-and-down and rotary motions of the beam and find the steady-state solution.

Hint. Replace the rotating part of the system by a vertical inertia force, a centrifugal force, a gravity force, and a torque.

2.17. Find an expression for the amplitude of the relative displacement x in the steady-state operation of a dynamic absorber of optimum design in which

$$\frac{\Omega}{\omega} = 1 + \frac{m}{M} \qquad \text{and} \qquad \left(\frac{c}{k}\right)^2 = \frac{3\gamma}{2\omega\Omega}$$

2.18. Design a dynamic absorber under the following conditions:
M = 500 lb
K = 100 lb/in.
F_0 = amplitude of disturbing force = 20 lb
$m < 50$ lb
D = coil diameter of the coil spring used for absorber spring
$D < 4$ in
S = shear stress in absorber spring $\qquad S < 40{,}000$ psi

2.19.

(*a*) Use the static deflection curve of the beam described in Exercise 2.9 to find the lower natural frequency by Rayleigh's method.
(*b*) Do the same for the beam in Exercise 2.10.

2.20. A steel shaft 1 in. in diameter overhangs a long bearing by 4 in. It carries at its free end a thin steel disk weighing 10 lb and having a radius of gyration of 4 in. Find the critical speed of the shaft, taking into account the gyroscopic effect due to forward whirling.

2.21. In the system shown let the imput signal be the motion (displacement) of the point P and the relative displacement between the two masses be considered as the response:

(*a*) Find the transfer function.
(*b*) Find the impulse response.

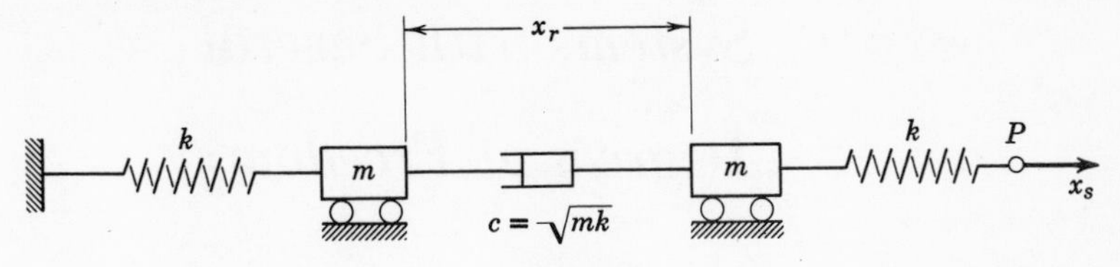

Exercise 2.21

2.22.

(*a*) A simple pendulum consisting of a mass m and a light rigid rod of length L is attached to the end of a vertical rod by a pin joint which allows rotation in only one plane. If the vertical rod is spinning with a constant speed ω_f, describe the small-oscillation behavior of the pendulum.
(*b*) If the pin joint is replaced by a universal joint, analyze the same.

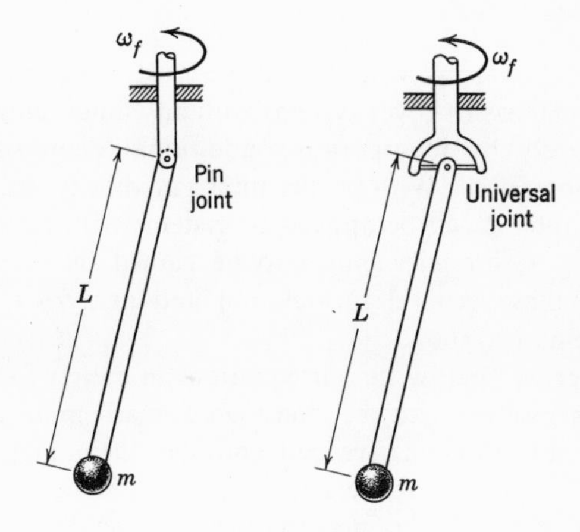

Exercise 2.22

CHAPTER 3

Systems with Several Degrees of Freedom

SECTION A. THEORY AND PRINCIPLES

3.0 Introduction

Having studied systems with two degrees of freedom, we can now generalize our analysis to cover systems with any finite number of degrees of freedom merely by incorporating additional coordinates into our mathematical operation. With proper minor modifications, all the results obtained in Chapter 2 can be applied to systems with several degrees of freedom. There is, however, much to be gained by re-examining our problem in its more general formulation and analyzing it with more powerful mathematical tools.

In this chapter we shall write our equations in matrix form. Although matrices by themselves can be considered mathematical entities, in application to our problems we can consider them merely a kind of shorthand. To help those readers to whom matrix notation is new, all the essentials of matrix algebra needed for our purpose are outlined in the Appendix. In the text we shall write our equations first in both the "longhand" and "shorthand" notations and gradually turn to writing in the shorthand notation only.

A few words are needed to defend the use of this mathematical tool, which is not indispensable for solving practical problems. Three justifications may be given. The first is that a simplified symbolism often provides a clearer picture of the physical theory it represents; a new formulation may reveal new ways of solving old problems. For instance, numerical multiplication or division can be carried out with either Roman or Arabic numerals, but the Arabic are not only more manageable, they also reveal more about the nature of the arithmetic processes themselves. The second justification is that matrix algebra is the unifying language of many seemingly unrelated subjects. Its use enables us to borrow the experience and feeling gained in analyzing one type of problem for the purpose of analyzing another. And the third is that matrix notation has become the accepted language for communication on the subject. Many technical papers which deal with the topics discussed in this chapter are written in this mathematical language. Furthermore, since the advent of electronic computers, it has become increasingly necessary for engineers to communicate with the people who run the computers or to "communicate" directly with the computers themselves. Both the operators and the computers can understand and help to solve an engineering problem readily when it is presented in matrix language.

3.1 Generalized Coordinates, Constraints, and Degrees of Freedom

We begin our study with a more thorough discussion of the terms mentioned in this heading. Any set of quantities, $q_1, q_2, \ldots, q_n$, can be considered as a set of *generalized coordinates* of a system if together with a time t they can be made to describe the configuration of the system. That is to say, when their values at any time t are known, the Cartesian coordinates of every mass particle in the system are determined. These generalized coordinates are said to be *kinematically independent* if the geometry of the system does not impose any interdependence relationships among them and their derivatives. In other words, it is possible for the system to have any set of values of q's and $\dot{q}$'s at any time t. On the other hand, if relationships such as

$$K(q_1, q_2, \cdots, q_n;\ \dot{q}_1, \dot{q}_2, \cdots, \dot{q}_n;\ t) = 0$$

exist, they are called the *equations of constraint*, or simple *constraints* of the system. The number of *degrees of freedom* of a system is the number of generalized coordinates, less the number of constraints among the coordinates. There are two types of constraints. One type is called the *integrable constraint* for which the function K contains no $\dot{q}$'s, or the q's can be eliminated by integration with respect to t. For example,

$$K(q_1, q_2) = q_1 + 2q_2 = 0$$

or

$$K(q_1, q_2, \dot{q}_1, \dot{q}_2) = q_1\dot{q}_2 + \dot{q}_1 q_2 = 0$$

With such constraints, some of the coordinates chosen beforehand can be eliminated. If all the constraints of a system are integrable, it becomes possible to have a set of generalized coordinates whose number is the same as the degrees of freedom of the system. Such a system is called a *holonomic system* and is the only type of system considered in this book.

As an example of a nonholonomic system, that is, a system with nonintegrable constraints, consider the motion of a coin of radius r, which can roll and spin without slipping on a rough horizontal table top. If it is

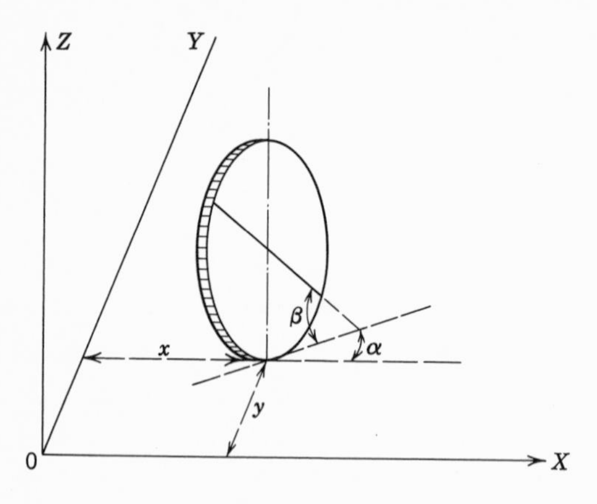

Figure 69

assumed that the coin plane remains perpendicular to the table top, the configuration can be specified by the Cartesian coordinates of the coin center, x and y, the bearing angle α of the coin plane, and the inclination β of a diameter fixed in the coin, as shown in Fig. 69. The nonintegrable constraint relationships among x, y, α, and β are

$$r\dot{\beta} \cos \alpha = \dot{x} \qquad r\dot{\beta} \sin \alpha = \dot{y}$$

This system therefore has only two degrees of freedom but needs at least four generalized coordinates to specify its configuration.

3.2 Energy Expressions in Generalized Coordinates for Linear Systems

We have seen in Chapter 2 that the vibratory motion of a system is governed by a set of linear differential equations, if its potential energy is a quadratic function of its coordinates and its kinetic energy is a quadratic function of the first derivatives of the coordinates. This is also true for linear systems with more than two degrees of freedom.

$$T = \tfrac{1}{2}(a_{11}\dot{q}_1{}^2 + a_{22}\dot{q}_2{}^2 + \cdots + a_{nn}\dot{q}_n{}^2 \cdots$$
$$+ 2a_{12}\dot{q}_1\dot{q}_2 + 2a_{13}\dot{q}_1\dot{q}_3 + 2a_{23}\dot{q}_2\dot{q}_3 + \cdots) \tag{1}$$

$$V = \tfrac{1}{2}(c_{11}q_1{}^2 + c_{22}a_2{}^2 + \cdots + c_{nn}q_n{}^2 \cdots$$
$$+ 2c_{12}q_1q_2 + 2c_{13}q_1q_3 + 2c_{23}q_2q_3 + \cdots) \tag{2}$$

In fact, we shall define a linear system as one whose energy expressions are as given above.

In addition to those systems that are genuinely linear many others can be considered approximately linear if their motions involve only small departures from their equilibrium configurations. To demonstrate this fact let us assume in what follows that the configurations of systems are determined by the generalized coordinates alone without having t entering explicitly. The potential energy of a system, being an energy of configuration, is then a function of the generalized coordinates, the q's.

$$V = V(q_1, q_2, \cdots, q_n)$$

Without losing generality, we may let $q_1 = 0$, $q_2 = 0, \ldots q_n = 0$, and $V(0, 0, \ldots 0) = 0$, when the system is at its equilibrium configuration. Thus the potential energy for any other set of values of the q's is, according to the mean value theorem,

$$V = \sum_i^n \left(\frac{\partial V}{\partial q_i}\right)_0 q_i + \frac{1}{2}\sum_i^n \sum_j^n \left(\frac{\partial^2 V}{\partial q_i\, \partial q_j}\right)_\eta q_i q_j \tag{3}$$

in which the subscript 0 of the first derivatives indicates that they are taken at the equilibrium position $(0, 0, 0, \ldots, 0)$ and the subscript of the second derivatives indicates that they are taken at some mean position $(\eta_1 q_1, \eta_2 q_2, \ldots, \eta_n q_n)$, with the η's lying between zero and unity.[1]

According to the principle of virtual work, when a system is in stable equilibrium its potential energy is at a minimum. Hence the first derivatives in (3) are zero. If we assume that the oscillation is small and the q's vary

[1] We assume that V is twice differentiable with respect to all the q's and the second derivatives are continuous in the neighborhood of the equilibrium configuration. More often one considers (3) as the Taylor series expansion, neglecting terms of third and higher orders. In that case, the second partial derivatives will also be taken at $q_i = 0$ and V will have to be continually differentiable.

in small ranges, the second derivatives can be considered as constants.[2] Then V may be written

$$V(q_1, q_2, \cdots, q_n) = \frac{1}{2}\sum_i^n \sum_j^n c_{ij} q_i q_j \tag{4}$$

where

$$c_{ij} = \left(\frac{\partial^2 V}{\partial q_i\, \partial q_j}\right)_\eta = c_{ji} \qquad (i, j = 1, 2, \cdots, n) \tag{5}$$

This double summation in (4) when expanded is the same as (2).

For the kinetic energy expression let us consider a generic mass element dm whose Cartesian coordinates x, y, and z are determined by the generalized coordinates as follows:

$$\begin{aligned} x &= x(q_1, q_2, \cdots, q_n) \\ y &= y(q_1, q_2, \cdots, q_n) \\ z &= z(q_1, q_2, \cdots, q_n) \end{aligned} \tag{6}$$

Its velocity in the x-direction, $\dot{x}$, is then

$$\dot{x} = \sum_i^n \frac{\partial x}{\partial q_i} \dot{q}_i \tag{7}$$

$$\dot{x}^2 = \sum_i^n \sum_j^n \frac{\partial x}{\partial q_i} \frac{\partial x}{\partial q_j} \dot{q}_i \dot{q}_j \tag{8}$$

Similar expressions for $\dot{y}^2$ and $\dot{z}^2$ yield the kinetic energy of the system.

$$\begin{aligned} T &= \frac{1}{2}\int_M (\dot{x}^2 + \dot{y}^2 + \dot{z}^2)\, dm \\ &= \frac{1}{2}\sum_i^n \sum_j^n \dot{q}_i \dot{q}_j \int_M \left(\frac{\partial x}{\partial q_i}\frac{\partial x}{\partial q_j} + \frac{\partial y}{\partial q_i}\frac{\partial y}{\partial q_j} + \frac{\partial z}{\partial q_i}\frac{\partial z}{\partial q_j}\right) dm \end{aligned} \tag{9}$$

Again, for small oscillations, the partial derivatives can be considered as constants with respect to t or the q's; and so is the last integral, being a definite integral over a fixed amount of mass M.

Hence

$$T = \frac{1}{2}\sum_i^n \sum_j^n a_{ij} \dot{q}_i \dot{q}_j \tag{10}$$

---

[2] Perhaps we are putting the cart before the horse, and should have defined the word "small" to mean small enough so that the second partial derivatives may be considered as constants.

where

$$a_{ij} = \int_M \left(\frac{\partial x}{\partial q_i} \frac{\partial x}{\partial q_j} + \frac{\partial y}{\partial q_i} \frac{\partial y}{\partial q_j} + \frac{\partial z}{\partial q_i} \frac{\partial z}{\partial q_j} \right) dm = a_{ji}$$

Again, this is a repetition of (1).

3.3 Summation Convention and Matrix Notation

Two conventions will be adopted for use in carrying out our analysis.

(A) THE SUMMATION CONVENTION

We notice, in all the equations studied so far, that whenever a certain subscript index is to be summed over all the available number of coordinates from 1 to n this index always appears twice in a given term. If this is always the case, the summation sign conveys no additional information and is therefore redundant. This is indeed generally the case for summation processes arising out of the types of operations we deal with. Thus the convention is hereby adopted that *whenever a particular subscript index repeats itself in a given term a summation process is understood, and no summation sign will be used.* Such an index is called a *dummy index.* In the meantime, a nonrepeating index is called a *free index.* It can take on any of the possible values $1, 2, \ldots, n$, but only one at a time. This convention is intimately connected with tensor calculus. The resulting notation may be called the *tensor notation*, although we may take it merely as a shorthand notation. For example, in the equation

$$f_i = c_{ij} q_j$$

i is nonrepeating, hence, a free index, whereas j is a dummy index. This equation is conventionally written

$$f_i = \sum_{j=1}^{n} c_{ij} q_j \qquad (i = 1, 2, \cdots, n)$$

which represents a set of simultaneous equations written in "longhand" as

$$\begin{aligned} f_1 &= c_{11} q_1 + c_{12} q_2 + \cdots + c_{1n} q_n \\ f_2 &= c_{21} q_1 + c_{22} q_2 + \cdots + c_{2n} q_n \\ &\cdots\cdots\cdots\cdots\cdots\cdots \\ f_n &= c_{n1} q_1 + c_{n2} q_2 + \cdots + c_{nn} q_n \end{aligned}$$

When an equation is written with the convention described, a free index must appear precisely once in every nonzero term of the equation. It is evident that the indexing denotes only a certain pairing or grouping relationship. Whether an index is named i or j or others is of no consequence as long as the proper pairing relationship is kept. For instance, the following two equations are identical in every respect because they are identical when written in longhand.

$$a_i = c_{ij}q_j + b_{ik}p_k$$

$$a_k = c_{km}q_m + b_{ki}p_i$$

(B) MATRIX NOTATION

Only three kinds of matrices are needed in our analysis. The notations adopted are as follows:

(i) An $n \times n$ square matrix is denoted by a bold sans serif letter in the upper case. The same letter in lower-case italic, with two subscript indices, denotes an element in the matrix. For example, $\mathbf{A}$ represents a square matrix, a_{12} represents the element of $\mathbf{A}$ belonging to the first row and second column, and a_{ij} is a generic element of $\mathbf{A}$.

(ii) An $n \times 1$ column matrix is denoted by bold sans serif letter in the lower case. The same letter in lower-case italic, with a single subscript index, represents an element of the column matrix. Thus $\mathbf{a}$ is a column matrix, a_2 is the second element of the column matrix $\mathbf{a}$, and a_i is a generic element of the column matrix $\mathbf{a}$.

(iii) A bar above a bold sans serif letter denotes the transpose of the matrix represented by this letter. Thus $\bar{\mathbf{A}}$ is the transpose of $\mathbf{A}$, and $\bar{\mathbf{a}}$ is a row matrix which is the transpose of the column matrix $\mathbf{a}$. A row matrix is always written as the transpose of a column matrix.

(iv) Greek letters with or without subscript and italic letters without subscript denote scalar quantities.

(v) In this type of analysis, the number n, which specifies the order of a matrix, is the same for all matrices within one problem. It is therefore not necessary to be specific.

With the notation adopted, an equation written in matrix notation can be readily translated into one in the tensor notation.

For example:

MATRIX NOTATION	TENSOR NOTATION
$\mathbf{a} + \mathbf{b} = \mathbf{0}$	$a_i + b_i = 0$
$\mathbf{A}\,\mathbf{B} = \mathbf{C}$	$a_{ij}b_{jk} = c_{ik}$
$\mathbf{A}\,\mathbf{f} + \mathbf{g} = \mathbf{0}$	$a_{ij}f_j + g_i = 0$
$\bar{\mathbf{p}}\,\mathbf{A}\,\mathbf{q} = \lambda$	$p_i a_{ij} q_j = \lambda$
$\mathbf{A}\,\mathbf{B}\,\mathbf{f} + \alpha\mathbf{f} = \mathbf{g}$	$a_{ij}b_{jk}f_k + \alpha f_i = g_i$

Note that in writing the tensor equation corresponding to a given matrix equation the last index of a matrix element must be the same as the first index of the following one. Similarly, to write the matrix equation from its corresponding tensor equation, the dummy indices should be arranged first to appear together. For example,

$$a_{ij}b_{kj}f_i = d_k$$

is first rearranged to give

$$b_{kj}\bar{a}_{ji}f_i = d_k$$

The corresponding matrix equation is

$$\mathbf{B}\,\bar{\mathbf{A}}\,\mathbf{f} = \mathbf{d}$$

The same equation can also be written as

$$f_i a_{ij} \bar{b}_{jk} = d_k$$

or

$$\bar{\mathbf{f}}\,\mathbf{A}\,\bar{\mathbf{B}} = \bar{\mathbf{d}}$$

This ambiguity is not important because the two matrix equations represent the same set of equations when written in longhand.

3.4 Free Vibrations of an Undamped System—An Eigenvalue Problem

(A) DETERMINATION OF THE NATURAL MODES

In this article we shall carry out our analysis both in the tensor notation (on the left) and in the matrix notation (on the right) and repeat some of the more important results in longhand form.

The energy expressions in (4) and (10) can be written with the tensor and matrix notations as

Tensor	Matrix	
$T = \frac{1}{2}a_{ij}\dot{q}_i\dot{q}_j$	$T = \frac{1}{2}\bar{\dot{\mathbf{q}}}\,\mathbf{A}\,\dot{\mathbf{q}}$	(11)
$V = \frac{1}{2}c_{ij}q_iq_j$	$V = \frac{1}{2}\bar{\mathbf{q}}\,\mathbf{C}\,\mathbf{q}$	

The matrices **A** and **C** are called the *inertia matrix* and the *elastic matrix*, respectively. They describe the inertial property and the elastic property of the system.

In free vibrations the principle of energy conservation demands that

$$\dot{T} + \dot{V} = 0$$

Tensor	Matrix
$\dot{T} = \frac{1}{2}(a_{ij}\dot{q}_i\ddot{q}_j + a_{ij}\ddot{q}_i\dot{q}_j)$	$\dot{T} = \frac{1}{2}(\bar{\dot{\mathbf{q}}}\,\mathbf{A}\,\ddot{\mathbf{q}} + \bar{\ddot{\mathbf{q}}}\,\mathbf{A}\,\dot{\mathbf{q}})$
Because both i and j are dummy and $a_{ij} = a_{ji}$,	Because $\dot{T}$ is scalar and **A** is symmetrical, the two terms in the parentheses are equal.
$\dot{T} = a_{ij}\dot{q}_i\ddot{q}_j$	$\dot{T} = \bar{\dot{\mathbf{q}}}\,\mathbf{A}\,\ddot{\mathbf{q}} \quad (\bar{\mathbf{A}} = \mathbf{A})$

Similarly,

$$\dot{V} = c_{ij}\dot{q}_i q_j \qquad \Bigg| \qquad \dot{V} = \bar{\dot{\mathbf{q}}}\,\mathbf{C}\,\mathbf{q} \quad (\bar{\mathbf{C}} = \mathbf{C})$$

The energy principle becomes

$$(a_{ij}\ddot{q}_j + c_{ij}q_j)\dot{q}_i = 0 \qquad \Bigg| \qquad \bar{\dot{\mathbf{q}}}(\mathbf{A}\,\ddot{\mathbf{q}} + \mathbf{C}\,\mathbf{q}) = 0 \tag{12}$$

Since $\dot{q}_i = 0$ or $\dot{\mathbf{q}} = \mathbf{0}$ are trivial cases, we have

$$a_{ij}\ddot{q}_j + c_{ij}q_j = 0 \qquad \Bigg| \qquad \mathbf{A}\,\ddot{\mathbf{q}} + \mathbf{C}\,\mathbf{q} = \mathbf{0} \tag{13}$$

In either form (13) represents the set of differential equations of motion conventionally written:

$$\begin{aligned}
a_{11}\ddot{q}_1 + c_{11}q_1 + a_{12}\ddot{q}_2 + c_{12}q_2 + \cdots + a_{1n}\ddot{q}_n + c_{1n}q_n &= 0\\
a_{21}\ddot{q}_1 + c_{21}q_1 + a_{22}\ddot{q}_2 + c_{22}q_2 + \cdots + a_{2n}\ddot{q}_n + c_{2n}q_n &= 0\\
\cdots\cdots\cdots\cdots\cdots\cdots\cdots\cdots\cdots\cdots\cdots\cdots &\\
a_{n1}\ddot{q}_1 + c_{n1}q_1 + a_{n2}\ddot{q}_2 + c_{n2}q_2 + \cdots + a_{nn}\ddot{q}_n + c_{nn}q_n &= 0
\end{aligned}$$

The a's are called the *inertia constants* and the c's, the *elastic* or *stiffness constants* of the system.

To solve this set of equations, assume as usual a typical solution:

$$q_i = l_i e^{i\omega t} \qquad \Bigg| \qquad \mathbf{q} = \mathbf{l}e^{i\omega t} \tag{14}$$

and substitute (14) in (13)

$$(-\omega^2 a_{ij} + c_{ij})l_j = 0 \qquad \Bigg| \qquad (-\omega^2\mathbf{A} + \mathbf{C})\,\mathbf{l} = \mathbf{0} \tag{15}$$

This is a set of linear homogeneous equations in l_j. The case that $l_j = 0$ or $\mathbf{l} = \mathbf{0}$ represents the trivial case of no motion. However, these equations can have nontrivial solutions; that is, if the determinant of the coefficients vanish.

$$|c_{ij} - \omega^2 a_{ij}| = 0 \qquad \Bigg| \qquad |\mathbf{C} - \omega^2\,\mathbf{A}| = 0 \tag{16}$$

Upon expanding the determinant, we obtain an algebraic equation in ω^2 of the nth degree, which is called the *frequency equation* or the *characteristic equation* of the system. It can be shown by theorems in algebra that since T and V are nonnegative the frequency equation will have n nonnegative roots.[3] Let these roots be

$$\omega^2 = \omega_1^{\,2} \qquad \omega_2^{\,2}, \cdots, \omega_n^{\,2}$$

They are the natural frequencies of the system. Let us assume for the time being the commoner situation in which these roots are *positive* and *distinct*. For each of the roots of ω^2 it is possible to solve (15), in the sense that it is possible to find the ratio among the l's.

$$l_1 : l_2 : l_3 : \cdots : l_n = r_1 : r_2 : r_3 : \cdots r_n$$

[3] See Whittaker, *Analytical Dynamics*, Cambridge University Press, 1937, p. 183.

or

$$l_i = \mu r_i \qquad \Big| \qquad \mathbf{l} = \mu \mathbf{r}$$

where μ is an arbitrary complex number, and the r's form a column matrix whose elements are real numbers determined to within an arbitrary multiplication factor. The elements of $\mathbf{r}$ are real because the coefficients of (15) are real. Therefore

$$q_i = r_i \mu e^{i\omega t} \qquad \Big| \qquad \mathbf{q} = \mathbf{r} \mu e^{i\omega t}$$

is a solution of (13), if ω satisfies (16) and $\mathbf{r}$ satisfies (15). The column matrix $\mathbf{r}$ specifies the amplitude ratio of a natural mode of vibration. It can be geometrically interpreted as a vector in n-space whose components are the elements of the matrix $\mathbf{r}$. Hence $\mathbf{r}$ is also called a *modal* vector.

Since μ is arbitrary, it is not necessary nor convenient to have $\mathbf{r}$ include an arbitrary multiplication factor also. To remove this unnecessary ambiguity in $\mathbf{r}$ let us adopt a so-called normalizing procedure, whereby the first non-zero element in $\mathbf{r}$ is taken to be unity. In this way all the other elements of $\mathbf{r}$ are uniquely[4] determined. From here on we shall assume that the modal vectors are normalized.

The basic procedure for determining the natural modes of vibration can thus be summarized as follows:

(i) Choose a set of appropriate generalized coordinates and obtain the expressions for T and V, from which the inertia matrix $\mathbf{A}$ and elastic matrix $\mathbf{C}$ are determined.

(ii) Set up the frequency equation (16), using the inertia and elastic constants of the system determined above, and find the roots of the equation.

(iii) Put each root of the frequency equation into (15) and solve for $l_2, l_3, \ldots, l_n$ with $l_1 = 1$. (If the solution is infinite with $l_1 = 1$, set $l_1 = 0$ and $l_2 = 1$; then solve for the rest of the l's. If this still does not give finite answers, set the next element of l equal to 1, and so forth.) A solution obtained this way is the normalized modal vector $\mathbf{r}$.

(B) GENERAL AND PARTICULAR SOLUTIONS

Let the modal vectors corresponding to the natural frequencies of a system, $\omega_1, \omega_2, \ldots, \omega_n$, be represented by the symbols $\mathbf{r}^{(1)}, \mathbf{r}^{(2)}, \ldots, \mathbf{r}^{(n)}$, respectively. The general solution of (13) is then

$$\mathbf{q} = \mathbf{r}^{(1)} \mu_1 e^{i\omega_1 t} + \mathbf{r}^{(2)} \mu_2 e^{i\omega_2 t} + \cdots \mathbf{r}^{(n)} \mu_n e^{i\omega_n t} \tag{17}$$

[4] We are assuming that the frequency equation has distinct roots. The case in which it has repeated roots is discussed later. Also, the normalization procedure described is one of the many possible. There is nothing physically unique about this procedure. See also Art. 3.12(B).

where $\mu_1, \mu_2, \ldots, \mu_n$ are arbitrary complex numbers which have to be determined by the initial conditions of the system.

The expressions for this general solution can be condensed and brought into more familiar matrix and tensor forms by introducing the following two artifices. Let us first form a square matrix **R**, called the *modal matrix*, by putting together all the column matrices **r** so that the jth column in **R** has the same elements as $\mathbf{r}^{(j)}$. Or

$$r_{ij} = r_i^{(j)} \qquad \Big| \qquad \mathbf{R} = [\mathbf{r}^{(1)}, \mathbf{r}^{(2)}, \cdots, \mathbf{r}^{(n)}] \tag{18}$$

Then let us form a column matrix **p** whose elements are given by

$$\mathbf{p} = \begin{bmatrix} p_1 \\ p_2 \\ \cdots \\ p_n \end{bmatrix} = \begin{bmatrix} \mu_1 e^{i\omega_1 t} \\ \mu_2 e^{i\omega_2 t} \\ \cdots \\ \mu_n e^{i\omega_n t} \end{bmatrix} \tag{19}$$

The solution can then be written simply as

$$q_i = r_{ij} p_j \qquad \Big| \qquad \mathbf{q} = \mathbf{R}\,\mathbf{p} \tag{20}$$

$$\begin{aligned} q_1(t) &= r_{11}p_1(t) + r_{12}p_2(t) + \cdots + r_{1n}p_n(t) \\ q_2(t) &= r_{21}p_1(t) + r_{22}p_2(t) + \cdots + r_{2n}p_n(t) \\ &\cdots\cdots\cdots\cdots\cdots\cdots\cdots\cdots \\ q_n(t) &= r_{n1}p_1(t) + r_{n2}p_2(t) + \cdots + r_{nn}p_n(t) \end{aligned}$$

The set of functions $p_i(t)$ is defined either by (19) with complex number representation or more conventionally by

$$\mathbf{p}(t) = \begin{bmatrix} p_1(t) \\ p_2(t) \\ \cdots \\ p_n(t) \end{bmatrix} = \begin{bmatrix} |\mu_1| \cos(\omega_1 t - \alpha_1) \\ |\mu_2| \cos(\omega_2 t - \alpha_2) \\ \cdots \\ |\mu_n| \cos(\omega_n t - \alpha_n) \end{bmatrix} \tag{21}$$

The relationship between μ, $|\mu|$, and α is

$$\mu = |\mu| e^{-i\alpha}$$

To obtain the particular solution satisfying a given set of initial conditions, these constants can be determined by the following procedure. Let $\mathbf{q}(0)$ and $\dot{\mathbf{q}}(0)$ be given. Put these into (20) to solve for $\mathbf{p}(0)$ and and $\dot{\mathbf{p}}(0)$.

$$\begin{aligned} q_i(0) &= r_{ij}p_j(0) \\ \dot{q}_i(0) &= r_{ij}\dot{p}_j(0) \end{aligned} \qquad \Bigg| \qquad \begin{aligned} \mathbf{q}(0) &= \mathbf{R}\,\mathbf{p}(0) \\ \dot{\mathbf{q}}(0) &= \mathbf{R}\,\dot{\mathbf{p}}(0) \end{aligned} \tag{22}$$

where $\dot{\mathbf{p}}(t)$ is defined by differentiating (19) or (21). When $\mathbf{p}(0)$ and $\dot{\mathbf{p}}(0)$ are found, the constants μ, $|\mu|$, and α can be determined from (19) or (20).

(c) EIGENVALUE PROBLEM

The method described for finding the frequencies and modal vectors becomes impractical when the number of degrees of freedom n is large. The number of arithmetic operations needed increases very rapidly with n. To devise other methods, it is necessary to introduce a new concept, the concept of an eigenvalue problem.

Stated in its most general form, an *eigenvalue problem* is a mathematical problem containing an unspecified parameter in such a way that the problem has only a trivial solution, unless this parameter takes on one of a certain set of values called the *eigenvalues* or *characteristic values* of the problem. The simplest and most important type of eigenvalue problem is illustrated by the following example. Given a square matrix $\mathbf{L}$, which represents a linear transformation of vectors in n-space, we are to find a vector $\mathbf{r}$ that is transformed by $\mathbf{L}$ into another vector in the same direction. In other words, the transformation $\mathbf{L}$ changes only the length but not the direction of $\mathbf{r}$. Such a vector is called an *eigenvector* of $\mathbf{L}$. The condition to be satisfied is represented by the equation

$$\mathbf{L}\,\mathbf{r} = \lambda\mathbf{r}$$

The scalar quantity λ represents the ratio between the lengths of the vectors before and after transformation, and it has to take on one of the eigenvalues for eigenvectors to be found. It is evident that eigenvectors are determined only to within an arbitrary multiplication constant. However, they can be normalized as desired.

The problem of determining the frequencies and amplitude ratios of the natural modes of vibration can be stated as an eigenvalue problem. Evidently the modal vectors satisfy (15)

$$(-\omega^2\mathbf{A} + \mathbf{C})\,\mathbf{r} = \mathbf{0}$$

This can be written

$$(\mathbf{A}^{-1}\,\mathbf{C})\,\mathbf{r} = \omega^2\mathbf{r} \tag{23}$$

Hence the modal vectors and the natural frequencies are the eigenvectors and eigenvalues of a linear transformation represented by the matrix product $(\mathbf{A}^{-1}\,\mathbf{C})$. Or, $\mathbf{L} = \mathbf{A}^{-1}\,\mathbf{C}$ and $\lambda = \omega^2$.

The problem of finding the eigenvalues and their associated eigenvectors is an integral problem. It is not necessary for one to be found before the other. In the classical procedure the eigenvalues are found first. There are other procedures in which the reverse is true or the eigenvalues and eigenvectors are found simultaneously.

A matter of practical interest is the fact that finding the eigenvalues and eigenvectors of a matrix has become a routine problem for electronic digital computers. In most computing laboratories the programming for solving such a problem is readily available.

3.5 Principal Coordinates and Orthogonal Property of Modal Vectors

(A) A TRANSFORMATION INTO PRINCIPAL COORDINATES

We have stated in Art. 3.1 that any set of quantities can be used as a set of generalized coordinates of a system if by specifying their values the configuration of the system is determined. It follows that if $q_1, q_2, \ldots, q_n$ are a set of generalized coordinates of a system any other set of quantities that will determine the q's uniquely can also be used as a set of generalized coordinates. According to (20) the set of quantities $p_1, p_2, \ldots, p_n$ determines $q_1, q_2, \ldots, q_n$; hence the p's can also be considered as generalized coordinates of the system. Obviously, when the coordinates used to describe a system are changed, the differential equations will be changed also. Now we want to see how the equations change when the coordinates are changed from $q_1, q_2, \ldots, q_n$ to $p_1, p_2, \ldots, p_n$. The matrix $\mathbf{q}$ satisfies (13).

$$\mathbf{A}\,\ddot{\mathbf{q}} + \mathbf{C}\,\mathbf{q} = \mathbf{0} \tag{13}$$

The matrix $\mathbf{p}$ then must satisfy

$$\mathbf{A}\,\mathbf{R}\,\ddot{\mathbf{p}} + \mathbf{C}\,\mathbf{R}\,\mathbf{p} = \mathbf{0}$$

This equation may be premultiplied by $(\mathbf{AR})^{-1}$ to yield

$$\ddot{\mathbf{p}} + (\mathbf{A}\,\mathbf{R})^{-1}\,\mathbf{C}\,\mathbf{R}\,\mathbf{p} = \mathbf{0}$$

or

$$\ddot{\mathbf{p}} + \mathbf{R}^{-1}\,\mathbf{A}^{-1}\,\mathbf{C}\,\mathbf{R}\,\mathbf{p} = \mathbf{0}$$

Let us define a matrix $\mathbf{W}^2$ as

$$\mathbf{W}^2 = \mathbf{R}^{-1}\mathbf{A}^{-1}\mathbf{C}\mathbf{R}$$

Then $\mathbf{p}$ satisfies

$$\ddot{\mathbf{p}} + \mathbf{W}^2\mathbf{p} = \mathbf{0} \tag{24}$$

In the meantime it is known that if $\mathbf{q}$ satisfies (13) and $\mathbf{p}$ is related to $\mathbf{q}$ by (20) $p_1, p_2, \ldots, p_n$ are a set of sinusoidal functions satisfying

$$\begin{aligned} \ddot{p}_1 + \omega_1^2 p_1 &= 0 \\ \ddot{p}_2 + \omega_2^2 p_2 &= 0 \\ &\cdots\cdots \\ \ddot{p}_n + \omega_n^2 p_n &= 0 \end{aligned}$$

This set of equations can be written in matrix form as

$$\begin{bmatrix} \ddot{p}_1 \\ \ddot{p}_2 \\ \cdot \\ \cdot \\ \cdot \\ \ddot{p}_n \end{bmatrix} + \begin{bmatrix} \omega_1^2 & 0 & \cdots & 0 \\ 0 & \omega_2^2 & \cdots & 0 \\ \cdot & \cdot & \cdot & \cdot \\ \cdot & \cdot & \cdot & \cdot \\ \cdot & \cdot & \cdot & \cdot \\ 0 & 0 & \cdots & \omega_n^2 \end{bmatrix} \begin{bmatrix} p_1 \\ p_2 \\ \cdot \\ \cdot \\ \cdot \\ p_n \end{bmatrix} = \begin{bmatrix} 0 \\ 0 \\ \cdot \\ \cdot \\ \cdot \\ 0 \end{bmatrix}$$

Comparing this equation with (24) we have[5]

$$\mathbf{R}^{-1}\mathbf{A}^{-1}\mathbf{C}\,\mathbf{R} = \mathbf{W}^2 = \begin{bmatrix} \omega_1^2 & 0 & \cdots & 0 \\ 0 & \omega_2^2 & \cdots & 0 \\ \cdot & \cdot & \cdot & \cdot \\ \cdot & \cdot & \cdot & \cdot \\ \cdot & \cdot & \cdot & \cdot \\ 0 & 0 & \cdots & \omega_n^2 \end{bmatrix} \tag{25}$$

In other words, $\mathbf{W}^2$ is a diagonal matrix, and the transformation of the coordinates from the q's into p's results in a separation of the variables in the differential equations of motion. The p's are therefore called the *principal coordinates.*[6]

It must be borne in mind that the relationship (25) is one between a matrix $\mathbf{A}^{-1}\,\mathbf{C}$, its eigenvectors which form the matrix $\mathbf{R}$, and its eigenvalues which form the matrix $\mathbf{W}^2$. It is a mathematical relationship not necessarily connected with the phenomenon of free vibration. For instance, in a forced vibration problem we shall see that the matrix equation is the nonhomogeneous equation

$$\mathbf{A}\,\ddot{\mathbf{q}} + \mathbf{C}\,\mathbf{q} = \mathbf{f} \tag{26}$$

The transformation procedure that leads from (13) to (24) transforms this equation into

$$\ddot{\mathbf{p}} + \mathbf{W}^2\,\mathbf{p} = \mathbf{R}^{-1}\,\mathbf{A}^{-1}\,\mathbf{f} \tag{27}$$

in which $\mathbf{W}^2$ is still a diagonal matrix and the unknowns $p_1, p_2, \ldots, p_n$ are separated in the set of differential equations represented by the foregoing matrix equation.

(B) ORTHOGONALITY OF MODAL VECTORS

A somewhat more convenient procedure of transformation into the principal coordinates is based on the so-called orthogonality properties

---

[5] We also have to take cognizance of the fact that the p's are linearly independent in order to arrive at (25).

[6] If a certain normalizing procedure, such as the one described in the Art. 3.4, is used, the principal coordinates become the *normal coordinates.*

of modal vectors. Two vectors **a** and **b** are said to be orthogonal with respect to a *symmetrical* matrix **S** if the product

$$\bar{\mathbf{a}}\,\mathbf{S}\,\mathbf{b} = \bar{\mathbf{b}}\,\mathbf{S}\,\mathbf{a} = 0$$

Now we want to show that any two modal vectors describing two natural vibrations of *different* frequencies are orthogonal with respect to both the inertia matrix **A** and the elastic matrix **C**. Let $\mathbf{r}^{(i)}$ and $\mathbf{r}^{(j)}$ be two modal vectors. They satisfy

$$\begin{aligned} \omega_i^2 \mathbf{A}\,\mathbf{r}^{(i)} &= \mathbf{C}\,\mathbf{r}^{(i)} \\ \omega_j^2 \mathbf{A}\,\mathbf{r}^{(j)} &= \mathbf{C}\,\mathbf{r}^{(j)} \end{aligned} \qquad \omega_i \neq \omega_j \tag{28}$$

Premultiply the two equations by $\bar{\mathbf{r}}^{(j)}$ and $\bar{\mathbf{r}}^{(i)}$, respectively.

$$\begin{aligned} \omega_i^2(\bar{\mathbf{r}}^{(j)}\,\mathbf{A}\,\mathbf{r}^{(i)}) &= \bar{\mathbf{r}}^{(j)}\,\mathbf{C}\,\mathbf{r}^{(i)} \\ \omega_j^2(\bar{\mathbf{r}}^{(i)}\,\mathbf{A}\,\mathbf{r}^{(j)}) &= \bar{\mathbf{r}}^{(i)}\,\mathbf{C}\,\mathbf{r}^{(j)} \end{aligned} \tag{29}$$

Because both **A** and **C** are symmetrical,

$$\begin{aligned} \bar{\mathbf{r}}^{(j)}\,\mathbf{C}\,\mathbf{r}^{(i)} &= \bar{\mathbf{r}}^{(i)}\,\mathbf{C}\,\mathbf{r}^{(j)} \\ \bar{\mathbf{r}}^{(j)}\,\mathbf{A}\,\mathbf{r}^{(i)} &= \bar{\mathbf{r}}^{(i)}\,\mathbf{A}\,\mathbf{r}^{(j)} \end{aligned} \tag{30}$$

Upon subtracting the two equations in (29) from each other, we have

$$(\omega_i^2 - \omega_j^2)(\bar{\mathbf{r}}^{(j)}\mathbf{A}\,\mathbf{r}^{(i)}) = 0$$

Since $\omega_i \neq \omega_j$, we have the proof that

$$\begin{aligned} \bar{\mathbf{r}}^{(j)}\,\mathbf{A}\,\mathbf{r}^{(i)} &= 0 \\ \bar{\mathbf{r}}^{(j)}\,\mathbf{C}\,\mathbf{r}^{(i)} &= 0 \end{aligned} \qquad \omega_i \neq \omega_j \tag{31}$$

In tensor notation these two equations are written

$$\begin{aligned} r_k^{(j)} a_{km} r_m^{(i)} &= 0 \\ r_k^{(j)} c_{km} r_m^{(i)} &= 0 \end{aligned} \qquad \omega_i \neq \omega_j$$

In either way of writing the equations contain only scalar products involving modal vectors. The same orthogonality property can also be described in terms of the modal matrix **R** given by (18). Let us form the matrix products

$$\begin{aligned} r_{kj} a_{km} r_{mi} &= m_{ji} \qquad & \bar{\mathbf{R}}\,\mathbf{A}\,\mathbf{R} &= \mathbf{M} \\ r_{kj} c_{km} r_{mi} &= k_{ji} \qquad & \bar{\mathbf{R}}\,\mathbf{C}\,\mathbf{R} &= \mathbf{K} \end{aligned}$$

We can see from (18) and (31) that if the natural frequencies for *different modes are distinct* the matrices **M** and **K** will have only diagonal terms. That is,

$$m_{ij} = 0 \qquad k_{ij} = 0 \qquad \text{when } i \neq j$$

The transformation of coordinates from q's to p's can now be performed on (13). Substitute (20) into (13) and premultiply the equation by $\bar{\mathbf{R}}$. The result is

$$\mathbf{A}\,\mathbf{R}\,\ddot{\mathbf{p}} + \mathbf{C}\,\mathbf{R}\,\mathbf{p} = \mathbf{0}$$

$$\bar{\mathbf{R}}\,\mathbf{A}\,\mathbf{R}\,\ddot{\mathbf{p}} + \bar{\mathbf{R}}\,\mathbf{C}\,\mathbf{R}\,\mathbf{p} = \mathbf{0}$$

or

$$\mathbf{M}\,\ddot{\mathbf{p}} + \mathbf{K}\,\mathbf{p} = \mathbf{0} \tag{32}$$

Since $\mathbf{M}$ and $\mathbf{K}$ have only diagonal terms, the longhand expression for (32) is

$$\begin{aligned} m_{11}\ddot{p}_1 + k_{11}p_1 &= 0 \\ m_{22}\ddot{p}_2 + k_{22}p_2 &= 0 \\ \cdots\cdots&\cdots\cdots \\ m_{nn}\ddot{p}_n + k_{nn}p_n &= 0 \end{aligned}$$

Evidently, since $\mathbf{p}$ is given by (19),

$$\frac{k_{11}}{m_{11}} = \omega_1^{\,2} \qquad \frac{k_{22}}{m_{22}} = \omega_2^{\,2}, \cdots, \frac{k_{nn}}{m_{nn}} = \omega_n^{\,2}$$

This can also be arrived at by the following operations:

$$\begin{aligned} \mathbf{M}^{-1}\,\mathbf{K} = (\bar{\mathbf{R}}\,\mathbf{A}\,\mathbf{R})^{-1}(\bar{\mathbf{R}}\,\mathbf{C}\,\mathbf{R}) &= \mathbf{R}^{-1}\,\mathbf{A}^{-1}\,\bar{\mathbf{R}}^{-1}\,\bar{\mathbf{R}}\,\mathbf{C}\,\mathbf{R} \\ &= \mathbf{R}^{-1}\,\mathbf{A}^{-1}\mathbf{C}\,\mathbf{R} = \mathbf{W}^2 \end{aligned} \tag{33}$$

The transformation from (13) to (32) is called *orthogonalization.*

The mathematical problem of determining the natural frequencies and modes of vibration is also one of finding a matrix $\mathbf{R}$ which will *diagonalize* two given symmetrical matrices $\mathbf{A}$ and $\mathbf{C}$ through

$$\bar{\mathbf{R}}\,\mathbf{A}\,\mathbf{R} = \mathbf{M} \qquad \text{and} \qquad \bar{\mathbf{R}}\,\mathbf{C}\,\mathbf{R} = \mathbf{K} \tag{34}$$

and will give the natural frequencies through

$$\mathbf{M}^{-1}\,\mathbf{K} = \mathbf{W}^2 \tag{35}$$

This approach is used in some numerical methods of solving the problem by successive approximation.

3.6 Rayleigh's Quotient

In Art. 3.5 the two equations (34) and (35) imply that if $\mathbf{r}$ is a modal vector the quotient

$$Q(\mathbf{r}) = \frac{\bar{\mathbf{r}}\,\mathbf{C}\,\mathbf{r}}{\bar{\mathbf{r}}\,\mathbf{A}\,\mathbf{r}}$$

is the natural frequency of vibration associated with that modal vector. Let us now investigate the nature of such a quotient formed with an *arbitrary* vector $\mathbf{u}$. This quotient is called *Rayleigh's quotient of* $\mathbf{u}$.

$$Q(\mathbf{u}) = \frac{\bar{\mathbf{u}}\,\mathbf{C}\,\mathbf{u}}{\bar{\mathbf{u}}\,\mathbf{A}\,\mathbf{u}} \tag{36}$$

Let us retain the assumption that the frequency equation has distinct roots. With this assumption, it is not difficult to show through the orthogonality property of the modal vectors that these vectors are linearly independent. (See Exercise 3.10.) An arbitrary vector $\mathbf{u}$ in n-space can thus be expressed in terms of a linear combination of the modal vectors

$$\mathbf{u} = v_1\mathbf{r}^{(1)} + v_2\mathbf{r}^{(2)} + \cdots + v_n\mathbf{r}^{(n)}$$

in which $v_1, v_2 \ldots$, and v_n are a set of coefficients. By utilizing definition (18), we can rewrite this equation in a form similar to (20):

$$u_i = r_{ij}v_j \qquad \Big| \qquad \mathbf{u} = \mathbf{R}\,\mathbf{v} \tag{37}$$

The meaning of (37) is, however, slightly different from (20), since (37) does not contain the time variable t.

Rayleigh's quotient formed with the vector $\mathbf{u}$ can thus be expressed

$$Q(\mathbf{u}) = \frac{\bar{\mathbf{v}}\,\bar{\mathbf{R}}\,\mathbf{C}\,\mathbf{R}\,\mathbf{v}}{\bar{\mathbf{v}}\,\bar{\mathbf{R}}\,\mathbf{A}\,\mathbf{R}\,\mathbf{v}} = \frac{\bar{\mathbf{v}}\,\mathbf{K}\,\mathbf{v}}{\bar{\mathbf{v}}\,\mathbf{M}\,\mathbf{v}} \tag{38}$$

Since $\mathbf{K}$ and $\mathbf{M}$ are diagonal matrices and $\mathbf{K} = \mathbf{M}\,\mathbf{W}^2$, we may write (38) in longhand form:

$$Q = \frac{m_{11}v_1^{\,2}\omega_1^{\,2} + m_{22}v_2^{\,2}\omega_2^{\,2} + \cdots + m_{nn}v_n^{\,2}\omega_n^{\,2}}{m_{11}v_1^{\,2} + m_{22}v_2^{\,2} + \cdots + m_{nn}v_n^{\,2}} \tag{39}$$

Consider Q as a function of n variables, $v_1, v_2, \ldots, v_n$, defined by (39). Since the denominator in (39) does not vanish except when $v_1 = v_2 = \ldots = v_n = 0$, the function is continuously differentiable except at the origin. Hence the function possesses a Taylor series expansion, and for small changes in the v's the change in Q is given by

$$\Delta Q = \frac{\partial Q}{\partial v_i}\,\Delta v_i + \frac{1}{2}\frac{\partial^2 Q}{\partial v_i\,\partial v_j}\,\Delta v_i\,\Delta v_j + \cdots \tag{40}$$

in which the summation convention is employed.

Let us assume now that $\mathbf{u}$ coincides in direction with one of the modal vectors, say $\mathbf{r}^{(1)}$; then $\mathbf{u} = v_1\mathbf{r}^{(1)}$ and $v_2 = 0, v_3 = 0, \ldots, v_n = 0$. Through routine differentiation of (39), it can be shown easily that under these conditions

$$\frac{\partial Q}{\partial v_1} = 0 \qquad \frac{\partial Q}{\partial v_2} = 0, \cdots, \frac{\partial Q}{\partial v_n} = 0 \tag{41}$$

Similarly, these partial derivatives vanish when $\mathbf{u}$ coincides with any modal vector $\mathbf{r}^{(i)}$. Hence Rayleigh's quotient *achieves a stationary value*[7] at any of the modal vectors. Furthermore, if $\omega_1 < \omega_2 < \ldots < \omega_n$, $\omega_1{}^2$ is the absolute minimum of Q. In other words, Rayleigh's quotient is always larger than or at least equal to the lowest natural frequency of the system. (See Exercise 3.11.)

By substituting (41) into (40), we obtain the relation

$$\Delta Q = \frac{1}{2} \frac{\partial^2 Q}{\partial v_i \, \partial v_j} \Delta v_i \, \Delta v_j + \cdots$$

which holds in the neighborhood of a modal vector. This relation indicates that if the difference between a vector and a modal vector is small, small changes in this vector will produce only second-order changes in the value of the corresponding Rayleigh's quotient. Since the value of Rayleigh's quotient for a modal vector is the square of the natural frequency of the corresponding mode, a vector that is a *first approximation* of a modal vector will yield, through its Rayleigh's quotient, *a better approximation* of the corresponding natural frequency. This approximate method of finding the natural frequency is called *Rayleigh's method.*

3.7 Forced Vibration of an Undamped System

(A) GENERALIZED FORCES

Since the coordinate system used in this analysis is in a generalized sense, it becomes necessary to have the corresponding concept of *generalized forces*. Let us first be reminded that our analysis is based on the study of energy forms, and our equations are derived from energy expressions. It is therefore obvious that those external forces which act on the system but do no work do not enter into the picture. Forces of this type are called forces of (nondissipative) constraint. Forces whose work upon the system is included in the potential energy expression are called *potential forces* and need not be considered again.[8] Therefore, only the forces that do work but are not accounted for in the potential energy of the system need to be added to the equations of motion (13).

Since the consideration here is energy, it is natural to define generalized forces by the work they perform on a system. The power, or the time rate

---

[7] A stationary value can be a maximum, a minimum, a minimax, an hyperbolic point, or others.

[8] For example, the gravity force does work on a simple pendulum; but this work is the potential energy of the system, and the force is taken into account in the change in potential energy.

of doing work, by external forces is a linear function of the velocity components of the mass particles on which the forces are acting. According to (7) the velocity components themselves are linear functions of the $\dot{q}$'s. Hence the power of external forces may be written as linear functions of the $\dot{q}$'s:

$$f_i\dot{q}_i = f_1\dot{q}_1 + f_2\dot{q}_2 + \cdots + f_n\dot{q}_n \tag{42}$$

The coefficients f's are called the *generalized forces* with respect to the coordinate system q_i. For linear systems and for systems in small oscillations these coefficients can be considered as independent of the q's and are functions of time t only.

With generalized forces acting on the system, the energy equation becomes

$$\dot{T} + \dot{V} = f_i\dot{q}_i \tag{43}$$

By following the same steps in the derivation of (13), we arrive at

$$a_{ij}\ddot{q}_j + c_{ij}q_j = f_i \quad \Big| \quad \mathbf{A}\,\ddot{\mathbf{q}} + \mathbf{C}\,\mathbf{q} = \mathbf{f} \tag{44}$$

(B) STEADY-STATE RESPONSE TO HARMONIC AND PERIODIC GENERALIZED FORCES

The special case in which every f_i is a harmonic function of time having the same frequency ω_f is now considered.

Let the generalized forces be represented by

$$f_i = g_i e^{i\omega_f t} \quad \Big| \quad \mathbf{f} = \mathbf{g}e^{i\omega_f t}$$

In this case the solution consists of a steady-state vibration of frequency ω_f and transient vibrations with the natural frequencies of the system. We are interested only in the former. Let the steady-state vibration be

$$q_i = l_i e^{i\omega_f t} \quad \Big| \quad \mathbf{q} = \mathbf{l}e^{i\omega_f t}$$

By putting this into (44) and canceling out $e^{i\omega_f t}$, we have

$$(-\omega_f^2 a_{ij} + c_{ij})l_j = g_i \quad \Big| \quad (-\omega_f^2\mathbf{A} + \mathbf{C})\,\mathbf{l} = \mathbf{g} \tag{45}$$

This is a set of linear simultaneous equations that can be solved by standard methods. If ω_f is equal to any one of the natural frequencies, resonance takes place. If $\mathbf{f}$ is a periodic force, it can be expanded into a Fourier series, and the response to $\mathbf{f}$ can be obtained by the method of superposition similar to that described in Art. 1.8.

(C) FORCED VIBRATION—GENERAL SOLUTION

For the general solution of a forced vibration problem let us begin with

$$\mathbf{A}\,\ddot{\mathbf{q}} + \mathbf{C}\,\mathbf{q} = \mathbf{f}$$

Transforming it into the principal coordinates, we have

$$\mathbf{A}\,\mathbf{R}\,\ddot{\mathbf{p}} + \mathbf{C}\,\mathbf{R}\,\mathbf{p} = \mathbf{f}$$

Premultiply both sides by $\overline{\mathbf{R}}$ and utilize (34) to obtain

$$\mathbf{M}\,\ddot{\mathbf{p}} + \mathbf{K}\,\mathbf{p} = \overline{\mathbf{R}}\,\mathbf{f} \tag{46}$$

or

$$\ddot{\mathbf{p}} + \mathbf{W}^2\,\mathbf{p} = \mathbf{M}^{-1}\,\overline{\mathbf{R}}\,\mathbf{f} \tag{47}$$

With $\mathbf{M}$ a diagonal matrix, $\mathbf{M}^{-1}$ is easy to compute since it is also a diagonal matrix with elements $m_{11}^{-1} = 1/m_{11}$, $m_{22}^{-1} = 1/m_{22}, \ldots, m_{nn}^{-1} = 1/m_{nn}$. It is also easy to show that (47) is the same as (27) by deducing from (34) that

$$\mathbf{M}^{-1}\overline{\mathbf{R}} = (\mathbf{A}\,\mathbf{R})^{-1}$$

Returning now to (46) and writing it in longhand form, we have

$$\begin{aligned}
m_{11}\ddot{p}_1 + k_{11}p_1 &= r_{11}f_1 + r_{21}f_2 + \cdots + r_{n1}f_n = j_1(t) \\
m_{22}\ddot{p}_2 + k_{22}p_2 &= r_{12}f_1 + r_{22}f_2 + \cdots + r_{n2}f_n = j_2(t) \\
&\cdots\cdots\cdots\cdots\cdots\cdots \\
m_{nn}\ddot{p}_n + k_{nn}p_n &= r_{1n}f_1 + r_{2n}f_2 + \cdots + r_{nn}f_n = j_n(t)
\end{aligned}$$

These equations can be solved separately. For instance, according to (76) in Art. 1.10, if the system is initially quiescent, the solution for p_1 is

$$p_1(t) = \frac{1}{\sqrt{m_{11}k_{11}}} \int_0^t j_1(\tau) \sin \omega_1(t - \tau)\, d\tau \tag{48}$$

where

$$j_1(\tau) = r_{11}\, f_1(\tau) + r_{21}f_2(\tau) + \cdots + r_{n1}\, f_n(\tau) \tag{49}$$

Let us define a matrix

$$\sin \mathbf{W}t = \mathbf{W}t - \frac{1}{3!}\mathbf{W}^3t^3 + \frac{1}{5!}\mathbf{W}^5t^5 \cdots \tag{50}$$

Since $\mathbf{W}$ is a diagonal matrix, the series above also represents a diagonal matrix, which is

$$\sin \mathbf{W}t = \begin{bmatrix} \sin \omega_1 t & 0 & 0 & \cdots & 0 \\ 0 & \sin \omega_2 t & 0 & \cdots & 0 \\ 0 & 0 & \ddots & & 0 \\ 0 & 0 & 0 & \cdots & \sin \omega_n t \end{bmatrix}$$

The solution to (46) or (47) can thus be written

$$\mathbf{p}(t) = \int_0^t (\mathbf{M}\,\mathbf{K})^{-1/2} \sin \mathbf{W}(t-\tau)\mathbf{j}(\tau)\,d\tau$$
$$= (\mathbf{M}\,\mathbf{K})^{-1/2} \int_0^t \sin \mathbf{W}(t-\tau)\overline{\mathbf{R}}\,\mathbf{f}(\tau)\,d\tau \tag{51}$$

if $\mathbf{p}(0) = \mathbf{0}$ and $\dot{\mathbf{p}}(0) = \mathbf{0}$.

The solution for $\mathbf{q}$ is therefore

$$\mathbf{q}(t) = \mathbf{R}\,\mathbf{p}\,(t) = \mathbf{R}(\mathbf{M}\,\mathbf{K})^{-1/2} \int_0^t \sin \mathbf{W}(t-\tau)\overline{\mathbf{R}}\,\mathbf{f}(\tau)\,d\tau \tag{52}$$

if $\mathbf{q}(0) = \mathbf{0}$ and $\dot{\mathbf{q}}(0) = \mathbf{0}$.

On the other hand, if the initial values do not vanish, the following terms must be added to (51) and (52), respectively:

$$\cos \mathbf{W}t\,\mathbf{p}(0) + \mathbf{W}^{-1} \sin \mathbf{W}t\,\dot{\mathbf{p}}(0)$$

and

$$\mathbf{R} \cos \mathbf{W}t\,\mathbf{R}^{-1}\,\mathbf{q}(0) + \mathbf{R}\,\mathbf{W}^{-1} \sin \mathbf{W}t\,\mathbf{R}^{-1}\,\dot{\mathbf{q}}(0)$$

The reader is left with the proof of this statement. (See Exercise 3.17.)

3.8 Free and Forced Vibrations of a Damped System

(A) FREE VIBRATIONS

When there are viscous forces acting on certain parts of the system, there is an energy dissipation. It is not difficult to see that if the forces are proportional to the velocities or relative velocities at certain parts of the system the rate of local energy dissipation is proportional to the square of the velocity of the parts affected by the damping force. This is true whether the damping forces are external or internal. According to (7) and (8), the squares of the velocities are quadratic functions of the generalized velocities $\dot{q}$'s. Hence the rate of energy dissipation for the entire system can be written as

$$2F = b_{ij}\dot{q}_i\dot{q}_j \qquad \Big| \qquad 2F = \overline{\dot{\mathbf{q}}}\,\mathbf{B}\,\dot{\mathbf{q}} \tag{53}$$

The energy equation for the system is then[9]

$$\dot{T} + \dot{V} + 2F = 0$$

Following the same argument used before, we arrive at

$$a_{ij}\ddot{q}_j + b_{ij}\dot{q}_j + c_{ij}q_j = 0 \qquad \Big| \qquad \mathbf{A}\,\ddot{\mathbf{q}} + \mathbf{B}\,\dot{\mathbf{q}} + \mathbf{C}\,\mathbf{q} = \mathbf{0} \tag{55}$$

[9] F is a scalar function called *Rayleigh's function*. The factor 2 is included to give F the same appearance as T and V and also to give certain symmetry to Lagrange's equation, modified by Lord Rayleigh.

Let the solution be of the type

$$q_i = l_i e^{st} \qquad \Big| \qquad \mathbf{q} = \mathbf{l} e^{st}$$

We have

$$(s^2 a_{ij} + s b_{ij} + c_{ij}) l_j = 0 \qquad \Big| \qquad (s^2 \mathbf{A} + s\mathbf{B} + \mathbf{C})\mathbf{l} = \mathbf{0} \tag{56}$$

For nontrivial solutions of (56) the determinant

$$D(s) = |s^2 a_{ij} + s b_{ij} + c_{ij}| = 0 \tag{57}$$

This is an algebraic equation in s of $2n$th degree. It has $2n$ roots, which may be real or complex. The rest of the procedure is similar to that discussed in Art. 2.7. The results can be stated as follows.

To each solution of (57), say $s = s^{(i)}$, there is a vector $\mathbf{l}^{(i)}$ such that

$$\mathbf{q} = \mathbf{l}^{(i)} e^{s^{(i)} t}$$

is a solution of (55). There are $2n$ such solutions, and the general solution of (55) is therefore

$$\mathbf{q} = \sum_{i=1}^{2n} \mathbf{l}^{(i)} e^{s^{(i)} t} \tag{58}$$

If $s^{(i)}$ is real, $\mathbf{l}^{(i)}$ has real elements. If it is complex, it must come as one of a complex conjugate pair, and the vector $\mathbf{l}$'s associated with this pair also form a complex conjugate pair. The real $\mathbf{l}$'s are determined only to within an arbitrary real multiplication factor, and the complex $\mathbf{l}$'s are determined only to within an arbitrary complex multiplication factor. In any event, there are $2n$ integration constants to be determined by the $2n$ initial conditions.

(B) FORCED VIBRATIONS

Forced vibrations of damped systems are described by a set of equations having the general form

$$a_{ij}\ddot{q}_j + b_{ij}\dot{q}_j + c_{ij} q_j = f_i(t)$$

or

$$\mathbf{A}\,\ddot{\mathbf{q}} + \mathbf{B}\,\dot{\mathbf{q}} + \mathbf{C}\,\mathbf{q} = \mathbf{f}(t) \tag{59}$$

(i) *Steady-state response to harmonic forces and transfer functions.* If $\mathbf{f}(t)$ is a sinusoidal function of time

$$f_i = g_i e^{i\omega_f t} \qquad \Big| \qquad \mathbf{f} = \mathbf{g} e^{i\omega_f t}$$

the steady-state solution of (59) can be obtained by assuming that it has the form

$$q_i = l_i e^{i\omega_f t} \qquad \Big| \qquad \mathbf{q} = \mathbf{l} e^{i\omega_f t} \tag{60}$$

This results in a set of linear simultaneous equations represented by

$$(-\omega_f^2\mathbf{A} + i\omega_f\mathbf{B} + \mathbf{C})\mathbf{I} = \mathbf{g} \tag{61}$$

Let us define a matrix function

$$\mathbf{D}(i\omega_f) = -\omega_f^2\mathbf{A} + i\omega_f\mathbf{B} + \mathbf{C} \tag{62}$$

The solution to (61) is then

$$\mathbf{I} = \mathbf{D}^{-1}(i\omega_f)\mathbf{g} \tag{63}$$

provided that the determinant

$$|\mathbf{D}(i\omega_f)| \neq 0$$

Otherwise steady-state solution is not possible, for the amplitude tends to grow without limit, and resonance is said to exist.

A problem of particular interest is that in which all but one of the g's vanish; that is

$$g_1 = g_2 = \cdots = g_{j-1} = g_{j+1} = \cdots = g_n = 0$$

and

$$g_j = 1 \tag{64}$$

In other words, $\mathbf{g}$ is equal to the unit vector of the jth coordinate. Let us call the amplitude of the response of a generic coordinate q_i to this unit harmonic force the *transfer function* t_{ij}. Evidently, the different transfer functions between the different pairs of coordinates can form a matrix. The elements of this matrix are obtained by substituting (64) into (63), and it is not difficult to see that this matrix is the inverse of the matrix $\mathbf{D}$.

$$t_{ij}(i\omega_f) = d_{ij}^{-1}(i\omega_f) \quad \Big| \quad \mathbf{T}(i\omega_f) = \mathbf{D}^{-1}(i\omega_f)$$

To extend the domain of definition of the functions into the complex plane, we replace the argument $i\omega_f$ by the complex variable s. Hence

$$\mathbf{T}(s) = \mathbf{D}^{-1}(s) = (s^2\mathbf{A} + s\mathbf{B} + \mathbf{C})^{-1} \tag{65}$$

This transfer function matrix is useful in studying the transient response of a damped system.

If the forcing functions represented by $\mathbf{f}$ are periodic, we can expand them into Fourier series and then apply the principle of superposition to obtain the steady-state solution in the usual way.

(ii) *Transient response—indicial response and impulse response.* The transient response of a damped system can be investigated through its indicial response and impulse response, as discussed in Art. 1.11. Similar to the situation with the transfer functions, for systems with many degrees of freedom there are many indicial response functions that can be defined. Let us use the symbol $u_i^{(j)}(t)$ to denote the indicial response of a generic coordinate q_i to a unit step force applied to the jth coordinate. In other words,

$$q_i = u_i^{(j)}(t) \qquad \Big| \qquad \mathbf{q} = \mathbf{u}^{(j)}(t)$$

satisfies (59) under the conditions

$$f_1 = f_2 = \cdots = f_{j-1} = f_{j+1} = \cdots = f_n = 0$$

and (66)

$$f_j = \mathcal{\Gamma}(t)$$

together with the initial conditions

$$\begin{aligned} q_i(0) &= 0 \\ \dot{q}_i(0) &= 0 \end{aligned} \qquad \Big| \qquad \begin{aligned} \mathbf{q}(0) &= \mathbf{0} \\ \dot{\mathbf{q}}(0) &= \mathbf{0} \end{aligned} \tag{67}$$

When the indicial response functions are continuous for $t \geq 0$ and differentiable for $t > 0$, the associated impulse response function can be obtained by differentiation with respect to t.

$$h_i^{(j)}(t) = \frac{d}{dt} u_i^{(j)}(t) \qquad \Big| \qquad \mathbf{h}^{(j)}(t) = \frac{d}{dt} \mathbf{u}^{(j)}(t)$$

According to the discussions in Art. 1.11, the general solution to (59) under the initial conditions (67) can now be constructed from the impulse response functions:

$$\begin{aligned} \mathbf{q}(t) &= \int_0^t [f_1(\tau)\mathbf{h}^{(1)}(t-\tau) + f_2(\tau)\mathbf{h}^{(2)}(t-\tau) \cdots f_n(\tau)\mathbf{h}^{(n)}(t-\tau)]\,d\tau \\ &= \int_0^t \sum_{j=1}^n f_j(\tau)\mathbf{h}^{(j)}(t-\tau)\,d\tau \end{aligned}$$

To simplify this expression, let us form two square matrices $\mathbf{U}$ and $\mathbf{H}$ whose columns are the vectors $\mathbf{u}$'s and $\mathbf{h}$'s, respectively; that is

$$u_{ij} = u_i^{(j)} \qquad h_{ij} = h_i^{(j)}$$

and

$$\mathbf{H} = \frac{d}{dt}\mathbf{U}$$

The solution to (59) can then be written

$$\begin{aligned} q_i(t) &= \int_0^t h_{ij}(t-\tau) f_j(\tau)\,d\tau \\ \mathbf{q}(t) &= \int_0^t \mathbf{H}(t-\tau)\mathbf{f}(\tau)\,d\tau \end{aligned} \tag{68}$$

The impulse response matrix $\mathbf{H}$ can be obtained by differentiating $\mathbf{U}$, the indicial response matrix, which is formed by the solutions to (59) under the conditions (66) and (67). The matrix $\mathbf{H}$ can also be obtained by integrating the transfer-function matrix $\mathbf{T}(s)$ with the integration factor e^{st}, as described in Art. 1.11(D).

$$\mathbf{H}(t) = \frac{d}{dt}\mathbf{U}(t) = \frac{1}{2\pi i}\int_{c-i\infty}^{c+i\infty} \mathbf{T}(s)e^{st}\,ds \tag{69}$$

in which c is any positive constant.

It is to be noted that in analyses of the vibrations of damped systems we do not try to orthogonalize the equations by a suitable linear transformation of the coordinates, as we do with undamped systems. There is an orthogonalization procedure,[10] but it is seldom utilized because of computational difficulties.

3.9 Semidefinite Systems

Most vibratory systems are connected with a stationary frame; as a matter of fact this stationary frame may be considered a part of the system. For such systems the equilibrium configuration is stable, and any variation in the generalized coordinates must be accompanied by a change in the potential energy of the systems. These systems are called positive-definite because their potential energy expression

$$V = \tfrac{1}{2}\,\bar{\mathbf{q}}\,\mathbf{C}\,\mathbf{q} > 0 \tag{70}$$

except at the equilibrium configuration

$$\mathbf{q} = \mathbf{0}$$

On the other hand, a system is called semidefinite if it is possible for V to vanish without having all the q's vanish simultaneously. In other words, $\mathbf{q} = \mathbf{0}$ corresponds to a condition of neutral equilibrium.

Mathematically, the necessary and sufficient condition for the potential energy expression to be nonnegative is that

$$c_{11} \geq 0 \qquad \begin{vmatrix} c_{11} & c_{12} \\ c_{12} & c_{22} \end{vmatrix} \geq 0 \qquad \begin{vmatrix} c_{11} & c_{12} & c_{13} \\ c_{12} & c_{22} & c_{23} \\ c_{13} & c_{23} & c_{33} \end{vmatrix} \geq 0$$

$$\cdots\cdots\cdots\cdots\cdots\cdots\cdots\cdots\cdots$$

$$|\mathbf{C}| = \begin{vmatrix} c_{11} & c_{12} & \cdots & c_{1n} \\ c_{12} & c_{22} & \cdots & c_{2n} \\ \cdots & \cdots & \cdots & \cdots \\ c_{1n} & c_{2n} & \cdots & c_{nn} \end{vmatrix} \geq 0$$

[10] See "Coordinates Which Uncouple the Equations of Motion of Damped Linear Dynamic Systems" by K. A. Foss, *Journal of Applied Mechanics*, Vol. 25 (1958), pp. 361–364.

For positive-definite systems all of the determinants are greater than zero and for semidefinite systems the last one or more of the determinants are equal to zero. In vibration study it is seldom necessary to evaluate these determinants, since an examination of the make-up of the system is usually enough to determine whether or not it is semidefinite. If the system does not include a stationary frame, or the stationary frame is not positively connected to some part of the system, the system is semidefinite.[11] Two such systems are illustrated in Fig. 70.

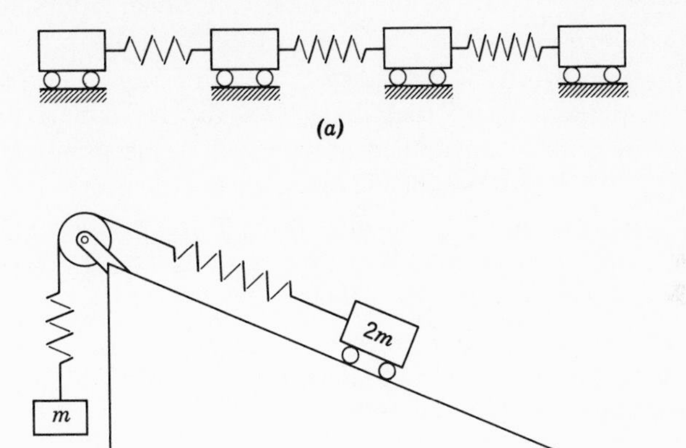

(a)

(b)

Figure 70

Note that we are not concerned about the kinetic energy expression, since any motion of a system must result in a positive amount of kinetic energy.

The analysis presented so far in this chapter is essentially valid for semidefinite as well as positive-definite systems, but there are certain features of semidefinite systems that we shall discuss.

Since for a semidefinite system

$$|c_{ij}| = 0 \qquad \Big| \qquad |\mathbf{C}| = 0 \tag{71}$$

one or more vectors $\mathbf{l}$ exist, so that

$$c_{ij} l_j = 0 \qquad \Big| \qquad \mathbf{C}\,\mathbf{l} = \mathbf{0} \tag{72}$$

This means that (15) can be satisfied with $\omega = 0$, and (13) can be satisfied by

$$q_j = l_j(\alpha t + \beta) \qquad \Big| \qquad \mathbf{q} = \mathbf{l}(\alpha t + \beta) \tag{73}$$

[11] We assume that the equilibrium configuration is at least not unstable so that the potential energy is nonnegative.

which represents motions having constant velocities. Semidefinite systems are thus associated with zero roots of the frequency equation (16). The number of independent nonzero $\mathbf{l}$'s which satisfies (72) is the same as the multiplicity of the root $\omega^2 = 0$ in (16). Together, they represent some of the natural modes of the system, which may be called the *zero modes.*

In mechanics there are two types of problems involving the study of semidefinite systems. In the first type we are given systems known to be semidefinite, systems such as a rotating shaft, a moving vehicle, or a rocket in free flight. We are to analyze their vibrational modes in addition to the known zero modes. In the second type of problem the potential energy expression V or the elastic matrix $\mathbf{C}$ includes some parameters that must be determined so that the system can be made semidefinite. This is the type of problem studied in theory of elastic stability.

For a positive-definite system the elements in the inverse of its elastic matrix, $\mathbf{C}^{-1}$, are known to be the *influence coefficients*. For a semidefinite system the matrix $\mathbf{C}$ is singular because of (71), so that its inverse is not defined. This agrees with the physical facts that when a system is in neutral equilibrium its influence coefficients are mostly undefined quantities. (See Exercise 3.15.) This has two practical consequences. The first is that we cannot write the alternate form of (23)

$$[\mathbf{C}^{-1}\,\mathbf{A}]\mathbf{r} = \frac{1}{\omega^2}\,\mathbf{r}$$

which is a desirable form for some methods of numerical computation, discussed in Art. 3.11. The second is that without the use of influence coefficients it becomes inconvenient to set up the equations of motion for some systems, such as a beam carrying three masses in free flight.

The zero modes of a semidefinite system are not of interest in vibration study. It is possible to "suppress" these modes by introducing constraints, which will reduce the number of degrees of freedom and in the meantime convert the system into a positive-definite one. This procedure is illustrated in Art. 2.9(A) and may be generalized as follows. Let $\mathbf{l}^0$ represent a zero mode. Then

$$\mathbf{C}\,\mathbf{l}^0 = \mathbf{0}$$

Since $\mathbf{C}$ is symmetrical,

$$\bar{\mathbf{l}}^0\,\mathbf{C} = \mathbf{0}$$

Premultiply (13) by $\bar{\mathbf{l}}^0$ to obtain

$$\bar{\mathbf{l}}^0\,\mathbf{A}\,\ddot{\mathbf{q}} + \bar{\mathbf{l}}^0\,\mathbf{C}\,\mathbf{q} = 0$$

or

$$\bar{\mathbf{l}}^0\,\mathbf{A}\,\ddot{\mathbf{q}} = 0 \qquad \bar{\mathbf{l}}^0\,\mathbf{A}\,\mathbf{q} = at + b$$

Suppressing the zero mode is equivalent to letting $a = 0$ and $b = 0$. In other words, only those motions orthogonal to the zero mode are considered. This results in a constraint relation between the q's. Written longhand, the relation is

$$(l_1{}^0 a_{11} + l_2{}^0 a_{12} + \cdots + l_n{}^0 a_{1n})q_1 + (l_1{}^0 a_{12} + l_2{}^0 a_{22} + \cdots + l_n{}^0 a_{2n})q_2 + \cdots + (l_1{}^0 a_{1n} + l_2{}^0 a_{2n} + \cdots + l_n{}^0 a_{nn})q_n = 0 \quad (74)$$

For each zero mode there is a constraint relation such as the one above. With these constraints, a corresponding number of the coordinate variables

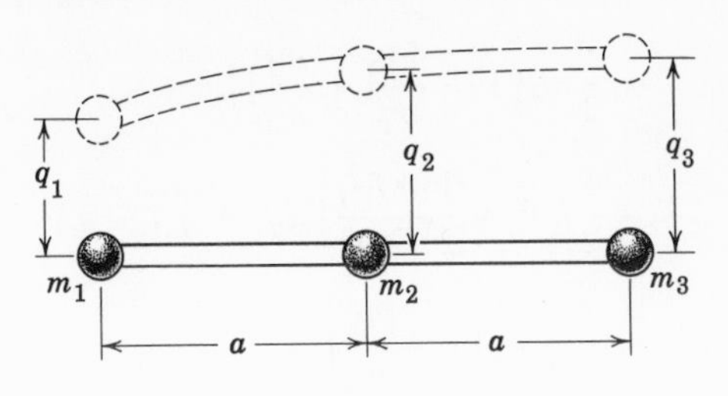

Figure 71

q's can be eliminated. This elimination process results in a positive-definite system having fewer degrees of freedom.[12]

It is not necessary that the constraint which suppresses the zero mode be obtained by finding nontrivial solutions of (72). In many cases it can be obtained by simple principles of mechanics. As an example, let us consider the free vibration of a light rectangular beam carrying three particle masses, as shown in Fig. 71. The beam is unsupported in free space. This vibration is often called the *free free-vibration.* Obviously, the degrees of freedom consist of three translations, three rotations, and two vibrations in the two principal planes of the beam cross section. Of the eight degrees of freedom, only two are nonzero modes. To solve this problem, we can suppress all the zero modes by assuming that the system has no linear momentum and no angular momentum. Furthermore, we restrict the motion in one of the two principal planes of bending of the beam. This is permissible, since obviously there is no coupling between the two vibrations in the two planes of bending. Referring to Fig. 71, we have therefore

$$m_1\dot{q}_1 + m_2\dot{q}_2 + m_3\dot{q}_3 = 0$$

$$m_1\dot{q}_1 \cdot (2a) + m_2\dot{q}_2 \cdot (a) = 0$$

[12] For an illustration of a similar problem see Art. 3.11(E).

Upon integration and setting the integration constants equal to zero, we have

$$q_2 = -\frac{2m_1}{m_2} q_1 \qquad \text{and} \qquad q_3 = \frac{m_1}{m_3} q_1$$

Hence

$$T = \frac{1}{2}(m_1\dot{q}_1{}^2 + m_2\dot{q}_2{}^2 + m_3\dot{q}_3{}^2)$$

$$= \frac{1}{2}\left(m_1\dot{q}_1{}^2 + \frac{4m_1{}^2}{m_2}\dot{q}_1{}^2 + \frac{m_1{}^2}{m_3}\dot{q}_1{}^2\right)$$

$$= \frac{1}{2}m_1\left(1 + \frac{4m_1}{m_2} + \frac{m_1}{m_3}\right)\dot{q}_1{}^2$$

$$V = \frac{1}{2}k\delta^2 = \frac{1}{2}\frac{48EI_1}{(2a)^3}[\tfrac{1}{2}(q_1 + q_3) - q_2]^2$$

$$= \frac{3EI_1}{a^3}\left[\frac{1}{2}\left(1 + \frac{m_1}{m_3}\right) + \frac{2m_1}{m_2}\right]^2 q_1{}^2$$

where EI_1 represents the bending stiffness of the beam cross section. For the vibration in the other plane of bending we need only change I_1 to I_2 in the potential energy expression.

3.10 Repeated Roots of the Frequency Equation

In Art. 3.5 it was shown that if the roots of the frequency equation (16)

$$|\mathbf{C} - \omega^2\mathbf{A}| = 0$$

are distinct there is a modal vector to each of these roots. These modal vectors are orthogonal to one another, with respect to both **A** and **C**.

$$\left.\begin{aligned} \bar{\mathbf{r}}^{(j)}\,\mathbf{A}\,\mathbf{r}^{(i)} &= 0 \\ \bar{\mathbf{r}}^{(j)}\,\mathbf{C}\,\mathbf{r}^{(i)} &= 0 \end{aligned}\right. \qquad \omega_i \neq \omega_j$$

The orthogonal relationship among the modal vectors also insures that they are linearly independent.

Now if some of the roots of the frequency equation repeat themselves, we will have fewer distinct natural frequencies. The question is then "Does the system have fewer natural modes?" The simple examples shown in Arts. 2.10 and 2.14(A) indicate that the answer is negative.

A rigorous mathematical treatment of the problem is not necessary for our purpose. We simply state that in the eigenvalue problem (23) arising from free-vibration analysis the coalescence of eigenvalues does not cause a coalescence of eigenvectors. This statement, however, is not generally true for an arbitrary eigenvalue problem.

$$\mathbf{L}\,\mathbf{r} = \lambda \mathbf{r}$$

To summarize, let

$$\omega^2 = \omega_r^{\,2}$$

be an r-time repeated root of the frequency equation (16). There are r linearly independent modal vectors, $\mathbf{r}^{(1)}, \mathbf{r}^{(2)}, \cdots, \mathbf{r}^{(r)}$, representing different modes of free vibrations having the same frequency. These modal vectors are orthogonal, with respect to $\mathbf{A}$ and $\mathbf{C}$, to all other modal vectors of the system not belonging to this set. Among themselves the orthogonality relationship may or may not hold. However, the set of modal vectors corresponding to a given repeated root are not uniquely determined because any linear combination of these vectors can also serve as a modal vector, since

$$(\mathbf{A}^{-1}\,\mathbf{C})(\alpha_1\mathbf{r}^{(1)} + \alpha_2\mathbf{r}^{(2)} + \cdots + \alpha_r\mathbf{r}^{(r)}) \\ = \omega_r^{\,2}(\alpha_1\mathbf{r}^{(1)} + \alpha_2\mathbf{r}^{(2)} + \cdots + \alpha_r\mathbf{r}^{(r)})$$

It now becomes possible to construct a new set of modal vectors by taking different linear combinations of the old set, so that the vectors in the new set are orthogonal among themselves with respect to $\mathbf{A}$ and $\mathbf{C}$. The method of construction is left to the reader as an exercise. (See Exercise 3.16.)

SECTION B. METHODS AND APPLICATIONS

3.11 Solution of Eigenvalue Problems by Matrix Iteration

The direct method of solving the eigenvalue problem

$$\omega^2\mathbf{A}\,\mathbf{r} = \mathbf{C}\,\mathbf{r}$$

as outlined in Art. 3.4, is not practical when a large number of coordinates is involved because of the excessive amount of arithmetic computations needed. There are several numerical procedures that simplify computational steps in one way or another. Aside from the amount of labor involved, the question of checks, control of round-off errors, susceptibility to mistakes, etc., must also be considered. Complete solution of large-scale eigenvalue problems is practicable only through the use of electronic digital computers. Numerical procedures, which are suited for programming on such computers, have requirements of their own, but this is a subject in itself and cannot be dealt with exhaustively here. In this article we can discuss only a few methods that may be used to solve problems of reasonable size with the help of a desk calculator and slide rule.

(A) DETERMINATION OF LARGEST EIGENVALUE BY ITERATION

The basic principle of the matrix iteration procedure is extremely simple.

Let the eigenvalues of a matrix $\mathbf{L}$ be

$$\lambda_1, \lambda_2, \cdots, \lambda_n$$

with

$$|\lambda_1| > |\lambda_2| \geq |\lambda_3| \cdots |\lambda_n|$$

Designate the corresponding eigenvectors by

$$\mathbf{r}^{(1)}, \mathbf{r}^{(2)}, \cdots, \mathbf{r}^{(n)}$$

Let $\mathbf{v}$ be an arbitrary vector. It can be thought of as a linear combination of the eigenvectors, since the eigenvectors are linearly independent.

$$\mathbf{v} = \alpha_1 \mathbf{r}^{(1)} + \alpha_2 \mathbf{r}^{(2)} + \cdots + \alpha_n \mathbf{r}^{(n)}$$

Hence

$$\begin{aligned} \mathbf{L}\,\mathbf{v} &= \alpha_1 \mathbf{L}\,\mathbf{r}^{(1)} + \alpha_2 \mathbf{L}\,\mathbf{r}^{(2)} + \cdots + \alpha_n \mathbf{L}\,\mathbf{r}^{(n)} \\ &= \alpha_1 \lambda_1 \mathbf{r}^{(1)} + \alpha_2 \lambda_2 \mathbf{r}^{(2)} + \cdots + \alpha_n \lambda_n\, \mathbf{r}^{(n)} \end{aligned}$$

By repeating this process, we have

$$\mathbf{L}^2\,\mathbf{v} = \mathbf{L}\,\mathbf{L}\,\mathbf{v} = \alpha_1 \lambda_1{}^2 \mathbf{r}^{(1)} + \alpha_2 \lambda^2{}_2 \mathbf{r}^{(2)} + \cdots + \alpha_n \lambda_n{}^2 \mathbf{r}^{(n)}$$

$$\cdots\cdots\cdots\cdots\cdots\cdots\cdots\cdots\cdots\cdots$$

$$\mathbf{L}^i\,\mathbf{v} = \alpha_1 \lambda_1{}^i \mathbf{r}^{(1)} + \alpha_2 \lambda_2{}^i \mathbf{r}^{(2)} + \cdots + \alpha_n \lambda_n{}^i \mathbf{r}^{(n)}$$

Since

$$|\lambda_1| > |\lambda_2| \geq \cdots |\lambda_n|$$

as i becomes sufficiently large, the first term on the right-hand side predominates over the rest of the terms and

$$\mathbf{L}^i\,\mathbf{v} \doteq \alpha_1 \lambda_1{}^i \mathbf{r}^{(1)}$$

$$\mathbf{L}\,(\mathbf{L}^i\,\mathbf{v}) \doteq \lambda_1(\mathbf{L}^i\,\mathbf{v})$$

Thus $\mathbf{L}^i\,\mathbf{v}$ is parallel to the eigenvector $\mathbf{r}^{(1)}$, and the corresponding eigenvalue λ_1 can be obtained by operating it once more by the matrix $\mathbf{L}$.

We thus have a method of determining the largest (in absolute value) eigenvalue and the associated eigenvector of a matrix $\mathbf{L}$. The method consists of repeated multiplication of an arbitrary vector by the matrix $\mathbf{L}$. The rapidity with which the eigenvector $\mathbf{r}^{(1)}$ is approached depends upon two things: the closer the starting vector $\mathbf{v}$ parallels $\mathbf{r}^{(1)}$, the faster the convergence. In other words, it is desirable that the coefficient α_1 be larger than the rest of the α's. Theoretically, there is a possibility that by accident a starting vector with $\alpha_1 = 0$ will be chosen. Then the iteration process described will converge to the eigenvector with the next largest eigenvalue. Practically, this possibility does not exist, for even if $\alpha_1 = 0$ in $\mathbf{v}$, unavoidable round-off errors will introduce a small component along $\mathbf{r}^{(1)}$ in the iterated vector, and this component will eventually dominate the rest. The second thing that enhances the rapidity of convergence is to have the eigenvalue λ_1 much larger in absolute value than the rest. This is especially important in large matrices.

Let us now illustrate the procedure by a simple example. One small modification will be made in the illustration. To keep the numerical value of the elements of the iterated vectors within a certain range, they are normalized after each iteration. A self-explanatory tabulation scheme is also used.

L			v	L v	v′	L v′	v″	L v″	v‴
5	0	−0.6	1	5.6	1.0	6.74	1.00	7.79	1.00
2	4	−1.2	1	7.2	1.3	10.68	1.86	15.02	1.93
−7	−4	5	−1	−16.0	−2.9	−26.7	−4.65	−37.69	−4.85

L			v‴	L v‴	v^iv	L v^iv	v^v	L v^v	λ
5	0	−0.6	1.00	7.91	1.00	7.96	1.00	7.98	(7.98)
2	4	−1.2	1.93	15.54	1.96	15.76	1.98	15.86	(8.01)
−7	−4	5	−4.85	−38.97	−4.93	−39.45	−4.96	−39.72	(8.01)

Thus the approximate answer is

$$\lambda_1 = (7.98 + 8.01 + 8.01)/3 = 8.00$$
$$\bar{\mathbf{r}}^{(1)} = [1.00 \quad 1.98 \quad -4.96]$$

The exact answer of this problem happens to be

$$\lambda_1 = 8.00$$
$$\bar{\mathbf{r}}^{(1)} = [1.00 \quad 2.00 \quad -5.00]$$

The procedure illustrated is straightforward. Such routine calculation can be put into the hands of untrained office help. On the other hand, if a little ingenuity is exercised, the process can be speeded up. For instance, we must realize that each iterated vector is a trial vector for the next step, so that it may be changed at will. After a few steps, a trend of changes in the elements is discernible. The trial vector of the succeeding step can be altered judiciously from that given by the previous step to hasten the convergence.

The matrix $\mathbf{L}$ used in this example was obtained from the following problem:

$$T = \tfrac{1}{2}(21\dot{q}_1^2 + 19\dot{q}_2^2 + 5\dot{q}_3^2 + 14\dot{q}_1\dot{q}_2 + 14\dot{q}_2\dot{q}_3 + 2\dot{q}_1\dot{q}_3)$$
$$V = \tfrac{1}{2}(14q_1^2 + 6q_2^2 + 2q_3^2 + 6q_1q_2 + 2q_2q_3 - 4q_1q_3) \times 10^3$$

$$\mathbf{A} = \begin{bmatrix} 21 & 7 & 1 \\ 7 & 19 & 7 \\ 1 & 7 & 5 \end{bmatrix} \qquad \mathbf{C} = \begin{bmatrix} 14 & 3 & -2 \\ 3 & 6 & 1 \\ -2 & 1 & 2 \end{bmatrix} \times 10^3$$

$$\mathbf{A}^{-1}\,\mathbf{C} = 125 \times \mathbf{L}$$

The reader will profit by solving this eigenvalue problem by the classical method. The answer is

$$\omega_1^2 = 1000 \qquad \omega_2^2 = 500 \qquad \omega_3^2 = 250$$

$$\mathbf{r}^{(1)} = \begin{bmatrix} 1 \\ 2 \\ -5 \end{bmatrix} \qquad \mathbf{r}^{(2)} = \begin{bmatrix} 1 \\ -4/3 \\ 5/3 \end{bmatrix} \qquad \mathbf{r}^{(3)} = \begin{bmatrix} 1 \\ 2 \\ 5 \end{bmatrix}$$

(B) DETERMINATION OF THE LOWEST NATURAL FREQUENCY

In the majority of vibration problems it is the lowest natural frequency that is of interest, whereas the method illustrated gives only the highest eigenvalue. This situation can easily be remedied if our eigenvalue problem is formulated as

$$(\mathbf{C}^{-1}\,\mathbf{A})\,\mathbf{r} = \frac{1}{\omega^2}\,\mathbf{r}$$

The largest eigenvalue of $\mathbf{C}^{-1}\,\mathbf{A}$ will then correspond to the lowest natural frequency. In this formulation the system must be positive-definite so that $\mathbf{C}^{-1}$ is defined.[13]

Example: Given

$$T = \tfrac{1}{2}[3\dot{q}_1 + 4\dot{q}_2^2 + 2\dot{q}_3^2 + \dot{q}_4^2 + 4\dot{q}_1\dot{q}_2 + 2\dot{q}_2\dot{q}_3 + 2\dot{q}_3\dot{q}_4] \times k_t$$
$$V = \tfrac{1}{2}[4q_1^2 + 5q_2^2 + q_3^2 + 2q_4^2 - 4q_1q_2 - 2q_2q_3] \times k_v$$

in which k_t and k_v are constants having appropriate units.

---

[13] For iteration of a semidefinite system see "Iteration in Semi-definite Eigenvalue Problems" by B. M. F. de Veubeke, *Journal of Aeronautical Sciences*, Vol. 22, No. 10, October 1955. Also, many physical problems are formulated by influence coefficients to begin with. The influence coefficients form the matrix $\mathbf{C}^{-1}$ and can be used directly in the ensuing computation.

To find the lowest natural frequency and the associated modal vector

$$\mathbf{A} = \begin{bmatrix} 3 & 2 & 0 & 0 \\ 2 & 4 & 1 & 0 \\ 0 & 1 & 2 & 1 \\ 0 & 0 & 1 & 1 \end{bmatrix} \times k_t \qquad \mathbf{C} \begin{bmatrix} 4 & -2 & 0 & 0 \\ -2 & 5 & -1 & 0 \\ 0 & -1 & 1 & 0 \\ 0 & 0 & 0 & 2 \end{bmatrix} \times k_v$$

$$\mathbf{C}^{-1} = \begin{bmatrix} 8 & 4 & 4 & 0 \\ 4 & 8 & 8 & 0 \\ 4 & 8 & 32 & 0 \\ 0 & 0 & 0 & 12 \end{bmatrix} \times \frac{1}{24k_v} = \begin{bmatrix} 2 & 1 & 1 & 0 \\ 1 & 2 & 2 & 0 \\ 1 & 2 & 8 & 0 \\ 0 & 0 & 0 & 3 \end{bmatrix} \times \frac{1}{6k_v}$$

$$\mathbf{C}^{-1}\mathbf{A} = \begin{bmatrix} 2 & 1 & 1 & 0 \\ 1 & 2 & 2 & 0 \\ 1 & 2 & 8 & 0 \\ 0 & 0 & 0 & 3 \end{bmatrix} \times \begin{bmatrix} 3 & 2 & 0 & 0 \\ 2 & 4 & 1 & 0 \\ 0 & 1 & 2 & 1 \\ 0 & 0 & 1 & 1 \end{bmatrix} = \begin{bmatrix} 8 & 9 & 3 & 1 \\ 7 & 12 & 6 & 2 \\ 7 & 18 & 18 & 8 \\ 0 & 0 & 3 & 3 \end{bmatrix} \times \frac{k_t}{6k_v}$$

The iteration of the last matrix:

L								a	b	c	d	e
8	9	3	1	1	21	1.0	27	1.0	29.6	1.00	29.80	1.000
7	12	6	2	1	27	1.3	38	1.4	41.8	1.41	42.12	1.412
7	18	18	8	1	51	2.5	79	2.9	86.8	2.93	87.68	2.935
0	0	3	3	1	6	0.3	8	0.3	9.6	0.32	9.75	0.327

A note about another scheme that often simplifies computation. We observe that in the foregoing tabulation

$$\mathbf{L\,a} = \mathbf{b} \quad \text{and} \quad \mathbf{L\,c} = \mathbf{d}$$

Hence

$$\mathbf{L}\,(\mathbf{c} - \mathbf{a}) = \mathbf{d} - \mathbf{b}$$

Or

$$\mathbf{d} = \mathbf{b} + \mathbf{L}\,(\mathbf{c} - \mathbf{a})$$

Since $(\mathbf{c} - \mathbf{a})$ is small, $\mathbf{d}$ can be conveniently obtained by applying a small correction to $\mathbf{b}$. Similarly, the next step is[14]

$$\mathbf{f} = \mathbf{d} + \mathbf{L}\,(\mathbf{e} - \mathbf{c})$$

$$= \begin{bmatrix} 29.80 \\ 42.12 \\ 87.68 \\ 9.75 \end{bmatrix} + \begin{bmatrix} 8 & 9 & 3 & 1 \\ 7 & 12 & 6 & 2 \\ 7 & 18 & 18 & 8 \\ 0 & 0 & 3 & 3 \end{bmatrix} \begin{bmatrix} 0 \\ 0.002 \\ 0.005 \\ 0.007 \end{bmatrix} = \begin{bmatrix} 29.84 \\ 42.19 \\ 87.86 \\ 9.78 \end{bmatrix}$$

[14] This correction can be carried out within the regular tabulation without writing out the numerical equation shown here.

As a final check, let us get the ratio between the corresponding elements of **f** and **e**.

$$\frac{29.84}{1.000} = 29.84 \qquad \frac{42.19}{1.412} = 29.88$$

$$\frac{87.86}{2.935} = 29.93 \qquad \frac{9.78}{0.327} = 29.91$$

Thus the lowest natural frequency of the system is

$$\omega_1^2 = \frac{6k_v}{k_t} \times \frac{1}{29.9} = 0.200\frac{k_v}{k_t}$$

and the amplitude ratio of this mode is

$$1 : 1.412 : 2.935 : 0.327$$

(C) USE OF RAYLEIGH'S QUOTIENT

If we are interested only in the natural frequency, we can stop the iteration process sooner and use Rayleigh's quotient. Suppose we stop at the vector **a**.

$$\mathbf{a} = [1 \quad 1.4 \quad 2.9 \quad 0.3]$$

Rayleigh's quotient can be computed by the following tabulation:

$$\mathbf{C} = k_v\begin{bmatrix} 4 & -2 & 0 & 0 \\ -2 & 5 & -1 & 0 \\ 0 & -1 & 1 & 0 \\ 0 & 0 & 0 & 2 \end{bmatrix} \qquad \begin{array}{c} \mathbf{a}\cdot\mathbf{C\,a} \\ 1.0 \times 1.2 = 1.20 \\ 1.4 \times 2.1 = 2.94 \\ 2.9 \times 1.5 = 4.35 \\ 0.3 \times 0.6 = 0.18 \\ \hline \bar{\mathbf{a}}\,\mathbf{C\,a} = 8.67 \times k_v \end{array}$$

$$\mathbf{A} = k_t\begin{bmatrix} 3 & 2 & 0 & 0 \\ 2 & 4 & 1 & 0 \\ 0 & 1 & 2 & 1 \\ 0 & 0 & 1 & 1 \end{bmatrix} \qquad \begin{array}{c} \mathbf{a}\cdot\mathbf{A\,a} \\ 1.0 \times 5.8 = 5.80 \\ 1.4 \times 10.5 = 14.70 \\ 2.9 \times 7.5 = 21.75 \\ 0.3 \times 4.6 = 0.96 \\ \hline \bar{\mathbf{a}}\,\mathbf{A\,a} = 43.2 \times k_t \end{array}$$

$$\omega_1^2 = \frac{8.67\,k_v}{43.6\,k_t} = 0.201\frac{k_v}{k_t}$$

(D) DETERMINATION OF A SECOND EIGENVECTOR

To get other eigenvectors by iteration, we need some supplementary theorems. These are now discussed.

Let the eigenvalues and the eigenvectors of a matrix $\mathbf{L}$ be

$$\lambda_1, \lambda_2, \cdots, \lambda_n$$

and

$$\mathbf{r}^{(1)}, \mathbf{r}^{(2)}, \cdots, \mathbf{r}^{(n)}$$

The matrices $\alpha\mathbf{L}$ and $\mathbf{L} - \beta\mathbf{I}$, in which $\mathbf{I}$ is the identity matrix, have the same eigenvectors and their eigenvalues, respectively, are

$$\alpha\lambda_1, \alpha\lambda_2, \cdots, \alpha\lambda_n$$

$$(\lambda_1 - \beta), (\lambda_2 - \beta), \cdots, (\lambda_n - \beta)$$

The proof of this theorem is simply as follows:

$$(\alpha\mathbf{L})\,\mathbf{r}^{(i)} = \alpha[\mathbf{L}\,\mathbf{r}^{(i)}] = \alpha\lambda_i\mathbf{r}^{(i)}$$

$$(\mathbf{L} - \beta\mathbf{I})\,\mathbf{r}^{(i)} = \mathbf{L}\,\mathbf{r}^{(i)} - \beta\mathbf{r}^{(i)} = (\lambda_i - \beta)\mathbf{r}^{(i)}$$

Next, let $\mathbf{L}$ and $\mathbf{M}$ be two matrices *having the same set of eigenvectors.* Let their eigenvalues be, respectively,

$$\lambda_1, \lambda_2, \cdots, \lambda_n$$

and

$$\mu_1, \mu_2, \cdots, \mu_n$$

The product matrix $\mathbf{P}$,

$$\mathbf{P} = \mathbf{L}\,\mathbf{M}$$

also has the same set of eigenvectors with eigenvalues

$$\lambda_1\mu_1, \lambda_2\mu_2, \cdots, \lambda_n\mu_n$$

This theorem is true because

$$\mathbf{P}\,\mathbf{r}^{(i)} = \mathbf{L}\,(\mathbf{M}\,\mathbf{r}^{(i)}) = \mathbf{L}\mu_i\mathbf{r}^{(i)} = \lambda_i\mu_i\mathbf{r}^{(i)}$$

From these two theorems we can deduce that the matrix

$$\mathbf{P} = \mathbf{L}(\lambda_1\mathbf{I} - \mathbf{L})$$

has the same eigenvectors as $\mathbf{L}$, and its eigenvalues are

$$0, \lambda_2(\lambda_1 - \lambda_2), \lambda_3(\lambda_1 - \lambda_3), \cdots, \lambda_n(\lambda_1 - \lambda_n)$$

This result gives us a way of evaluating eigenvalues, other than the largest one, by the same iteration process described.

Let us assume that we are given a matrix $\mathbf{L}$ whose eigenvalues are known to be *real positive* numbers:

$$\lambda_1 > \lambda_2 > \lambda_3 \cdots > \lambda_n > 0$$

First find λ_1 and $\mathbf{r}^{(1)}$ by iteration. Afterwards, form the matrix

$$\mathbf{P} = \mathbf{L}(\lambda_1\mathbf{I} - \mathbf{L})$$

which has the same set of eigenvectors as $\mathbf{L}$. Then iterate $\mathbf{P}$ to get the eigenvector with the largest eigenvalue. This eigenvector cannot be the $\mathbf{r}^{(1)}$ just found, since the eigenvalue of $\mathbf{P}$ corresponding to $\mathbf{r}^{(1)}$ is zero and therefore cannot be the largest one. To which of the eigenvectors the iteration of **P** will converge cannot always be established beforehand. We have, however, a useful clue. If

$$\lambda_1 > (\lambda_2 + \lambda_3)$$

it is easy to show that

$$\lambda_2(\lambda_1 - \lambda_2) > \lambda_3(\lambda_1 - \lambda_3) > \lambda_4(\lambda_1 - \lambda_4) \cdots$$

In that case the iteration of **P** will yield the eigenvalue-eigenvector pair

$$\lambda_2(\lambda_1 - \lambda_2) \qquad \text{and} \qquad \mathbf{r}^{(2)}$$

We can also show by theory of algebraic equations that the sum of the diagonal elements of **L** is equal to the sum of its eigenvalues. Or

$$l_{11} + l_{22} + \cdots + l_{nn} = \lambda_1 + \lambda_2 + \lambda_3 + \cdots + \lambda_n$$

Hence, knowing λ_1, we know also the value of $\lambda_2 + \lambda_3 + \ldots + \lambda_n$. Very often this sum is less than λ_1 and the inequality

$$\lambda_1 > \lambda_2 + \lambda_3$$

is assured.

Let us now return to our previous example. There we have found the largest eigenvalue λ_1 of the matrix **L**.

$$\mathbf{L} = \begin{bmatrix} 8 & 9 & 3 & 1 \\ 7 & 12 & 6 & 2 \\ 7 & 18 & 18 & 8 \\ 0 & 0 & 3 & 3 \end{bmatrix} \qquad \lambda_1 \doteq 30$$

The sum of all four eigenvalues of **L** is $8 + 12 + 18 + 3 = 41$. Hence λ_1 is larger than the rest of the eigenvalues combined, and the largest eigenvalue of the matrix[15]

$$\mathbf{P} = \mathbf{L}(\lambda_1 \mathbf{I} - \mathbf{L})$$

is

$$\lambda_2(\lambda_1 - \lambda_2)$$

$$\mathbf{P} = \begin{bmatrix} 8 & 9 & 3 & 1 \\ 7 & 12 & 6 & 2 \\ 7 & 18 & 18 & 8 \\ 0 & 0 & 3 & 3 \end{bmatrix} \times \begin{bmatrix} (30-8) & -9 & -3 & -1 \\ -7 & (30-12) & -6 & -2 \\ -7 & -18 & (30-18) & -8 \\ 0 & 0 & -3 & (30-3) \end{bmatrix}$$

$$\begin{bmatrix} 92 & 36 & -45 & -23 \\ 28 & 45 & -27 & -25 \\ -98 & -63 & 63 & 29 \\ -21 & -54 & 27 & 57 \end{bmatrix}$$

---

[15] It is not necessary to use the exact value of λ_1 in the procedure that follows.

Iteration of this matrix yields

$$\overline{\mathbf{r}}^{(2)} = [1.000 \quad 0.565 \quad -1.261 \quad -0.670]$$

and

$$\lambda_2(30 - \lambda_2) = 184.5$$

or

$$\lambda_2^2 - 30\lambda_2 + 184.5 = 0$$

$$\lambda_2 = \frac{30 - \sqrt{900 - 738}}{2} = 8.62$$

The other root of the quadratic equation has no meaning. To get accuracy as well as a check, we should go back to the original matrix and compute $\mathbf{L}\,\mathbf{r}^{(2)}$.

$$\begin{vmatrix} 8 & 9 & 3 & 1 \\ 7 & 12 & 6 & 2 \\ 7 & 18 & 18 & 8 \\ 0 & 0 & 3 & 3 \end{vmatrix} \begin{matrix} 1.000 \\ 0.565 \\ -1.261 \\ -0.670 \end{matrix} \begin{vmatrix} 8.634 \\ 4.874 \\ -10.882 \\ -5.793 \end{vmatrix} \begin{matrix} 1.000 \\ 0.565 \\ -1.261 \\ -0.671 \end{matrix}\Bigg|$$

The answer checks out, and the eigenvalue is $\lambda_2 = 8.63$.

To get another eigenvector, we can form the matrix $\mathbf{Q}$,

$$\mathbf{Q} = \mathbf{L}(30\mathbf{I} - \mathbf{L})(8.63\mathbf{I} - \mathbf{L})$$

and repeat the process as before.

We conclude this discussion with two remarks.

(i) Although theoretically by iterating the matrix $(\lambda_1\mathbf{I} - \mathbf{L})$ we should get the eigenvector $\mathbf{r}^{(n)}$ having the smallest eigenvalue, it is usually not practical to do so because the first few eigenvalues of this matrix $(\lambda_1 - \lambda_n)$, $(\lambda_1 - \lambda_{n-1})$, etc., are often close together so that convergence is very slow.

(ii) The multiplication of two $n \times n$ square matrices represents as much computational labor as multiplying a square matrix to a column matrix n times. Therefore, for moderately large matrix iteration problems labor may be saved by not getting the product matrix $\mathbf{P}$ (or $\mathbf{Q}$) first. Instead, we can iterate a trial vector by multiplying it alternately with $(\lambda_1\mathbf{I} - \mathbf{L})$ and $\mathbf{L}$.

It is not even necessary to iterate with these two matrices alternately. One can be used more often than the other. The principle is as follows. Let the starting vector be

$$\mathbf{v} = \alpha_1\mathbf{r}^{(1)} + \alpha_2\mathbf{r}^{(2)} + \cdots + \alpha_n\mathbf{r}^{(n)}$$

After being operated on by $(\lambda_1\mathbf{I} - \mathbf{L})$, the result is

$$\mathbf{v}' = \epsilon\mathbf{r}^{(1)} + \alpha_2(\lambda_1 - \lambda_2)\mathbf{r}^{(2)} + \cdots + \alpha_n(\lambda_1 - \lambda_n)\mathbf{r}^{(n)}$$

Theoretically, ϵ is zero, but because of unavoidable round-off errors as well as the error in the value of λ_1, $\mathbf{v}'$ still retains a small component in $\mathbf{r}^{(1)}$. Next, we operate $\mathbf{v}'$ with $\mathbf{L}$ i times:

$$\mathbf{L}^i\,\mathbf{v}' = \epsilon\lambda_1{}^i\mathbf{r}^{(1)} + \alpha_2\lambda_2{}^i(\lambda_1 - \lambda_2)\mathbf{r}^{(2)} + \cdots + \alpha_n\lambda_n{}^i(\lambda_1 - \lambda_n)\mathbf{r}^{(n)}$$

By this time the coefficient of $\mathbf{r}^{(1)}$, that is $\epsilon\lambda_1{}^i$, may become a fair amount. So we suppress it by operating again with $(\lambda_1\mathbf{I} - \mathbf{L})$ and then follow by operations with $\mathbf{L}$.

The sequence of operation is thus

$$\cdots\,\mathbf{L}^i(\lambda_1\mathbf{I} - \mathbf{L})\,\mathbf{L}^i(\lambda_1\mathbf{I} - \mathbf{L})\,\mathbf{v}$$

It is clear that the greater the precision in the value of λ_1 previously obtained and the smaller the round-off errors the less often it is necessary to use the matrix $(\lambda_1\mathbf{I} - \mathbf{L})$. It is also true that if additional eigenvalues are to be found, regardless of the scheme adopted, the preceding eigenvalues must be determined with greater accuracy. The last remark applies also to the method discussed below.

(E) DETERMINATION OF SUCCESSIVE EIGENVALUES BY SUCCESSIVE REDUCTION OF THE ORDER OF THE PROBLEM

When one of the modes of vibration is known, it is possible to reduce the order of the problem by one. The situation is exactly the same as that discussed in Art. 3.9, in which a semidefinite system is reduced to a positive-definite system by introducing the constraint relation (74) to suppress the zero mode. The procedure is best illustrated by an example. Take the eigenvalue problem we have just studied. After we have found the first eigenvector,

$$\mathbf{r}^{(1)} = [1.000 \quad 1.412 \quad 2.935 \quad 0.327]$$

we introduce either of the constraint relations

$$\bar{\mathbf{r}}\,\mathbf{C}\,\mathbf{r}^{(1)} = 0 \qquad \text{and} \qquad \bar{\mathbf{r}}\,\mathbf{A}\,\mathbf{r}^{(1)} = 0$$

This is equivalent to restricting the vibrations only in the remaining modes, which are all orthogonal to $\mathbf{r}^{(1)}$ with respect to either $\mathbf{C}$ or $\mathbf{A}$. Putting in numerical values, we have for this example

$$(4 \times 1.000 - 2 \times 1.412)r_1 + (-2 \times 1.000 + 5 \times 1.412 - 1 \times 2.935)r_2 + (-1 \times 1.412 + 1 \times 2.935)r_3 + (2 \times 0.327)r_4 = 0$$

or

$$r_1 = -1.810r_2 - 1.301r_3 - 0.531r_4$$

By substituting this relation into the original problem,

$$\begin{bmatrix} 8 & 9 & 3 & 1 \\ 7 & 12 & 6 & 2 \\ 7 & 18 & 18 & 8 \\ 0 & 0 & 3 & 3 \end{bmatrix} \begin{bmatrix} r_1 \\ r_2 \\ r_3 \\ r_4 \end{bmatrix} = \lambda \begin{bmatrix} r_1 \\ r_2 \\ r_3 \\ r_4 \end{bmatrix}$$

we will have four linear equations with three unknowns. One of these equations can be considered redundant and be left out. If we leave out the first of the equations, the following reduced system is obtained:

$$\begin{bmatrix} 12 - (7 \times 1.810) & 6 - (7 \times 1.301) & 2 - (7 \times 0.531) \\ 18 - (7 \times 1.810) & 18 - (7 \times 1.301) & 8 - (7 \times 0.531) \\ 0 - (0 \times 1.810) & 3 - (0 \times 1.301) & 3 - (0 \times 0.531) \end{bmatrix} \begin{bmatrix} r_2 \\ r_3 \\ r_4 \end{bmatrix} = \lambda \begin{bmatrix} r_2 \\ r_3 \\ r_4 \end{bmatrix}$$

This procedure can be generalized as follows. Find a constraint relation through the orthogonality property of eigenvectors and express it as

$$r_1 = \alpha_2 r_2 + \alpha_3 r_3 + \cdots + \alpha_n r_n$$

The problem is then to find the eigenvalues of the reduced matrix $\mathbf{L}'$:

$$\mathbf{L}' = \begin{bmatrix} l_{22} + l_{21}\alpha_2 & l_{23} + l_{21}\alpha_3 & \cdots & l_{2n} + l_{21}\alpha_n \\ l_{32} + l_{31}\alpha_2 & l_{33} + l_{31}\alpha_3 & \cdots & l_{3n} + l_{31}\alpha_n \\ \cdots & \cdots & \cdots & \cdots \\ l_{n2} + l_{n1}\alpha_2 & l_{n3} + l_{n1}\alpha_3 & \cdots & l_{nn} + l_{n1}\alpha_n \end{bmatrix}$$

The eigenvectors of $\mathbf{L}'$ have only $(n - 1)$ elements, which are the same as the corresponding elements of $(n - 1)$ eigenvectors of $\mathbf{L}$. The remaining elements of the eigenvectors of $\mathbf{L}$ are obtained by the constraint relation imposed.

(F) REMARKS

So far, in this article and in the next, the discussion centers on the mathematical problem of determining the eigenvalues and eigenvectors of a square matrix. To connect this discussion with the solution of physical problems, the following remarks are presented to bring together pertinent results previously obtained.

Assume that we are dealing with vibrations of systems in which damping forces can be neglected. For such systems the first thing of interest is the natural frequencies and modes of vibration. This we have shown to be an eigenvalue problem of the square matrix $\mathbf{A}^{-1}\mathbf{C}$ or $\mathbf{C}^{-1}\mathbf{A}$. Since the numerical methods discussed always give the largest eigenvalue first and since in practice we are more interested in the lower frequencies, the matrix product $\mathbf{C}^{-1}\mathbf{A}$ (hence $\mathbf{C}^{-1}$) has to be found. The matrix $\mathbf{C}^{-1}$ is formed by the influence coefficients between different pairs of generalized coordinates. If these coefficients can be computed directly, a tedious and error-producing inversion procedure can be eliminated. For systems such as beams and frames, carrying masses, the influence coefficients are directly obtainable from formulas in strength of material, whereas the elastic constants, which form the elastic matrix **C**, are not. On the other hand, there are systems whose potential energy expressions in terms of generalized coordinates can be readily obtained. For such systems it is more convenient to determine **C** first and then invert it to obtain $\mathbf{C}^{-1}$.

After the matrix product $\mathbf{C}^{-1}\,\mathbf{A}$ is obtained, the methods described can be used to determine the natural frequencies and amplitude ratios of the system in free vibration. Ordinarily, only the first few modes are of practical interest. This is because of two facts. First, the frequencies of external disturbances are usually far below the higher natural frequencies. Second, the assumptions required in setting up the differential equations are often very unrealistic for the higher modes of vibration, although they may be justified for the lower modes.

When the numerical procedure is terminated after the determination of, say, the first k modes, only the first k columns of the modal matrix **R** defined by (18) are known. By knowing the first k columns of **R**, we can compute the first k diagonal elements of the matrices **M** and **K**, since

$$\mathbf{M} = \overline{\mathbf{R}}\,\mathbf{A}\,\mathbf{R} \qquad \text{and} \qquad \mathbf{K} = \overline{\mathbf{R}}\,\mathbf{C}\,\mathbf{R}$$

In this way the first k equations represented by (46) can be obtained. By solving these equations for $p_1, p_2, \ldots, p_k$ and then assuming $p_{k+1} = p_{k+2} = \ldots = p_n = 0$, we can get an approximate solution for $q_1, q_2, \ldots, q_n$ in a forced vibration problem. This procedure is permissible when the frequency of the external force or forces is low in comparison with the higher natural frequencies of the system. For example, a system having 7 degrees of freedom is under an external sinusoidal force of 60 cycles per second. The first three natural frequencies were found to be 44, 185, and 602 cycles per second. The system's approximate response to this external force can then be determined without finding all of its natural modes.

3.12 Additional Theorems and Methods

(A) ENCLOSURE THEOREM

In many practical problems the generalized coordinates of the system are the displacements of the different inertia elements with respect to some fixed reference system. For such problems the kinetic energy expression contains only the squares of $\dot{q}$'s.

$$T = \tfrac{1}{2}(a_{11}\dot{q}_1^{\,2} + a_{22}\dot{q}_2^{\,2} + \cdots + a_{nn}\dot{q}_n^{\,2})$$

In other words, the matrix $\mathbf{A}$ is a *diagonal* with *positive* diagonal elements.

$$a_{ij} = 0 \quad \text{when } i \neq j \qquad \text{and} \qquad a_{ij} > 0 \quad \text{when } i = j$$

In matrix iteration of the eigenvalue problem for such a system we have the so-called *enclosure theorem*, which can be stated as follows. Let

$$\mathbf{L} = \mathbf{A}^{-1}\,\mathbf{C}$$

and

$$\mathbf{v}' = \mathbf{L}\,\mathbf{v}$$

in which $\mathbf{v}$ is an *arbitrary* vector. Let the ratios between corresponding elements in $\mathbf{v}'$ and $\mathbf{v}$ be

$$\lambda_1' = \frac{v_1'}{v_1}, \qquad \lambda_2' = \frac{v_2'}{v_2}, \cdots, \lambda_n' = \frac{v_n'}{v_n}$$

Let the largest of these ratios be $\lambda'_{\max}$ and the smallest, $\lambda'_{\min}$. The theorem then asserts that between these two limits there is at least one eigenvalue of $\mathbf{L}$.[16]

The conditions stated for the validity of this theorem are rather stringent. For example, it does not apply to the case

$$\mathbf{L}\,\mathbf{v} = (\mathbf{C}^{-1}\,\mathbf{A})\,\mathbf{v} = \mathbf{v}'$$

in which $\mathbf{A}$ is diagonal and $\mathbf{C}^{-1}$ is symmetric. However, these conditions are sufficient conditions. Although we have examples to show that the theorem is not valid for arbitrary $\mathbf{L}$, it is suspected that it is valid under more liberal conditions, which at present are not known. Experience seems to indicate that when $\lambda'_{\max}$ and $\lambda'_{\min}$ are reasonably close together they usually bracket an eigenvalue.

(B) EIGENVALUE PROBLEM OF A SYMMETRICAL MATRIX AND SYMMETRIZATION OF A GENERAL EIGENVALUE PROBLEM

The eigenvalue problem of a symmetrical matrix

$$\mathbf{S}\,\mathbf{r} = \lambda\mathbf{r} \qquad (\mathbf{S} = \overline{\mathbf{S}})$$

has many convenient features. One is that the enclosure theorem just discussed is valid; another is that Rayleigh's quotient of vectors during an iteration process is easily computed:

$$R(\mathbf{v}) = \frac{\overline{\mathbf{v}}\mathbf{S}\,\mathbf{v}}{\overline{\mathbf{v}}\,\mathbf{v}} = \frac{\overline{\mathbf{v}}\,\mathbf{v}'}{\overline{\mathbf{v}}\,\mathbf{v}}$$

---

[16] See *Eigenwertaufgaben mit technischer Anwendung*, by L. Collatz, Akademische Verlagsgesellschaft, Leipzig, 1949, p. 289.

Still another is that the eigenvectors are mutually orthogonal in the *ordinary geometrical* sense; that is

$$\bar{\mathbf{r}}^{(i)}\,\mathbf{r}^{(j)} = 0 \qquad i \neq j$$

Among other things, this simplifies the procedure described in Art. 3.11(D). Moreover, if the eigenvectors are *normalized in length*, that is, by proper scaling of these vectors so that

$$\bar{\mathbf{r}}^{(i)}\,\mathbf{r}^{(i)} = 1$$

then the modal matrix formed by the $\mathbf{r}$'s will have the very desirable property that

$$\bar{\mathbf{R}}\,\mathbf{R} = \mathbf{I} \qquad \text{or} \qquad \bar{\mathbf{R}} = \mathbf{R}^{-1}$$

The truth of these statements can be readily verified.

Now we want to show how a general free vibration problem can be converted into that of a symmetrical matrix. The idea is simply to convert one of the energy expressions into a sum of squares by a convenient linear transformation of variables. Suppose we choose the potential energy expression for this maneuver.

$$V = \tfrac{1}{2}\bar{\mathbf{q}}\,\mathbf{C}\,\mathbf{q}$$

First we find a matrix $\mathbf{F}$ such that

$$\bar{\mathbf{F}}\,\mathbf{F} = \mathbf{C}$$

This is always possible when $\mathbf{C}$ is symmetrical. Introduce a new set of coordinates represented by $\mathbf{g}$.

$$\mathbf{g} = \mathbf{F}\,\mathbf{q} \qquad \text{or} \qquad \mathbf{q} = \mathbf{F}^{-1}\,\mathbf{g}$$

This transformation changes the energy expression into

$$V = \tfrac{1}{2}\bar{\mathbf{q}}\,\mathbf{C}\,\mathbf{q} = \tfrac{1}{2}\bar{\mathbf{q}}\,\bar{\mathbf{F}}\,\mathbf{F}\,\mathbf{q} = \tfrac{1}{2}\bar{\mathbf{g}}\,\mathbf{g}$$

$$T = \tfrac{1}{2}\bar{\dot{\mathbf{q}}}\,\mathbf{A}\,\dot{\mathbf{q}} = \tfrac{1}{2}\bar{\dot{\mathbf{g}}}(\bar{\mathbf{F}}^{-1}\,\mathbf{A}\,\mathbf{F}^{-1})\,\dot{\mathbf{g}} = \tfrac{1}{2}\bar{\dot{\mathbf{g}}}\,\mathbf{S}\,\dot{\mathbf{g}}$$

where

$$\mathbf{S} = \bar{\mathbf{F}}^{-1}\,\mathbf{A}\,\mathbf{F}^{-1}$$

can be shown to be symmetrical. The eigenvalue problem then becomes

$$\mathbf{S}\,\mathbf{r} = \lambda\mathbf{r} \qquad \lambda = \frac{1}{\omega^2}$$

Similarly, if we make

$$\bar{\mathbf{F}}\,\mathbf{F} = \mathbf{A} \qquad \text{and} \qquad \bar{\mathbf{F}}\,\mathbf{S}\,\mathbf{F} = \mathbf{C}$$

we have a symmetrical eigenvalue problem with $\lambda = \omega^2$.

At first glance it appears that in our effort to symmetrize the problem a great deal of additional labor of computation is introduced to defeat our original purpose. But this is not so, for by a proper choice of $\mathbf{F}$ the computational labor involved will be no more than that of getting $\mathbf{C}^{-1}\mathbf{A}$ or $\mathbf{A}^{-1}\mathbf{C}$, and in many ways it is more convenient to manage.

The matrix equation

$$\bar{\mathbf{F}}\mathbf{F} = \mathbf{C}$$

represents a system of n^2 linear simultaneous equations, of which $n(n-1)/2$ repeat themselves because $\mathbf{C}$ is symmetrical. Therefore, the elements of $\mathbf{F}$ are not uniquely determined and $n(n-1)/2$ of the elements may take arbitrarily assigned values. Since the object is to find as simple an $\mathbf{F}$ as possible, we will assign zero as the value of these elements. The most advantageous way of placing these zeros turns out to be all at one side of the diagonal line. In other words, $\mathbf{F}$ is a *triangular matrix.*

$$\mathbf{F} = \begin{bmatrix} f_{11} & f_{12} & f_{13} & \cdots & f_{1n} \\ 0 & f_{22} & f_{23} & \cdots & f_{2n} \\ 0 & 0 & f_{33} & \cdots & f_{3n} \\ \cdot & \cdot & \cdot & \cdot & \cdot \\ 0 & 0 & 0 & \cdots & f_{nn} \end{bmatrix}$$

The expansion of the matrix equation $\bar{\mathbf{F}}\mathbf{F} = \mathbf{C}$ yields the following simple relations:

$$\begin{aligned}
&f_{11}^2 = c_{11} \\
&f_{11}f_{12} = c_{12}, \quad f_{11}f_{13} = c_{13}, \cdots, f_{11}f_{1n} = c_{1n} \\
&f_{22}^2 = c_{22} - f_{12}^2 \\
&f_{22}f_{23} = c_{23} - f_{12}f_{13}, \quad f_{22}f_{24} = c_{24} - f_{12}f_{14}, \cdots \\
&f_{33}^2 = c_{33} - f_{13}^2 - f_{23}^2 \\
&f_{33}f_{34} = c_{34} - f_{13}f_{14} - f_{23}f_{24}, \quad f_{33}f_{35} = c_{35} - f_{13}f_{15} - f_{23}f_{25}, \cdots \\
&\cdots\cdots\cdots\cdots\cdots\cdots\cdots\cdots \\
&f_{nn}^2 = c_{nn} - f_{1n}^2 - f_{2n}^2 - \cdots, f_{n-1}^2
\end{aligned}$$

The salient feature of these equations is that the elements of $\mathbf{F}$ can be computed one at a time starting from the left to the right in each row and then row after row. A convenient tabulating schedule can be set up to handle this computation.

After having found $\mathbf{F}$, we will now find $\mathbf{F}^{-1}$. Again a triangular matrix has the advantage that its inverse can be computed one element at a time in a simple way. This is in marked contrast to the determination of the inverse of an arbitrary matrix. As a matter of fact, there is a number of practical schemes for the determination of the inverse of a matrix based on the principle of splitting the matrix into two triangular matrices.

Since $f_{ij} = 0$ when $i > j$, the expansion of

$$\mathbf{F}^{-1}\,\mathbf{F} = \mathbf{I}$$

is

$$\begin{aligned}
&f_{11}^{-1}f_{11} = 1, \\
&f_{11}^{-1}f_{12} + f_{12}^{-1}f_{22} = 0 \\
&f_{11}^{-1}f_{13} + f_{12}^{-1}f_{23} + f_{13}^{-1}f_{33} = 0 \\
&\cdots\cdots\cdots\cdots\cdots\cdots \\
&f_{11}^{-1}f_{1n} + f_{12}^{-1}f_{2n} + \cdots + f_{1n}^{-1}f_{nn} = 0 \\
&f_{21}^{-1}f_{11} = 0 \qquad \text{or} \qquad f_{21}^{-1} = 0 \\
&f_{22}^{-1}f_{22} = 1, \qquad f_{22}^{-1}f_{23} + f_{23}^{-1}f_{33} = 0 \\
&\cdots\cdots\cdots\cdots\cdots\cdots \\
&\cdots\cdots\cdots\cdots\cdots\cdots \\
&f_{n1}^{-1} = 0, \qquad f_{n2}^{-1} = 0, \qquad f_{n3}^{-1} = 0 \\
&f_{nn}^{-1}f_{nn} = 1
\end{aligned}$$

It is seen that $\mathbf{F}^{-1}$ is also a triangular matrix, and its elements can be computed from $\mathbf{F}$ one at a time in a simple way.

3.13 Chain Systems—Holzer's Method

One way of obtaining the frequency equation of the vibration problem embodied in

$$(c_{ij} - a_{ij}\omega^2)r_j = 0 \qquad \Big| \qquad (\mathbf{C} - \mathbf{A}\omega^2)\mathbf{r} = \mathbf{0}$$

is as follows. Set aside one of the n simultaneous equations represented by this matrix equation. Solve the remaining $n - 1$ equations by assigning an arbitrary value to one of the coordinate variables. The solution will be in terms of ω^2. By substituting this solution into the equation that has been set aside, we obtain an equation in ω^2, which is the frequency equation of the system. This method is usually too tedious. Under some special circumstances, however, the principle of this method can be applied to determine the natural modes.

Consider the torsional vibration of a shaft carrying a number of disks, as shown in Fig. 72. The eigenvalue problem for this system is that of the following set of algebraic equations. [See Art. 2.9(A).]

$$\begin{aligned}
0 \qquad\qquad &+ I_1\omega^2\phi_1 = k_{12}(\phi_1 - \phi_2) \\
k_{12}(\phi_1 - \phi_2) &+ I_2\omega^2\phi_2 = k_{23}(\phi_2 - \phi_3) \\
k_{23}(\phi_2 - \phi_3) &+ I_2\omega^2\phi_3 = k_{34}(\phi_3 - \phi_4) \\
&\cdots\cdots\cdots\cdots\cdots\cdots \\
k_{n-1,n}(\phi_{n-1} - \phi_n) &+ I_n\omega^2\phi_n = 0
\end{aligned}$$

Physically these equations describe how the torque of the shaft changes from one section to the next. We start from zero torque at the left and end up with zero torque at the right end.

Holzer's method of solving this problem is as follows. Assume first a value for ω^2 and assign the value 1 to ϕ_1, which can be arbitrary anyhow. From the first equation we then get $\phi_1 - \phi_2$ and ϕ_2. By putting these into the second equation, we obtain $\phi_2 - \phi_3$ and ϕ_3, and so forth. When we reach the $(n - 1)$th equation, we shall have all the values of the ϕ's. The last equation then tells us whether or not our assumed value for ω^2 is correct. By trial and error a value for ω^2 will eventually be found that will

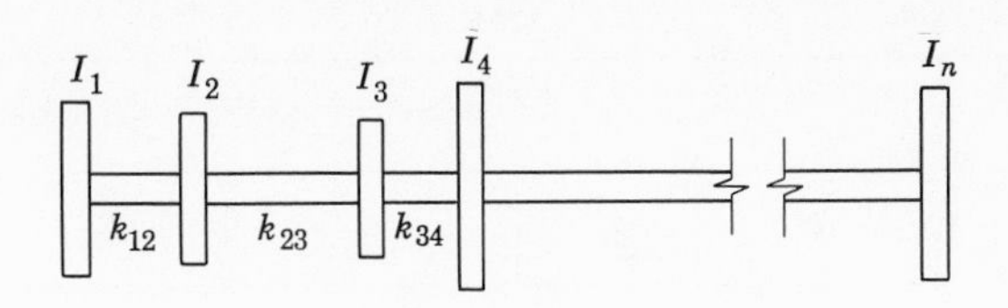

Figure 72

make the left-hand side of the last equation vanish or become very small. This value is the square of a natural frequency, and the corresponding values of $\phi_1, \phi_2, \ldots, \phi_n$ represent the elements of the corresponding modal vector.

To facilitate the setting up of a tabular method for the computations, the preceding set of equations are rewritten:

$$I_1\omega^2\phi_1 = k_{12}(\phi_1 - \phi_2)$$
$$I_1\omega^2\phi_1 + I_2\omega^2\phi_2 = k_{23}(\phi_2 - \phi_3)$$
$$I_1\omega^2\phi_1 + I_2\omega^2\phi_2 + I_3\omega^2\phi_3 = k_{34}(\phi_3 - \phi_4)$$
$$\cdots\cdots\cdots\cdots\cdots\cdots$$
$$I_1\omega^2\phi_1 + I_2\omega^2\phi_2 + \cdots + I_n\omega^2\phi_n = 0$$

The computation for each trial value of ω^2 consists in filling out Table 1.

Columns A and F are first computed from the given data with an assumed value of ω^2. The rest of the places are filled in according to the sequence indicated. Item D_n represents the left-hand side of the last equation, which is a function of the value of ω^2 assumed beforehand. The idea is to determine the value of ω^2 for which

$$D_n(\omega^2) = 0$$

To start the trial-and-error procedure, we must have a reasonable estimate of the correct ω^2, lest the labor needed be prohibitive. To this end we first compute Rayleigh's quotient with a roughly estimated amplitude ratio $\phi_1 : \phi_2 : \ldots : \phi_n$. Since the system is semidefinite with a zero mode, it is necessary that this estimated ratio satisfies

$$I_1\phi_1 + I_2\phi_2 + \cdots + I_n\phi_n = 0$$

Rayleigh's quotient obtained with this constraint will always be larger than the square of the lowest nonzero natural frequency of the system. It is therefore preferable to start our trial-and-error procedure with a value of ω^2 somewhat lower than that of Rayleigh's quotient.[17]

TABLE 1

	$\omega^2 =$					
	A	B	C	D	E	F
	$I\omega^2$	ϕ	$I\omega^2\phi$	$\Sigma I\omega^2\phi = k\,\Delta\phi$	$\dfrac{\Sigma I\omega^2\phi}{k} = \Delta\phi$	$1/k$
(1)	$I_1\omega^2$	1.000	A_1B_1	C_1	D_1F_1	$1/k_{12}$
(2)	$I_2\omega^2$	$B_1 - E_1$	A_2B_2	$C_2 + D_1$	D_2F_2	$1/k_{23}$
(3)	$I_3\omega^2$	$B_2 - E_2$	A_3B_3	$C_3 + D_2$	D_3F_3	$1/k_{34}$
.	.	.	.	.	.	.
.	.	.	.	.	.	.
.	.	.	.	.	.	.
(n)	$I_n\omega^2$			D_n		

After the first trial, it becomes necessary to have a way of knowing which way to correct the ω^2 value for the second trial. In other words, we must know how D_n varies with ω^2 in the vicinity of the trial value. It was mentioned previously that $D_n(\omega^2) = 0$ is the frequency equation[18] if ω^2 were left in as a variable instead of an assumed numerical value. The value of D_n is therefore bounded and is a continuous function of ω^2 for all finite and positive ω^2. A plot of D_n versus ω^2 must be of the form shown in Fig. 73. The curve crosses over the abscissae at n places, including the origin. These correspond to the natural frequencies. At the origin the curve must have a positive slope, since for a very small but positive ω^2 the sequence of computation must lead to a positive D_n. Hence in our

[17] We are assuming that generally we want to find the lowest natural frequency first.
[18] This equation may differ from (16) only by a multiplication constant.

trial to locate the lowest nonzero frequency a positive D_n indicates that the trial value is too small and vice versa.

In practical applications Holter's method is most widely used for analyzing the torsional vibration of the crankshaft of a multicylinder engine connected to a generator or other driven systems. In such applications there are usually two or three large inertia elements representing generator rotor, flywheel, damper inertia, etc., and a number of small

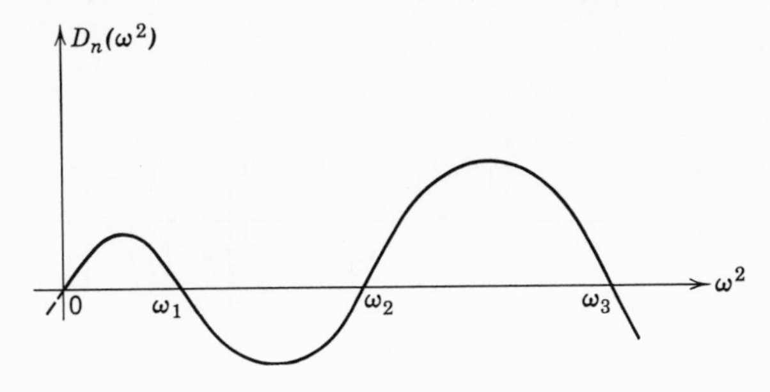

Figure 73

inertia elements representing the pistons, connecting rods, and crankshaft mass of the cylinders. To obtain an estimate of the lower natural frequencies of such a system, we may simplify it by "lumping" the smaller moments of inertia with the larger ones near to them. Then the simplified system has only one or two nonzero modes whose frequencies can be determined quickly with methods described in the preceding chapters. These frequencies may now serve as the starting values for Holzer's method.

Holzer's method may also be used alternately with Rayleigh's method. After a trial run Rayleigh's quotient for the amplitude ratio can be obtained by the following simple relation:

$$\omega'^2 = R(\phi_1, \phi_2, \cdots, \phi_n) = \frac{\Sigma k\, \Delta\phi^2}{\Sigma I\phi^2} = \frac{(D_1E_1 + D_2E_2 + \cdots + D_{n-1}E_{n-1})\omega^2}{(B_1C_1 + B_2C_2 + \cdots + B_nC_n)}$$

in which the symbols refer to items in Table 1. If $D_n = 0$, ω' naturally is equal to ω, and the correct frequency is obtained. If D_n is small, ω' is a better approximation than ω and can be used for the next run of computations by Holzer's method. If D_n is large, a corrective procedure, which is described later, may be needed.

We shall now work an example. Let the crankshaft of a 4-cylinder engine and the attached inertia elements be equivalent to the system shown in Fig. 74*a*. The values of the I's and k's are

$$I_1 = 150 \qquad I_2 = 20 \qquad I_3 = I_4 = I_5 = I_6 = 2 \qquad I_7 = 10$$

$$k_{12} = 1 \qquad k_{23} = 6 \qquad k_{34} = k_{45} = k_{56} = 3 \qquad k_{67} = 4$$

All are in their proper units, so that the unit of ω will be *10^3 radians per second.*

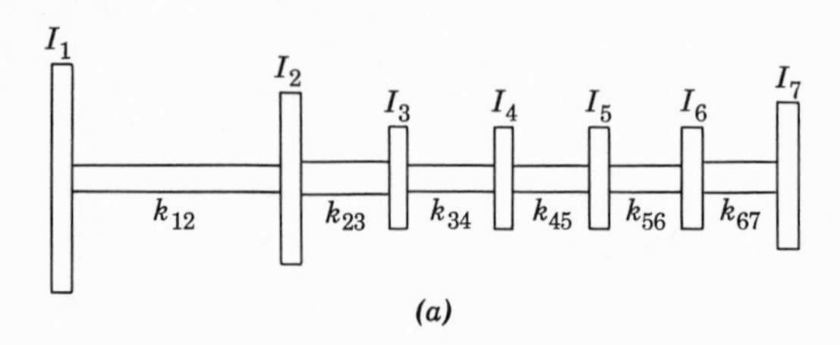

(*a*)

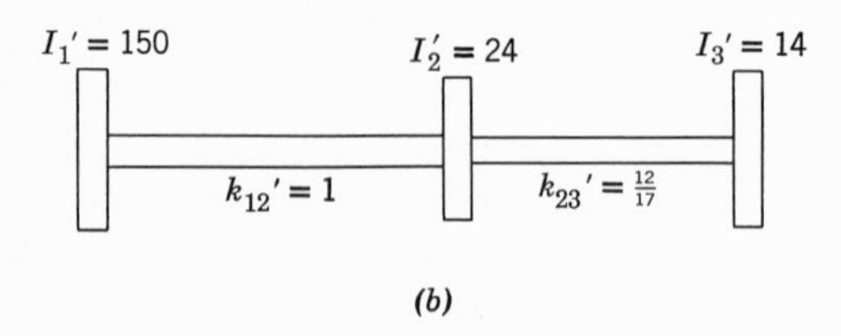

(*b*)

Figure 74

If we lump I_3 and I_4 with I_2 and I_5 and I_6 with I_7, we have the approximately equivalent system shown in Fig. 74*b*, in which

$$I_1' = 150 \qquad I_2' = 24 \qquad I_3' = 14$$

$$k_{12}' = 1 \qquad k_{23}' = \frac{1}{\frac{1}{6} + \frac{1}{3} + \frac{1}{3} + \frac{1}{3} + \frac{1}{4}} = \frac{12}{17}$$

By substituting these into (53) of Art. 2.9(A), we obtain the following frequency equation:

$$\begin{vmatrix} -150\omega^2 + \left(1 + \dfrac{150}{24}\right) & \dfrac{14}{24} \\ \dfrac{12}{17}\left(\dfrac{150}{24}\right) & -14\omega^2 + \dfrac{12}{17}\left(1 + \dfrac{14}{24}\right) \end{vmatrix} = 0$$

This quadratic equation gives

$$\omega^2 = 0.0262 \qquad \text{or} \qquad 0.1000\ (10^3\ \text{rad/sec})^2$$

We can now proceed to construct Holzer's table, Table 2, with $\omega^2 = 0.0262$.

TABLE 2

	$\omega^2 = 0.0262$					
	A	*B*	*C*	*D*	*E*	*F*
	$I\omega^2$	ϕ	$I\omega^2\phi$	$k\,\Delta\phi$	$\Delta\phi$	$1/k$
1	3.930	1.000	3.930	3.930	3.930	1
2	0.524	−2.930	−1.536	2.394	0.399	0.1666
3	0.0524	−3.329	−0.175	2.219	0.740	0.3333
4	0.0524	−4.069	−0.213	2.016	0.672	0.3333
5	0.0524	−4.741	−0.248	1.768	0.589	0.3333
6	0.0524	−5.330	−0.280	1.488	0.372	0.250
7	0.2620	−5.702	−1.495	$-0.007 = D_7$		

Since the value of D_n in our first trial is sufficiently small, we have the first natural frequency of the system; $\omega_1{}^2 = 0.0262 \times 10^6$.

Of course, we cannot always be lucky enough to have the estimated answer so close to the true answer. For the purpose of illustration, let us now work the same problem with a much poorer initial estimate. Suppose by some scheme we obtain an initial estimate of $\omega^2 = 0.0328$. This estimate results in Table 3.

Since $D_n = -1.084 < 0$, we know that the trial ω^2 is too large. We can decrease this value and try again. A better way would be to compute Rayleigh's quotient with the approximate modal vector represented by column *B* of Table 3. According to our previous discussion,

$$\omega'^2 = \frac{D_1E_1 + D_2E_2 + \cdots + D_6E_6}{B_1C_1 + B_2C_2 + \cdots + B_7C_7}\,\omega^2$$

$$= \frac{28.43}{35.74} \times 0.0328 = 0.0261$$

Thus we see that Rayleigh's quotient of the modal vector obtained from a roughly estimated value of ω^2 gives remarkably accurate results.

The modal vector obtained from column B of a first trial generally does not satisfy the constraint relationship $\Sigma I\phi = 0$, since $D_n \neq 0$. It therefore contains a rigid-body motion. If D_n is not too large, we may disregard this discrepancy. If D_n is moderately large, a correction may be necessary.

TABLE 3

$\omega^2 = 0.0328$

	A	B	C	D	E	F
	$I\omega^2$	ϕ	$I\omega^2\phi$	$k\ \Delta\phi$	$\Delta\phi$	$1/k$
1	4.920	1.000	4.920	4.920	4.920	1
2	0.656	−3.920	−2.572	2.348	0.392	0.1666
3	0.0656	−4.311	−0.282	2.066	0.689	0.3333
4	0.0656	−5.000	−0.328	1.738	0.579	0.3333
5	0.0656	−5.579	−0.366	1.372	0.457	0.3333
6	0.0656	−6.036	−0.396	0.976	0.244	0.2500
7	0.328	−6.280	−2.060	$-1.084 = D_7$		

The correction consists of deducting from the denominator of Rayleigh's quotient a term representing the kinetic energy of the zero mode. This is permissible because of the orthogonality relation of the modal vectors. The correction term is the first term of the denominator of (39). For the present problem it is

$$\epsilon = (I_1 + I_2 + \cdots + I_n)\,\phi_{\text{mean}}^2$$

in which

$$\phi_{\text{mean}} = \frac{I_1\phi_1 + I_2\phi_2 + \cdots + I_n\phi_n}{I_1 + I_2 + \cdots + I_n}$$

In terms of quantities in the tabulated computation, we can see easily that

$$\epsilon = \frac{D_n{}^2}{(A_1 + A_2 + \cdots + A_n)\omega^2}$$

Applying this formula to the example of Table 3,

$$\epsilon = \frac{1.084^2}{7.162\omega^2} = \frac{0.164}{\omega^2}$$

Rayleigh's quotient corrected is then

$$\omega'^2 = \frac{28.43}{(35.74 - 0.16)}\,\omega^2 = 0.0262$$

although in this example this correction is too small to warrant the effort.

To obtain the second nonzero mode, we begin by assuming $\omega^2 = 0.1000$. The computations are tabulated as Tables 4 and 5.

TABLE 4

$\omega^2 = 0.1000$

	A	B	C	D	E	F
1	15.000	1.000	15.000	15.000	15.000	1.000
2	2.000	−14.000	−28.000	−13.000	−2.166;	0.1666
3	0.200	−11.833	−2.367	−15.367	−5.122	0.3333
4	0.200	−6.711	−1.342	−16.709	−5.570	0.3333
5	0.200	−1.141	−0.228	−16.937	−5.641	0.3333
6	0.200	4.505	0.901	−16.036	−4.009	0.2500
7	1.000	8.514	8.514	$-7.522 = D_7$		

$\Sigma DE = 586 \qquad \Sigma BC = 526 \qquad D_7{}^2/\Sigma A = 3$

$$\omega'^2 = \frac{586}{527 - 3}(0.1000) = 0.113$$

By this time it appears very probable that the iteration process will approach the answer from below. Rayleigh's quotient in Table 5 is most likely to be very near but slightly lower than the true answer. The first trial results in a 13 per cent increase and the second trial, a 5 per cent increase. For the final trial we will use an "anticipated" answer, which is about 2 per cent larger.

This time, D_7 is positive but very small, so that we know the true answer is slightly below 0.121.

TABLE 5

$\omega^2 = 0.113$					
A	B	C	D	E	F
16.95	1.000	16.95	16.95	16.95	1.000
2.26	−15.95	−36.05	−19.10	−3.37	0.1666
0.226	−12.58	−2.84	−21.94	−7.31	0.1333
0.226	−5.27	−1.19	−23.13	−7.71	0.1333
0.226	2.44	0.55	−22.58	−7.53	0.1333
0.226	9.97	2.25	−20.33	−5.08	0.2500
1.130	15.05	17.05	$-3.28 = D_7$		

$\Sigma DE = 964 \qquad \Sigma BC = 914;$

$$\omega'^2 = \frac{964}{914} \times 0.113 = 0.119$$

TABLE 6

$\omega^2 = 0.119 \times 1.02 = 0.121$					
A	B	C	D	E	F
18.15	1.000	18.15	18.15	18.15	1.000
2.42	−17.15	−41.50	−23.30	−3.88	0.1666
0.242	−13.27	−3.21	−26.51	−8.84	0.3333
0.242	4.43	−1.07	−27.58	−9.19	0.3333
0.242	4.76	1.15	−26.43	−8.81	0.3333
0.242	13.56	3.28	−23.15	−5.79	0.2500
1.210	19.35	23.40	$+0.25 = D_7$		

3.14 Electrical Analog of Mechanical Systems and Electromechanical Systems

(A) ELECTRICAL ANALOG

We have emphasized on different occasions that vibratory systems may have entirely different physical appearances, yet their motions are governed by common mathematical equations, so that it is not always necessary to analyze each individual system having a different make-up. We may go one step further and observe that the differential equations of motion

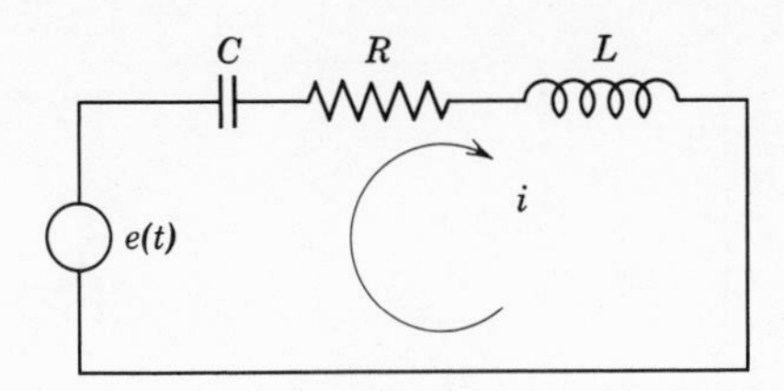

Figure 75

which describe vibratory phenomena also govern the behavior of many other types of systems. These systems are called analogous systems, and they also come under the same treatment. The analogous systems most closely related to mechanical vibratory systems are electrical networks. Except for a different placing of emphasis, network theory is almost indistinguishable from vibration theory. Historically, these theories have always been borrowing results from each other.

Consider the simple circuit shown in Fig. 75. It consists of a resistance R, an inductance L, a capacitance C, and a time-dependent voltage source $e(t)$ connected in series. If $i(t)$ denotes the loop current, Kirchhoff's law will lead to the following integro-differential equation:

$$L\dot{i} + Ri + \frac{1}{C}\int i\,dt = e(t) \tag{i}$$

The indefinite integral above contains an integration constant to be determined by the initial condition. By defining

$$q(t) = \int i\,dt \tag{ii}$$

we can write this integro-differential equation as

$$L\ddot{q} + R\dot{q} + \frac{1}{C}q = e(t) \tag{iii}$$

This equation is then the same as that for the forced vibration of a single-degree-freedom system.

$$m\ddot{q} + c\dot{q} + kq = f(t)$$

The electrical circuit in Fig. 75 is thus an analogous system of a spring-mass-damper system in the sense that a time-dependent voltage source will produce a current in the circuit in an analogous way as a time-dependent force gives a velocity to the mass of a spring-mass-damper system. This analogy is often called the *direct analogy* or the *force-voltage analogy.*

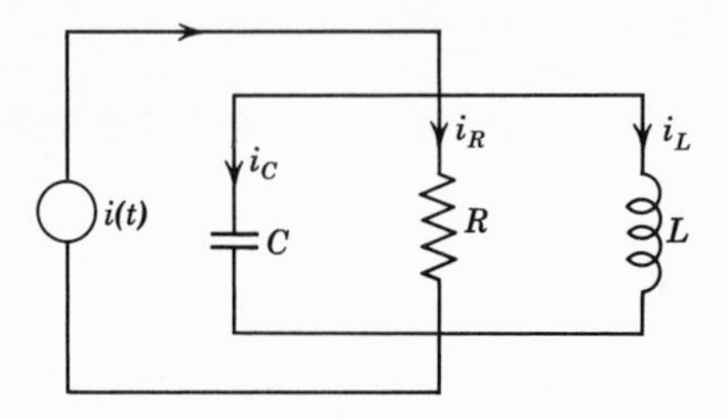

Figure 76

A different electrical analog of the same mechanical system is the circuit shown in Fig. 76. There we have a capacitance, a resistance, and an inductance connected in parallel to a time-dependent current source $i(t)$. Let $v(t)$ be the voltage drop across the three parallel elements. The branch currents flowing in these elements are, respectively,

$$i_C = C\dot{v} \qquad i_R = \frac{v}{R} \qquad \text{and} \qquad i_L = \frac{1}{L}\int v\,dt$$

Since the sum of the branch currents must be equal to the current from the current source, we have

$$C\dot{v} + \frac{1}{R}v + \frac{1}{L}\int v\,dt = i(t) \tag{iv}$$

This integro-differential equation has exactly the same mathematical form as the one before, and because the indefinite integral contains an arbitrary constant this integro-differential equation can also be changed into a differential equation of the second order by defining a function[19] $q(t)$ as

$$q(t) = \int v(t)\,dt$$

$$C\ddot{q} + \frac{1}{R}\dot{q} + \frac{1}{L}q = i(t)$$

[19] This definition is intended to have mathematical meaning only. Although the integral $\int i\,dt$ previously represented the physical quantity, electrical charge, this physical meaning is not essential to our discussion.

This analogy is called an *indirect analogy* or a *force-current analogy*. Here the voltage response to a current source is analogous to the velocity response of a mechanical system to an applied force.

The foregoing simple examples show that when we speak of analogous systems we must have in mind some specific phenomena with which the analogy is to be drawn. In the present case the phenomena in question are the signal-response relationships between analogous pairs of physical quantities.

We must realize also that both the mechanical system and the electrical systems used for illustrations are merely models of other systems to which they are analytically equivalent. Hence the analogy exists not only between two specific systems but between two classes of equivalent systems.

An electrical analog to a mechanical system, which consists of a simple arrangement of springs, mass elements, and dampers, can be conceived by inspection without writing the differential equations of motion. There are rules available whereby an analogous circuit can be drawn simply by replacing mechanical elements with appropriate electrical elements and mechanical arrangements with analogous electrical arrangements. These rules permit a person who is more familiar with one type of system to analyze the other type with which he is not as familiar. It is, however, not our intention to analyze a mechanical system by converting it into a network problem or to analyze an electrical circuit by vibration theory. Our purpose of studying analogy is partly to create an awareness of its existence and partly to enable us to build electrical analogs for complex mechanical systems whose signal-response relations can then be determined experimentally on the analog. (It can be readily appreciated that experiments on electrical circuits are usually more economical than those on mechanical models.) Therefore, in the following discussion it is assumed that we know how to write the governing equations for both types of systems when they are needed for the construction of analogous systems.

Let us now study an example of a mechanical system having two degrees of freedom, as shown in Fig. 77*a*. The differential equations of motion are

$$m_{11}\ddot{x}_1 + c_{11}\dot{x}_1 + k_{11}x_1 + c_{12}(\dot{x}_1 - \dot{x}_2) + k_{12}(x_1 - x_2) = f_1(t)$$

$$m_{22}\ddot{x}_2 + c_{22}\dot{x}_2 + k_{22}x_2 + c_{12}(\dot{x}_2 - \dot{x}_1) + k_{12}(x_2 - x_1) = f_2(t)$$

The two electrical analogs of this system are shown in Figs. 77*b* and 77*c*. The reader can verify that by applying Kirchhoff's law to the two loops in Fig. 77*b* the loop currents are governed by the same set of equations, and by summing up the branch currents at the two nodes in Fig. 77*c* the nodal voltage are also governed by the same equations. The following tables help to describe the analogous relationships:

MECHANICAL SYSTEM	FORCE-VOLTAGE ANALOG	FORCE-CURRENT ANALOG
D'Alembert's principle	Kirchhoff's law	Continuity law
Degrees of freedom	Loops	Nodes (not including datum node)
Generalized velocity	Loop currents	Nodal voltage
Generalized force	Voltage source	Current source
Inertia element	Inductance	Capacitance
Damping element	Resistance	Conductance
Elastic element	1/capacitance	1/inductance
Coupling elements	Elements common to two loops	Elements between the nodes
Stationary frame		Datum node

The electrical analogs of mechanical systems, which consist of masses, springs, and dampers connected in a simple way, can be constructed according to the analogous relations given in the foregoing tables. For others, in which the couplings among the different degrees of freedom are not obvious by inspection, it is necessary that the differential equations of motion be obtained first. Take for instance the system shown in Fig. 53 and studied in Art. 2.11. There are no ready-made rules by which we can construct the electrical analogs for such a system without first writing down the differential equations of motion; these equations were found to be

$$(M + m)\ddot{q}_1 + Kq_1 - m\cos\theta\ddot{q}_2 - Kq_2 = 0$$

$$-m\cos\theta\ddot{q}_1 - Kq_1 + m\ddot{q}_2 + (K + k)q_2 = 0$$

in which

$$q_1 = X \qquad \text{and} \qquad q_2 = x$$

For the purpose of constructing electrical analogs we rearrange the equations to read

$$(M + m - m\cos\theta)\ddot{q}_1 + m\cos\theta(\ddot{q}_1 - \ddot{q}_2) + K(q_1 - q_2) = 0$$

$$(m - m\cos\theta)q_2 + k\ddot{q}_2 + m\cos\theta(\ddot{q}_2 - \ddot{q}_1) + K(q_2 - q_1) = 0$$

From this set of equations we deduce that the two electrical analogs are as shown in Fig. 78.

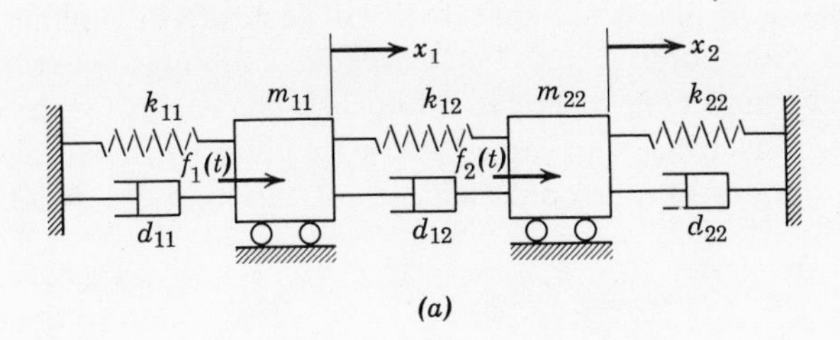

(*a*)

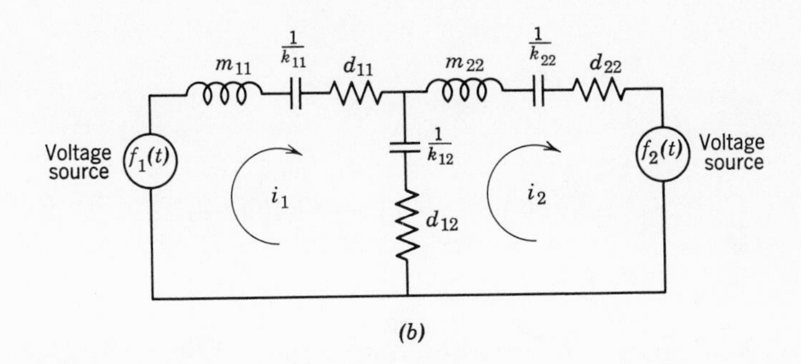

(*b*)

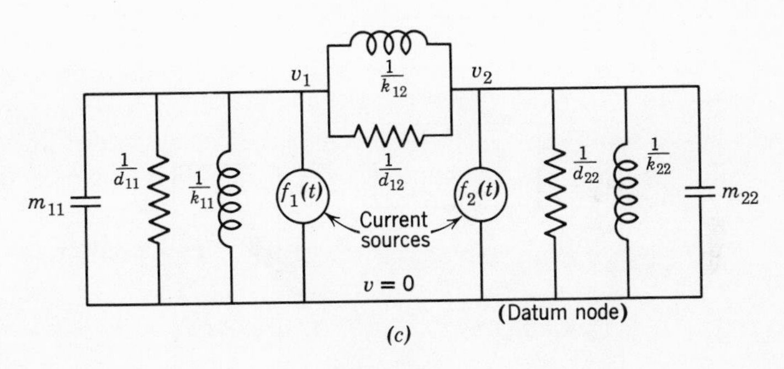

(*c*)

Figure 77

For a more complex example let us consider a mechanical system whose motion is described by

$$\mathbf{A}\,\ddot{\mathbf{q}} + \mathbf{B}\,\dot{\mathbf{q}} + \mathbf{C}\,\mathbf{q} = \mathbf{f}$$

with

$$\mathbf{A} = \begin{bmatrix} 10 & 5 & -1 \\ 5 & 8 & 2 \\ -1 & 2 & 7 \end{bmatrix} \quad \mathbf{B} = \begin{bmatrix} 9 & 4 & -3 \\ 4 & 12 & 6 \\ -3 & 6 & 11 \end{bmatrix} \quad \mathbf{C} = \begin{bmatrix} 21 & 3 & -11 \\ 3 & 17 & 4 \\ -11 & 4 & 15 \end{bmatrix} \times 10^{-6}$$

From the signs of the off-diagonal elements of these matrices we observe that in a force-voltage analog for this system the loop currents must be arranged to flow in such a way that there will be positive couplings between loops 1 and 2 and loops 2 and 3 and negative couplings between loops 1 and 3. The arrangement is shown in Fig. 79. The values for the coupling inductances, resistances, and capacitances are given by the *absolute values* of the appropriate off-diagonal elements of the matrices **A**, **B**, and **C**.

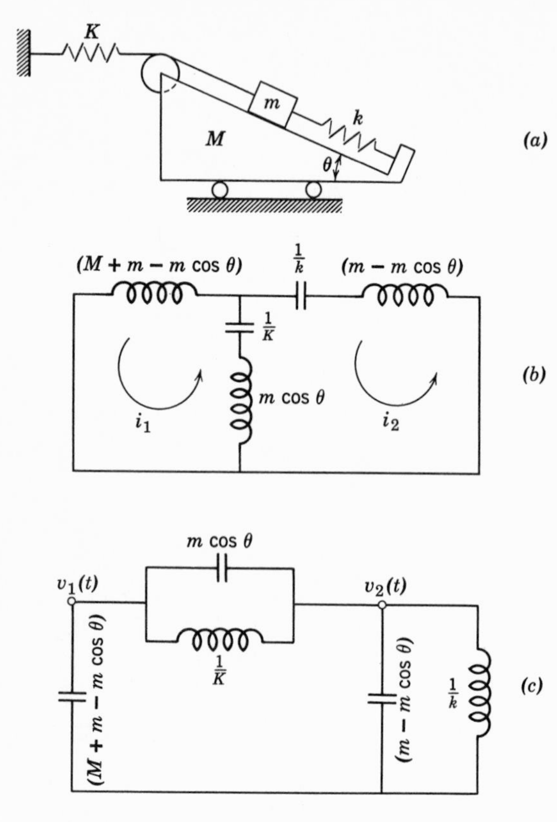

Figure 78

Additional electrical elements are then placed in the loops to make the total inductance, resistance, and capacitance in each loop equal to the values of the appropriate diagonal elements of the matrices. Voltage sources are placed in each loop to fit the column matrix **f**. The polarities shown in Fig. 79 are for positive values of the elements in **f**.

The construction of a force-current analog of the same system follows the same idea. It is left to the reader as an exercise. (See Exercise 3.21.)

The types of analog circuits described so far contain only passive circuit elements, which are capacitances, resistances, and self-inductances with positive values. If these are the only kinds of circuit elements that may be used, it is not always possible to construct analog circuits from a set of differential equations obtained from a real mechanical system because to do so may require circuit elements with negative values. On the other hand, there are electronic devices that can be made to behave like negative

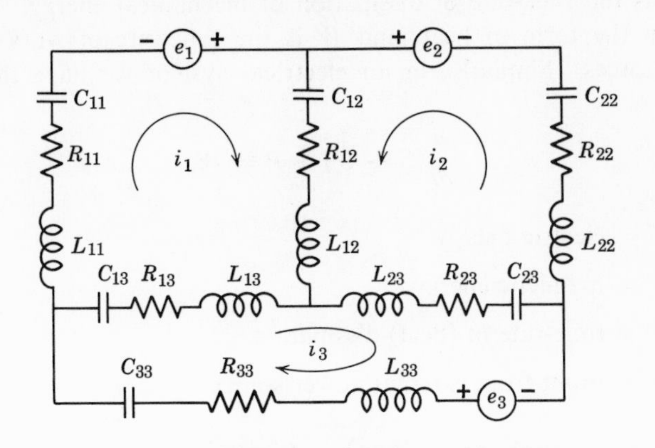

$$\begin{cases} L_{12} = 5 \\ L_{13} = 1 \\ L_{23} = 2 \end{cases} \qquad \begin{cases} C_{12} = \frac{1}{3} \times 10^{-6} \\ C_{13} = \frac{1}{11} \times 10^{-6} \\ C_{22} = \frac{1}{4} \times 10^{-6} \end{cases} \qquad \begin{cases} R_{12} = 4 \\ R_{13} = 3 \\ R_{23} = 6 \end{cases}$$

$$\begin{cases} L_{11} = 10 - 5 - 1 = 4 \\ R_{11} = 9 - 4 - 3 = 2 \\ C_{11} = \dfrac{10^{-6}}{21 - 3 - 11} = \frac{1}{7} \times 10^{-6} \end{cases} \begin{cases} L_{22} = 8 - 5 - 2 = 1 \\ R_{22} = 12 - 6 - 4 = 2 \\ C_{22} = \dfrac{10^{-6}}{17 - 4 - 3} = 10^{-7} \end{cases} \begin{cases} L_{33} = 7 - 2 - 1 = 4 \\ R_{33} = 11 - 6 - 3 = 2 \\ C_{33} = \dfrac{10^{-6}}{15 - 11 - 4} = \infty \end{cases}$$

(short circuit)

Figure 79

capacitances, resistances, and inductances. These devices contain energy sources in themselves and therefore are not passive elements. They are commonly used in analog computers, which are nothing but electrical analogs designed with a greater flexibility of operation.[20]

(B) ELECTRO-MECHANICAL SYSTEMS

The analogy between vibratory mechanical systems and electrical circuits is a particularly intimate one because in both types of systems the phenomenon of interest is the transformation of energy forms viewed

[20] For a brief account of analog computers see *Engineering Systems Analysis* by R. L. Sutherland, Addison-Wesley Publishing Co., Inc., Reading, Mass., 1958, Chapters 7 and 8.

against the background of time. In a pure mechanical system the fundamental relation is

$$\frac{d}{dt}(T + V) + P = W$$

where P is the time-rate of dissipation of mechanical energy,[21] which is usually in the form of heat, and W is the time-rate of work done by external forces. Similarly, in an electrical system we have the energy relation

$$\frac{d}{dt}(S + U) + P = W \tag{v}$$

where S = electric energy

U = magnetic energy

P = time-rate of (heat) dissipation

W = input from external power source

Consider the simple circuit shown in Fig. 75 as an example. In terms of the loop current i the energy expressions are

$$S = \frac{1}{2}\frac{q^2}{C} \qquad U = \frac{1}{2}Li^2 \qquad P = Ri^2 \qquad \text{and} \qquad W = ei$$

where q is defined by (ii). If we substitute these expressions into the energy equation (v) and cancel out an i, the result is the equation from Kirchhoff's law (i):

$$L\dot{i} + Ri + \frac{1}{C}\int i\,dt = e(t)$$

Now take the circuit shown in Fig. 76. In terms of the variable v, in this case the energy expressions are

$$S = \frac{1}{2}Cv^2 \qquad U = \frac{1}{2L}\left(\int v\,dt\right)^2 \qquad P = \frac{v^2}{R} \qquad \text{and} \qquad W = iv$$

and the energy relationship leads to the nodal current equation (iv):

$$c\dot{v} + \frac{1}{R}v + \frac{1}{L}\int v\,dt = i(t)$$

[21] The function P is the same as $2F$, F being Rayleigh's function described in Art. 3.8.

It is well known that mechanical energies and electromagnetic energies from the point of view of thermodynamics are *reversibly* convertible. Hence a mechanical system may be coupled to an electrical system to form a so-called *electromechanical* system. The first law of thermodynamics for such a composite system can be written

$$\frac{d}{dt}[T + V + S + U] + P = W \tag{vi}$$

where P becomes the heat dissipation and W becomes the work input. The term "work" is to be interpreted in the general thermodynamic sense, which includes energy input by virtue of Newtonian forces as well as electromotive forces. The generalized coordinates for an electromechanical system consist of geometrical variables (displacements, angles, etc.) for the mechanical part and electrical variables (loop currents and nodal voltages) for the electrical part. Where the two parts are coupled, energy conversion takes place and imposes a relation between a pair of variables, one mechanical and the other electrical. This relationship serves as an equation of constraint, which describes the dependence of one on the other.

An energy transfer between a mechanical phenomenon and an electromagnetic phenomenon can take place in a number of ways. The most important is that which takes place when a current-carrying electrical conductor moves in a magnetic field. Take, for example, the simple case of the moving coil instrument studied in Art. 1.15. The basic construction can be schematically represented by Fig. 80.

If we let θ = angular deflection of the meter coil

i = current flowing in the coil

J = moment of inertia of the coil

k = constant of the restoring spring

R_g = resistance of the coil

R = resistance external to the coil

e = externally impressed emf

the energy expressions are then

$$T = \tfrac{1}{2}J\dot{\theta}^2 \qquad V = \tfrac{1}{2}k\theta^2$$

$$P = i^2(R + R_g) \qquad \text{and} \qquad W = ei$$

We assume that the capacitance and the self-inductance of the coil are negligible and so is the viscous damping. By substituting these into the energy equation (vi), we have

$$(J\ddot{\theta} + k\theta)\dot{\theta} + i^2(R + R_g) = ei \tag{vii}$$

This equation contains both the geometrical variable θ and the electrical variable i. These, however, are related by an equation of constraint, which

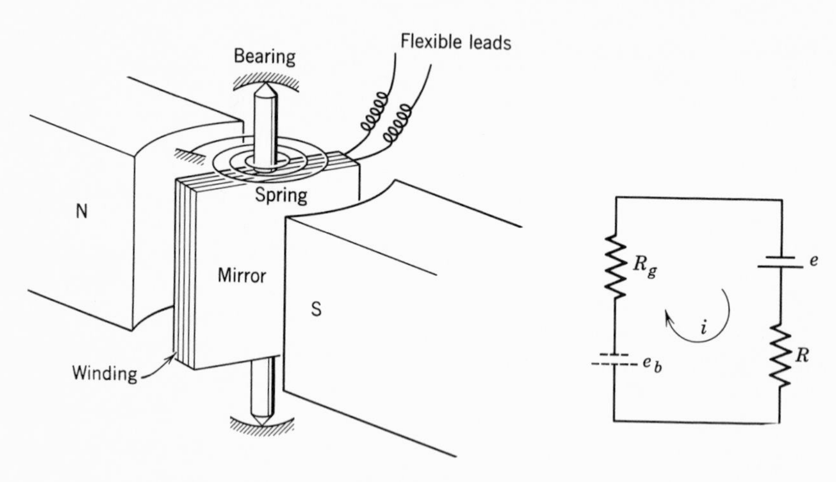

Figure 80

may be found by the following reasoning, based on Faraday's law. As the coil turns, a back emf e_b is produced, which is proportional to the angular velocity $\dot{\theta}$.

$$e_b = B\dot{\theta} \tag{viii}$$

in which B is determined by the field strength of the pole pieces[22] and the geometry of the coil design. By applying Kirchhoff's law to the loop, the relationship between $\dot{\theta}$ and i is then

$$e - e_b = e - B\dot{\theta} = i(R + R_g) \tag{ix}$$

By eliminating the variable i between (vii) and (ix), we obtain finally

$$J\ddot{\theta} + \frac{B^2}{R + R_g}\dot{\theta} + k\theta = \frac{B}{R + R_g}e(t) \tag{x}$$

[22] It is generally the case that the magnetic field produced by the pole pieces is so strong and the coil so designed that the field strength is undisturbed by the current flowing in the coil.

As it was pointed out before, the dependence relation between $\dot{\theta}$ and i originates from the process of converting mechanical energy into electrical energy, or vice versa. From this point of view we see that if the torque produced in the coil by the interaction between the current and the magnetic field is denoted by T_b the rate of energy conversion is given by

$$T_g\dot{\theta} = e_b i \qquad \text{(xi)}$$

Hence the torque per unit current flowing in the coil is

$$\frac{T_b}{i} = \frac{e_b}{\dot{\theta}} = B \qquad \text{(xii)}$$

The dynamic equilibrium equation of the coil is

$$J\ddot{\theta} + k\theta = T_b = Bi \qquad \text{(xiii)}$$

Elimination of i between (xiii) and (ix) results again in (x). Incidentally, (x) is the same equation as (i) of Art. 1.15 because of (xii).

Although a moving coil instrument is a very simple electromechanical system, the analysis of its operation illustrates adequately the principles available for studying the class of system in which the conversion of mechanical energies into electrical energy, or vice versa, is effected by the motion of a conductor in a magnetic field. There are other types of conversion mechanisms which cannot be discussed here. Most of these involve highly nonlinear conversion relationships.

Exercises

3.1. A bent wire is contained in a vertical plane. Its shape is described by

$$y = ax^2 \qquad \text{for } x \geq 0$$

$$(R - y)^2 = R^2 - x^2 \qquad \text{for } x \leq 0$$

A small ring slides on the wire without friction. What must the relation be between a and R so that the system may be approximated by a linear system for a small interval of x near $x = 0$?

3.2. Write the energy expressions for the systems shown, using as generalized coordinates the quantities indicated. How are these expressions "linearized" for small oscillations? (The correct word is perhaps "bilinearized," but it is awkward.)

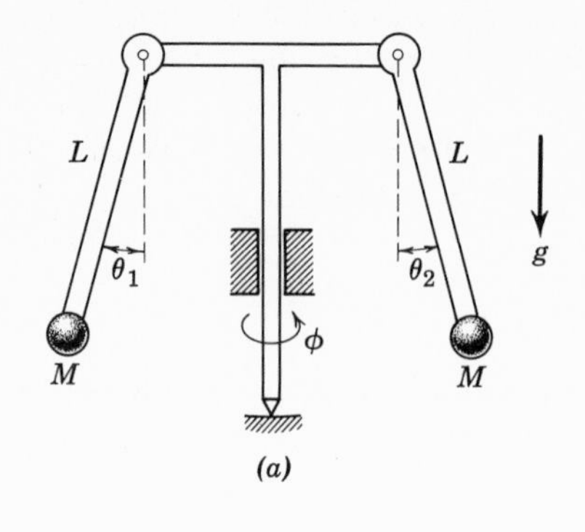

(a)

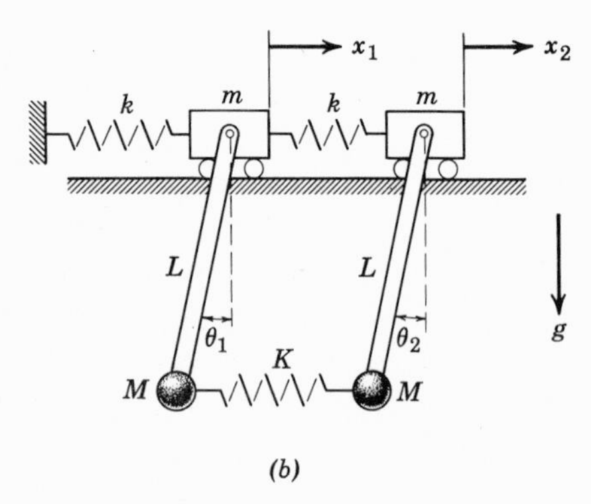

(b)

Exercise 3.2

3.3. Rewrite the following matrix equations first in tensor notation, then in longhand for $n = 3$.

$$\mathbf{A}\,\mathbf{f} + \alpha\mathbf{g} = \mathbf{h} \qquad \bar{\mathbf{g}}\,\mathbf{A}\,\mathbf{B}\,\mathbf{f} = \lambda$$

3.4. Rewrite the following equations in matrix notation:

$$a_{ij}b_{ik} = c_{jk} \qquad a_{ij}b_{km}x_j x_k = c_{mi}$$

3.5. Write out in longhand the determinant in (16).

3.6. Illustrate equations (12) to (16) with a numerical example using

$$\mathbf{A} = \begin{bmatrix} 21 & 7 & 1 \\ 7 & 19 & 7 \\ 1 & 7 & 5 \end{bmatrix} \qquad \mathbf{C} = \begin{bmatrix} 14 & 3 & -2 \\ 3 & 6 & 1 \\ -2 & 1 & 2 \end{bmatrix} \times 10^3$$

Solve the frequency equation obtained and determine the modal vector corresponding to each frequency.

3.7. To which of the equations in Chapter 2 are the following equations in this chapter equivalent: (12), (13), (14), (15), (16), (17), (19), (20) and (21)?

3.8. By matrix iteration, determine the smallest eigenvalue and the associated eigenvector of the problem in which

$$\mathbf{A} = \begin{bmatrix} 5.83 & 1.21 & 3.12 \\ 1.21 & 4.60 & 2.57 \\ 3.12 & 2.57 & 6.95 \end{bmatrix} \qquad \mathbf{C} = \begin{bmatrix} 13 & 3 & 7 \\ 3 & 9 & 4 \\ 7 & 4 & 5 \end{bmatrix} \times 10^4$$

3.9.

(*a*) Find a second eigenvector for Exercise 3.8 by the method described in Art. 3.11(D).
(*b*) Reduce the order of the problem of Exercise 3.8 to $n = 2$ by the method described in Art. 3.11(E).

3.10. Show that a set of mutually orthogonal vectors must be linearly independent. That is

$$\alpha_1 r^{(1)} + \alpha_2 r^{(2)}, \cdots, \alpha_n r^{(n)} \neq 0$$

unless $\alpha_1 = \alpha_2, \ldots, \alpha_n = 0$.

3.11. Prove that

$$Q(\mathbf{u}) \geq \omega_1^2$$

by the fact that both the denominator and the numerator in (36) or (38) must be positive for arbitrary **u**.

Hint. Show first that the elements of the diagonal matrix **M** are always non-negative.

3.12. Derive equations (47) and (48) in Art. 2.8.

3.13. Set up the differential equations of motion for the beam shown.

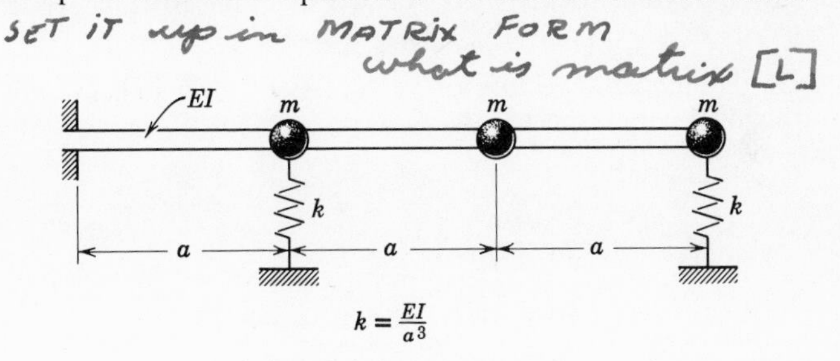

Exercise 3.13

3.14. Find the steady-state solution of

$$\mathbf{A}\ddot{\mathbf{q}} + \mathbf{C}\mathbf{q} = \mathbf{f}e^{i\omega_f t}$$

in which **A** and **C** are given in Exercise 3.6, and

$$\bar{\mathbf{f}} = [3, 4, 5] \qquad \omega_f = 20$$

(*a*) by method discussed in Art. 3.7(B), (*b*) by methods discussed in Art. 3.7(C).

3.15. Find $\mathbf{C}$ for the system shown. Does $\mathbf{C}^{-1}$ exist for this system? Can any of the influence coefficients be defined?

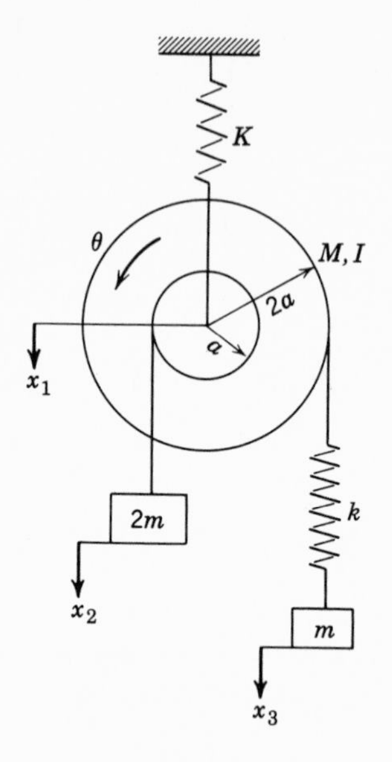

Exercise 3.15

3.16. Given a symmetrical matrix $\mathbf{A}$ and a set of linearly independent vectors $\mathbf{r}^{(1)}, \mathbf{r}^{(2)}, \ldots, \mathbf{r}^{(n)}$:

(*a*) Show that the set of vectors $\mathbf{v}^{(1)}, \mathbf{v}^{(2)}, \ldots, \mathbf{v}^{(n)}$ defined below are mutually orthogonal with respect to $\mathbf{A}$.

$$\mathbf{v}^{(1)} = \mathbf{r}^{(1)}$$

$$\mathbf{v}^{(2)} = \mathbf{r}^{(2)} - \frac{\bar{\mathbf{v}}^{(1)}\mathbf{A}\,\mathbf{r}^{(2)}}{\bar{\mathbf{v}}^{(1)}\mathbf{A}\,\mathbf{v}^{(1)}}\,\mathbf{v}^{(1)}$$

$$\mathbf{v}^{(3)} = \mathbf{r}^{(3)} - \frac{\bar{\mathbf{v}}^{(2)}\mathbf{A}\,\mathbf{r}^{(3)}}{\bar{\mathbf{v}}^{(2)}\mathbf{A}\,\mathbf{v}^{(2)}}\,\mathbf{v}^{(2)} - \frac{\bar{\mathbf{v}}^{(1)}\mathbf{A}\,\mathbf{r}^{(3)}}{\bar{\mathbf{v}}^{(1)}\mathbf{A}\,\mathbf{v}^{(1)}}\,\mathbf{v}^{(1)}$$

$$\mathbf{v}^{(n)} = \mathbf{r}^{(n)} - \frac{\bar{\mathbf{v}}^{(n-1)}\mathbf{A}\,\mathbf{r}^{(n)}}{\bar{\mathbf{v}}^{(n-1)}\mathbf{A}\,\mathbf{v}^{(n-1)}}\,\mathbf{v}^{(n-1)} - \cdots - \frac{\bar{\mathbf{v}}^{(1)}\mathbf{A}\,\mathbf{r}^{(n)}}{\bar{\mathbf{v}}^{(1)}\mathbf{A}\,\mathbf{v}^{(1)}}\,\mathbf{v}^{(1)}$$

(*b*) Show that if the $\mathbf{r}$'s satisfy

$$\mathbf{C}\,\mathbf{r} = \lambda\mathbf{A}\,\mathbf{r} \qquad \lambda \neq 0$$

the $\mathbf{v}$'s defined are also mutually orthogonal with respect to $\mathbf{C}$.

3.17. Verify the statement following (52).

3.18. Make up an eigenvalue problem for which the answer is

$$\mathbf{r}^{(1)} = \begin{bmatrix} 1 \\ 2 \\ 2 \\ 1 \end{bmatrix} \qquad \mathbf{r}^{(2)} = \begin{bmatrix} 1 \\ 1 \\ -2 \\ -2 \end{bmatrix} \qquad \mathbf{r}^{(3)} = \begin{bmatrix} 1 \\ -2 \\ -2 \\ 1 \end{bmatrix} \qquad \mathbf{r}^{(4)} = \begin{bmatrix} 1 \\ -2 \\ 1 \\ -1 \end{bmatrix}$$

$$\lambda_1 = 1 \qquad \lambda_2 = 4 \qquad \lambda_3 = 8 \qquad \lambda_4 = 20$$

Note: The answer will not be unique.

3.19. Find the lowest two natural frequencies by Holzer's method for the following torsional system

I_1	I_2	I_3	I_4	I_5	I_6	unit
200	10	10	10	10	40	lb-ft-sec^2

k_{12}	k_{23}	k_{34}	k_{45}	k_{56}	unit
1000	8000	8000	8000	4000	lb-ft

3.20. Draw the force-voltage and the force-current analogs of the mechanical systems shown.

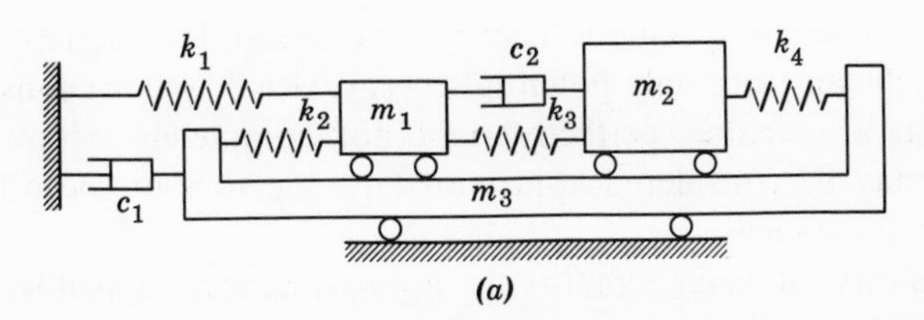

(a)

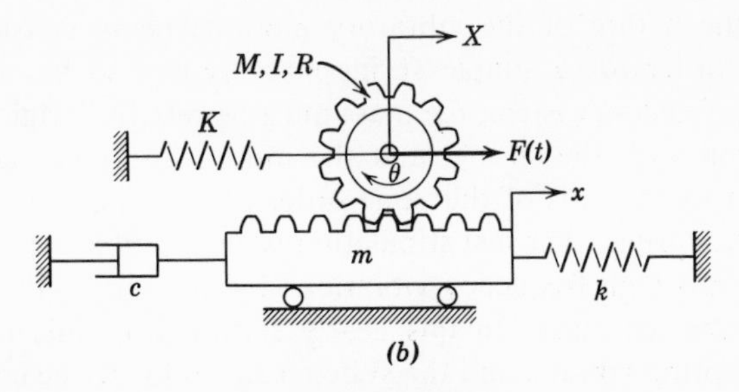

(b)

Exercise 3.20

CHAPTER 4

Vibration of Elastic Bodies

4.0 Introduction

Vibratory systems having a finite number of degrees of freedom are only idealized models of certain real systems. The essential property of such systems is that the inertia forces are those due to a finite number of rigid bodies, and the potential and dissipative forces are the interactions between pairs of these rigid bodies. We have, therefore, rigid bodies, which can store[1] only kinetic energy, and weightless bodies and force fields, which can store only potential energy. Real systems consist of real bodies that are neither perfectly rigid nor completely without inertia, but they may be considered approximately one way or the other under certain circumstances.

The validity of such simplifying approximations depends upon the relative rigidity and amount of mass in the different parts of the system as well as the nature of the vibratory motions being considered. For instance, in order for a simple spring-mass system to be considered a single-degree-freedom system, the mass must be relatively rigid and heavy in comparison with the spring, and the motion must be such that the amplitude of the mass is of the same order of magnitude as that of any portion of the spring. The last stipulation is necessary because the system may be set into high frequency vibrations by "stroking" the spring. In such vibrations the mass remains nearly stationary, while the different parts of the spring vibrate, and the system can no longer be considered as having only one degree of freedom.

[1] The concept of energy stored in bodies is sometimes convenient but cannot bear close scrutiny. The meaning of the word "stored" is not to be taken too literally in the present context.

In this chapter we discuss the vibration of elastic bodies, which cannot be considered as rigid or as without inertia. The configuration of the systems containing such bodies thus cannot be described by a finite number of generalized coordinates. The analysis of these systems is naturally more complex. The increased complexities, however, lie mostly with the mechanics of elastic deformation (theory of elasticity) and the mathematics of solving boundary-value problems. There are no general methods in dealing with these two aspects of the problem. On the other hand, the conceptual matters related to theory of vibration can be discussed by a general treatment. This treatment we shall emphasize. Complete solutions for a few simple problems are carried out as illustrations. With these examples it is hoped that the reader will have enough understanding to analyze more involved problems, once he has also acquired the necessary knowledge of the theory of elasticity and the necessary mathematical tools.

4.1 Coordinates and Constraints

In order to describe the configuration of an elastic body, it is necessary to specify the spatial location of every mass particle in the body. The most direct method of description is then to use the displacement of the particles as the coordinates. But the so-called mass particles in an elastic body are not discrete. They have a continuous distribution in space.[2] Therefore, it is not possible to label them by integer indices or to assign finite values for their masses.

Let x, y, and z be the Cartesian coordinates of a generic point P in an elastic body in static equilibrium. Let $\rho(x, y, z)$ be the mass density at P. A generic mass element $dm = \rho(x, y, z)\, dV$ then plays the role of a mass particle. Let u, v, and w be the three components of the displacement of this mass element from its equilibrium location. These components are both space and time dependent.

$$u = u(x, y, z, t)$$
$$v = v(x, y, z, t)$$
$$w = w(x, y, z, t)$$

These displacement functions[3] can be considered as the coordinates of the system. The space variables x, y, and z are used to designate the particular

[2] We are looking at things macroscopically, not microscopically.

[3] Those who have studied fluid dynamics should note that they furnish essentially the Lagrangian description of the motion of a deformable body.

element being considered. These variables play the role that was played by subscripts before.

Since there are infinitely many combinations of x, y, and z, each corresponding to a mass element, there are infinitely many degrees of freedom in the vibration of an elastic body. At first glance it appears that the number of degrees of freedom is not only infinite but noncountable, since the mass elements in a continuous medium are not countable.[4] This, we shall see, is not the case unless the body is infinite in extent. The question of countability is of interest because we have seen that with each degree of freedom there is associated a natural frequency. If the degrees of freedom are countable, the natural frequencies will be discrete; that is, we can list them in an infinite sequence $\omega_1, \omega_2, \ldots, \omega_n, \ldots$.

The coordinates u, v, and w, however, are not completely independent. They are subject to certain constraints. At the boundary where the body comes into contact with its support or with another medium the displacement functions are often subjected to certain restrictions, which are called *boundary conditions*. In the interior of the body other types of restrictions prevail, such as the requirement that the displacement function be continuous and differentiable a certain number of times with respect to space variables. Restrictions also arise out of assumptions. For instance, in specifying the deformed shape of a slender beam, we may assume that the points on a given cross section move together as a rigid plane.

Because of the different kinds of constraints described it is often possible to express a displacement function as the sum of an infinite series of given functions. For instance, in describing the shape of the elastic curve of a deflected beam simply supported at the ends, we may use the trigonometric series

$$w = \sum_{n=1}^{\infty} q_n \sin \frac{n\pi x}{L}$$

By specifying a set of values for the coefficients $q_1, q_2, \ldots, q_n, \ldots$, which are infinite but countable, the configuration of the beam is uniquely specified. Hence the set of q's may be considered as the generalized coordinates of the system. This method of describing the configurations of elastic bodies is important because it allows us to borrow the results from the analysis in Chapter 3.

---

[4] By "countable" or "denumerable" we mean that the set of things can be put into one-to-one correspondence with integers 0, 1, 2, 3, ... It can be shown, for instance, that rational numbers are countable, whereas the number of points on a line segment is not.

4.2 Formulation of a Problem by Differential Equation

The direct application of Newton's second law to a mass element results in

$$\rho \frac{\partial^2 u}{\partial t^2} dV = df_x$$

$$\rho \frac{\partial^2 v}{\partial t^2} dV = df_y$$

$$\rho \frac{\partial^2 w}{\partial t^2} dV = df_z \tag{1}$$

in which df_x, df_y, and df_z are elemental forces acting on the elemental volume dV. In free vibrations these are elastic forces caused by local deformations of the body. They are related to u, v, and w by the laws of elastic deformation, which relate forces to stresses, stresses to strains, and strains to displacements. General equations are available from theory of elasticity to express these forces in terms of displacements.[5] Since such general equations are seldom solved in practice, we shall dispense with the exact expressions here. It is sufficient to say that the equations are of the form

$$\rho \frac{\partial^2 u}{\partial t^2} = \mathsf{L}_x(u, v, w)$$

$$\rho \frac{\partial^2 v}{\partial t^2} = \mathsf{L}_y(u, v, w) \tag{2}$$

$$\rho \frac{\partial^2 w}{\partial t^2} = \mathsf{L}_z(u, v, w)$$

in which the L's are linear differential operators involving partial derivatives with respect to space variables of different orders.

$$\mathsf{L} = \mathsf{L}\left(\frac{\partial}{\partial x}, \frac{\partial}{\partial y}, \frac{\partial}{\partial z}, \text{elastic constants}\right)$$

It is to be noted that time t does not enter explicitly at the right-hand side.

The partial differential equations so obtained are merely statements of Newton's law of motion and Hooke's law of elastic deformation, with certain references to the mass distribution and elastic property of the material that makes up the elastic body. These equations are, however,

---

[5] These equations are associated with the name of Navier.

not specific enough to define a vibration problem. They must be supplemented by other conditions. The first set of conditions is called the *boundary conditions*, which describe how the elastic body is supported and how it comes into contact with other media along its boundary. Differential equations of motion, together with a set of boundary conditions, constitute a *boundary-value problem.* Such a problem specifies the types of vibratory motions a given elastic system may have. It is often *the* problem of practical interest. If, however, the problem is to find out how a given body actually vibrates, we shall also have to know how it was set into vibration to begin with. This information is furnished by so-called *initial conditions*, which specify the displacement and velocity distributions at a certain instant $t = t_0$.

Let us now illustrate the discussion with a few examples.

(A) LONGITUDINAL VIBRATION OF A SLENDER BAR AND MATHEMATICALLY ANALOGOUS VIBRATION PROBLEMS

During longitudinal vibration each elemental length of the bar undergoes compression and extension alternately. If the bar is relatively slender, the inertia forces in the transverse directions, due to the contraction and expansion of the cross sections, are negligible. The internal forces in the bar are then essentially axial. The stress-displacement relationship in a bar subjected only to axial forces is given by Hooke's law as

$$\sigma_x = E\epsilon_x = E\frac{\partial u}{\partial x} \tag{3}$$

in which the x-axis is parallel to the axis of the bar, and σ, ϵ, and E are the stress, strain, and Young's modulus, respectively (see Fig. 81).

Consider now the equilibrium condition for an elemental length of the bar between two cross sections spaced dx apart. Application of Newton's second law results in

$$\rho A\frac{\partial^2 u}{\partial t^2} = \frac{\partial}{\partial x}\left(EA\frac{\partial u}{\partial x}\right) \tag{4}$$

For bars with uniform cross sections the equation simplifies into

$$\frac{\partial^2 u}{\partial t^2} = \frac{E}{\rho}\frac{\partial^2 u}{\partial x^2} \tag{5}$$

Since there is only one space variable, namely x, the mathematical model of the bar has only two boundary points corresponding to the two ends of the bar.[6] Various boundary conditions are possible.

[6] The boundary of the physical body itself naturally is a surface having an infinite number of points. The mathematical model reduces the bar into a one-dimensional object.

At a fixed end the displacement is zero.

$$u = 0$$

At a free end the stress is zero.

$$\frac{\partial u}{\partial x} = 0$$

At an end at which a mass M is attached the inertia force of M and the elastic force at the end of the bar must be in equilibrium.

$$M \frac{\partial^2 u}{\partial t^2} + EA \frac{\partial u}{\partial x} = 0$$

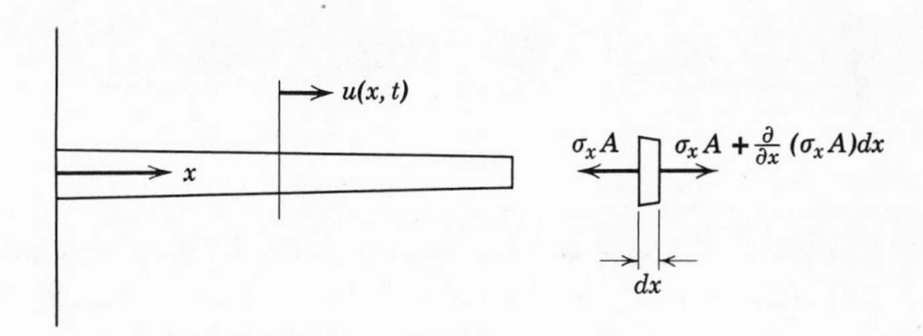

Figure 81

At an end at which a spring of constant K is attached, the two elastic forces must be in equilibrium.

$$Ku + EA \frac{\partial u}{\partial x} = 0$$

Each of these boundary conditions, when valid, is supposed to hold only for one particular value of x but for all values of t.

All of these boundary conditions are *linear homogeneous* because they contain only first power terms of the dependent variable u and its derivatives. The linear differential equation (4), and a set of linear boundary conditions together make the problem linear, and the superposition theorem holds; it is easy to see that if $u_1(x, t)$ and $u_2(x, t)$ are two solutions to the boundary-value problem, their linear combination $c_1u_1 + c_2u_2$ is also a solution.

The boundary condition of the first type $u = 0$ is described by the term "*imposed*" or "*geometrical*." The other types are called *natural* or *dynamical* boundary conditions. The significance of this differentiation is discussed in Art. 4.7(B).

The initial conditions needed to specify a particular solution of the vibration problem are of the form

$$u(x, 0) = f(x)$$

and

$$\left(\frac{\partial u}{\partial t}\right)_{t=0} = g(x)$$

These conditions are linear but not homogeneous, since the right-hand sides are not zero. The statement of the superposition theorem as applied to an initial-value problem appears in Art. 1.10.

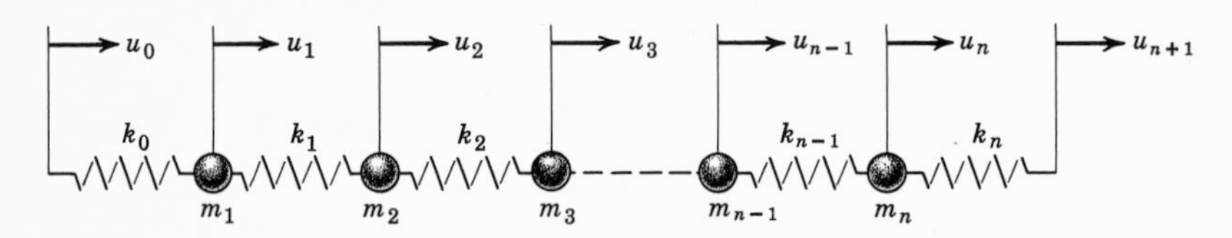

Figure 82

It is a worthwhile digression to compare the formulation of this problem with that of a similar problem in which the mass distribution is not continuous. Consider a system made up of n masses, $m_1, m_2, \ldots, m_n$, connected by $n + 1$ springs, $k_0, k_1, k_2, \ldots, k_n$, into a continuous chain. (Fig. 82.) If all the masses are constrained to move along a straight line, with $u_1, u_2, \ldots, u_n$ as their respective displacements, the equation of motion for the ith mass is

$$m_i \frac{d^2u_i}{dt^2} = k_i(u_{i+1} - u_i) - k_{i-1}(u_i - u_{i-1}) \qquad i = 1, 2, \cdots, n$$

In writing this general expression, u_0 and u_{n+1} are taken to be the displacements of the outer ends of the two end springs. To use the notation of difference equation, we set

$$\Delta u_i = u_{i+1} - u_i$$

$$\Delta u_{i-1} = u_i - u_{i-1}$$

$$\Delta(k_i \, \Delta u_i) = k_i \, \Delta u_i - k_{i-1} \, \Delta u_{i-1}$$

Hence the general expression becomes

$$m_i \frac{d^2u_i}{dt^2} = \Delta(k_i \, \Delta u_i) \qquad i = 1, 2, \cdots, n$$

If all the k's are equal, we have

$$\frac{d^2u_i}{dt^2} = \frac{k}{m_i}\,\Delta^2 u_i \qquad i = 1, 2, \cdots, n$$

These difference equations are "images" of the partial differential equations (4) and (5).

The description of this system, as given by the difference equations, is not complete without some reference to the two end springs which terminate

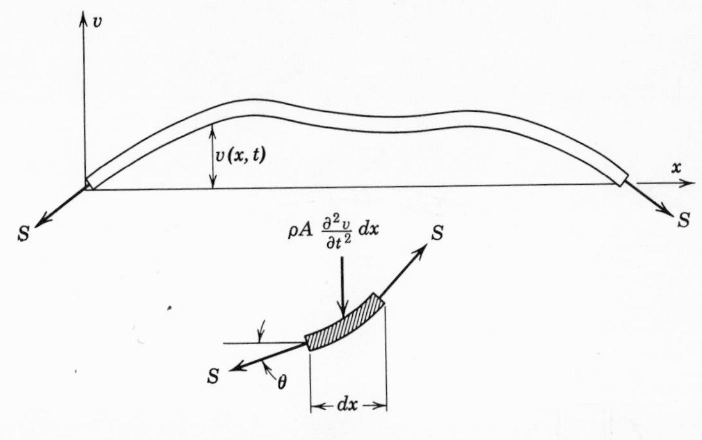

Figure 83

the chain. For instance, if one end of k_n is fastened to a fixed point, we must also specify that

$$u_{n+1} = 0$$

and, if one end of k_n is completely free,

$$u_{n+1} - u_n = \Delta u_n = 0$$

These conditions correspond to the boundary conditions of the partial differential equation.

Two other vibration phenomena have the same governing differential equation as the longitudinal vibration of a bar. The first is the *torsional vibration* of a shaft with a circular cross section. Let the axis of the shaft be in the x-direction and the rotation of a generic shaft cross section be denoted by

$$\theta = \theta(x, t)$$

The torsion formula states

$$\frac{\partial\theta}{\partial x} = \frac{M}{JG}$$

in which M is the torque, G the modulus of rigidity, and J the polar moment of inertia of the cross section. On the other hand, Newton's law of motion leads to

$$\rho J \frac{\partial^2 \theta}{\partial t^2} = \frac{\partial M}{\partial x}$$

Upon elimination of M, the resulting equation is

$$\rho J \frac{\partial^2 \theta}{\partial t^2} = \frac{\partial}{\partial x}\left(JG \frac{\partial \theta}{\partial x}\right)$$

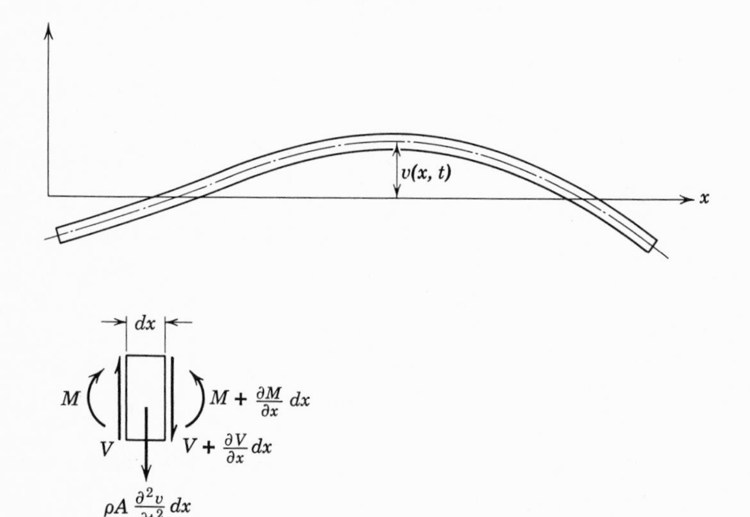

Figure 84

For shafts with uniform cross sections

$$\frac{\partial^2 \theta}{\partial t^2} = \frac{G}{\rho} \frac{\partial^2 \theta}{\partial x^2} \tag{6}$$

Except for interpretation of the symbols, these equations are identical to (4) and (5).

The second analogous phenomenon is the transverse vibration of a thin stretched string. Assume that the vibration is constrained within the xy-plane. The configuration of the string during vibration is described by (Fig. 83):

$$v = v(x, t)$$

with $v = 0$ being the equilibrium configuration. The force-acceleration relationship of an elemental length of the string in the y-direction is

$$\rho A \frac{\partial^2 v}{\partial t^2} dx = dS_y$$

in which S_y is the y-component of the tension S existing in the string. Neglecting second-order terms of $\partial v/\partial x$, we have

$$S_y = S \sin \theta \doteq S \frac{\partial v}{\partial x}$$

$$dS_y = \frac{\partial}{\partial x}\left(S \frac{\partial v}{\partial x}\right) dx$$

Hence

$$\rho A \frac{\partial^2 v}{\partial t^2} = \frac{\partial}{\partial x}\left(S \frac{\partial v}{\partial x}\right)$$

This is a nonlinear relation, as S depends also on v. However, if the initial tension is strong and vibration v small, S may be taken as a constant. We then have

$$\frac{\partial^2 v}{\partial t^2} = \frac{\sigma}{\rho} \frac{\partial^2 v}{\partial x^2}$$

where $\sigma = S/A$.

(B) LATERAL VIBRATION OF A SLENDER BAR

When a slender bar enters into a transverse vibration, the stress and strain distributions produced in the bar are approximately the kind described by the elementary theory of beam for static bending under lateral loads. That is to say, the inertia forces due to such things as shear strain and anticlastic deformation of the cross sections can be ignored.

Let us choose a *right-handed* coordinate system such that the x-axis is the centroidal axis of the bar and the xz-plane is the neutral plane of the bar during symmetrical bending. The deformed shape of the bar is then described by the equation of the so-called elastic curve, which lies in the xy-plane (Fig. 84):

$$v = v(x, t)$$

in which v is the displacement of points on the centroid axis from its unstressed position. For small deformation, the flexural formula states

$$EI \frac{\partial^2 v}{\partial x^2} = M \tag{7}$$

in which M is the internal bending moment and I is the moment of inertia of the cross section.[7] The elementary theory of bending states further that in the absence of externally applied moment

$$\frac{\partial M}{\partial x} = V = \text{internal shear} \tag{8}$$

and

$$\frac{\partial V}{\partial x} = f_y \tag{9}$$

in which f_y is the distribution of externally applied force in the y-direction.

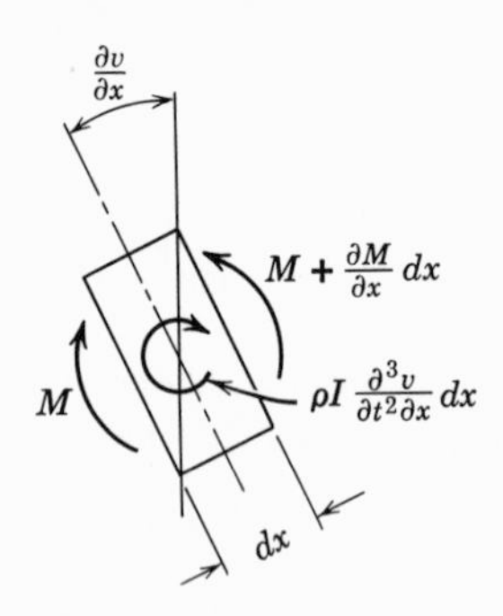

Figure 85

In a dynamics problem f_y is replaced by inertia force. Hence

$$-\rho A \frac{\partial^2 v}{\partial t^2} = \frac{\partial V}{\partial x} = \frac{\partial^2}{\partial x^2}\left(EI\frac{\partial^2 v}{\partial x^2}\right) \tag{10}$$

For bars with uniform cross sections we have

$$-\frac{\partial^2 v}{\partial t^2} = \frac{EI}{\rho A}\frac{\partial^4 v}{\partial x^4} \tag{11}$$

Let us insert a few remarks about our assumption of slenderness of the bar. In the deviation of (10) and (11) this assumption enters into a number of places. As a rough guide we may say that most of the results from elementary theory of bending are valid when the square of the depth-to-length ratio of a beam, $(c/L)^2$, is much less than one. This is so in static bending, where the applied loads are predominantly in one direction and

[7] The sign conventions used here for bending moments and shear are those commonly adopted by modern textbooks on strength of materials. It is also permissible to consider the sign conventions as being defined by (7) and (8).

the length of the beam enters as the distance between points of zero deflections or of zero moment. In vibratory motions, however, a beam may have deflections of the form ⌒ or of the form ∿∿ . Thus a given bar may be considered as slender in one kind of vibration but not in the other kind. The quantity L is therefore more appropriately interpreted as the "wavelength" of the deflected form during vibration.

If the ratio c/L is small but not altogether negligible, whereas $(c/L)^2$ is negligible, the equation of motion may be corrected for the inertia effect of the rotation of the cross sections. The correction begins with (8).

$$\frac{\partial M}{\partial x}\,dx = V\,dx - \text{moment of inertia force on } dx$$

or

$$\frac{\partial M}{\partial x}\,dx = V\,dx + \rho I\,\frac{\partial^2}{\partial t^2}\left(\frac{\partial v}{\partial x}\right)dx$$

Together with (7) and (9), this relation leads to

$$\frac{\partial^2}{\partial x^2}\left(EI\,\frac{\partial^2 v}{\partial x^2}\right) = -\rho A\,\frac{\partial^2 v}{\partial t^2} + \rho I\,\frac{\partial^4 v}{\partial t^2\,\partial x^2} \tag{12}$$

It is interesting to note that this equation is not in the general form of (2). The reason for this deviation is that in our scheme of describing the deformation of the bar we think of it as being made of elemental rigid slices, each having a translation v and a rotation $\partial v/\partial x$. Hence the displacement function v is not really the displacement of a generic mass element in the elastic body.

Depending on end conditions, appropriate boundary conditions must be prescribed. A few of the frequently encountered boundary conditions are as follows (Fig. 86):

At a fixed or built-in end,

$$v = 0 \qquad \text{and} \qquad \frac{\partial v}{\partial x} = 0$$

At a pinned end, where $M = 0$,

$$v = 0 \qquad \text{and} \qquad \frac{\partial^2 v}{\partial x^2} = 0$$

At a free end, where $M = 0$ and $V = 0$,

$$\frac{\partial^2 v}{\partial x^2} = 0 \qquad \text{and} \qquad \frac{\partial}{\partial x}\left(EI\,\frac{\partial^2 v}{\partial x^2}\right) = 0$$

Still other types of boundary conditions are possible. These are discussed in specific problems.

For this problem those boundary conditions involving *only* v and $\partial v/\partial x$, which describe the displacement and the slope at an end, are called imposed or geometrical; those involving $\partial^2 v/\partial x^2$ or $\partial^3 v/\partial x^3$, which describe the moment on shear at an end, are called natural or dynamic.

The initial conditions required to specify a particular solution of the vibratory motion are given by

$$v(x, t_0) = f(x)$$

$$\frac{\partial v}{\partial t}(x, t_0) = g(x)$$

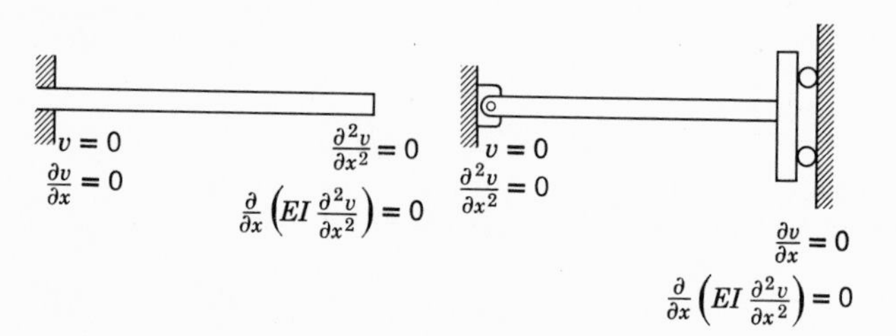

Figure 86

(c) VIBRATIONS OF STRETCHED ELASTIC MEMBRANES AND OF FLAT THIN PLATES

These problems are two-dimensional extensions of the problems for vibrating strings and beams. We shall not derive the differential equations of motion here, since what is involved in the derivations belongs to the theory of elasticity. It is not difficult, however, for readers to accept the following results.

For transverse vibration of a membrane lying in xy-plane when at rest the differential equation of motion is

$$\rho h \frac{\partial^2 w}{\partial t^2} = S\left(\frac{\partial^2}{\partial x^2} + \frac{\partial^2}{\partial y^2}\right) w = S\,\nabla^2 w \tag{13}$$

in which h is the thickness of the membrane and S is the surface tension in the membrane, which is assumed to be constant. For a membrane initially stretched to a constant surface tension the only boundary condition physically realizable is that

$$w = 0$$

on all boundary points. This equation, as well as its one-dimensional and three-dimensional counterparts, is called the *wave equation*. These equations are studied extensively in acoustics and in hydrodynamics. In other applications the boundary conditions may also contain normal derivative $\partial w/\partial n$, which is the rate of change of w along a direction normal to the boundary of the system.

The equation for the vibration of a thin plate is the two-dimensional extension of that for a beam. It reads

$$-\rho h \frac{\partial^2 w}{\partial t^2} = \left(\frac{\partial^2}{\partial x^2} + \frac{\partial^2}{\partial y^2}\right)\left[E'I'\left(\frac{\partial^2 w}{\partial x^2} + \frac{\partial^2 w}{\partial y^2}\right)\right] = \nabla^2(E'I'\nabla^2 w) \tag{14}$$

in which $E' = E/(1 - \nu^2)$, ν = Poisson's ratio, $I = h^3/12$, and h = plate thickness.

4.3 Separation of Time Variable from Space Variables—Reduction to Eigenvalue Problems

Most of the boundary-value and initial-value problems used for illustrations in Art. 4.2 can be solved under a number of circumstances. Before we get into the details of solving particular problems and thereby lose sight of the over-all picture, let us study our problem in general terms for a little while longer. Without losing too much generality, we do wish, however, to restrict the discussion to equations having only a single dependent variable,[8] which we shall call q in all cases.

All of the equations used for illustrations in Art. 4.2 can be put into the general form of

$$\mathsf{M}\ddot{q} + \mathsf{L}q = 0 \tag{15}$$

in which M and L are two linear differential operators involving only space variables x, y, and z, and the dots over the q represent partial differentiation with respect to time. For instance, in (12)

$$\mathsf{M} = \left(\rho A - \rho I \frac{\partial^2}{\partial x^2}\right)$$

$$\mathsf{L} = \frac{\partial^2}{\partial x^2}\left(EI \frac{\partial^2}{\partial x^2}\right)$$

and in (14)

$$\mathsf{M} = \rho h$$

$$\mathsf{L} = \nabla^2(E'I'\nabla^2)$$

[8] It is also possible to write a single vectorial equation to replace the three scalar equations in (2).

In form, at least, if in nothing else, (15) resembles (13) of Chapter 3. This resemblance gives us ideas about possible subsequent developments. As we recall, what we used to do in studying free vibrations was first to see if the system could vibrate in such a way that all the coordinates varied as a harmonic function of time. To this end we let

$$q_i(t) = r_i \cos(\omega t - \alpha)$$

Similarly, for the present problem, we may let

$$q(x, y, z, t) = r(x, y, z) \cos(\omega t - \alpha) \tag{16}$$

Introducing this assumption[9] into (15), we have

$$-\omega^2 \mathsf{M}r + \mathsf{L}r = 0 \tag{17}$$

This is a differential equation containing no t, just as the matrix equation (16) in Chapter 3 does not contain t. A more formal way of arriving at (17) is by a method called the *separation of variables*. Here we let

$$q = r(x, y, z)p(t) \tag{18}$$

and (15) becomes

$$\ddot{p}\,\mathsf{M}r + p\mathsf{L}r = 0$$

or

$$\frac{\mathsf{L}r}{\mathsf{M}r} = -\frac{\ddot{p}}{p} = \lambda$$

Since the first ratio cannot contain t and the second cannot contain x, y, z, neither ratio can contain any variable and λ must be a constant. Furthermore, it is not difficult to see that λ must be positive so that p will not be an exponential function that grows with time. Thus by setting $\lambda = \omega^2$, we have

$$\ddot{p} + \omega^2 p = 0$$

$$\mathsf{L}r = \omega^2 \mathsf{M}r \tag{19}$$

These two equations share in common only the parameter ω^2, whereas both the dependent variables and the independent variables in them are different. For every solution we can find for this pair we have a solution for the original equation (15). But the reverse is not true, since a solution of (15) may or may not be expressed in the form of (16) or (18). We can, however, entertain hopes that since ω^2 is yet undetermined there is more than one set of solutions for (19) and the totality of linear combinations of these solutions may include all the solutions of (15). This is again a

[9] For the time being the possibility of a solution in the form (16) is only an assumption yet to be proven.

situation similar to that encountered in Chapter 3, where a particular solution in free vibration is representable by a linear combination of principal modes.

So far the discussion has been centered around the differential equation of motion which does not by itself define a physical problem. The accessory conditions concerning the initial values and the boundary values must also be considered. Let us take up the boundary conditions first, since these are an integral part of the problem that defines the possible ways in which a system may vibrate. The boundary conditions can be expressed in the general form

$$\mathsf{N}(q) = 0$$

in which N is a linear differential operator of the space variables and sometimes also of the time variable t. If N does not contain t, the replacement of q by rp according to (18) will result in

$$\mathsf{N}(r) = 0$$

because $\mathsf{N}(q)$ is linear and homogeneous in q. If N contains t, it is because the boundary condition says something about an inertia force. In this case t enters only in the form of $\partial^2/\partial t^2$. Since

$$\frac{\partial^2}{\partial t^2} q = \ddot{p}r = -\omega^2 pr$$

if q is in the form of pr, the boundary $\mathsf{N}(q)$ leads to $\mathsf{N}'(r)$ where N' is obtained by replacing $\partial^2/\partial t^2$ in N with $-\omega^2$.

To recapitulate, we now have the problem of finding a function $r(x, y, z)$ that satisfies a linear homogeneous differential equation

$$\mathsf{L}(r) = \omega^2 \mathsf{M}(r)$$

and a set of linear homogeneous boundary conditions of the form

$$\mathsf{N}(r) = 0$$

where ω^2 is a parameter yet unspecified and N may or may not contain ω^2.

In many vibration problems in which M is merely a multiplication factor that can be incorporated in L, the differential equation simplifies into

$$\mathsf{L}(r) = \omega^2 r$$

In any event, the problem is markedly similar to the eigenvalue problem we dealt with in Chapter 3. We expect, and we shall find, that the situation is as follows:

(i) The problem has a nontrivial solution only when ω^2 takes on one of a set of values called *eigenvalues* ω_1^2, ω_2^2, ... To each eigenvalue is associated a solution $r_i(x, y, z)$ called the *eigenfunction* belonging to ω_i^2; together they describe the frequency and the deformation of a natural mode of vibration of an elastic body.

(ii) Since the degrees of freedom of an elastic body are infinite, there are infinitely many natural modes. All motions of a given elastic body in free vibration can be represented by a linear combination of its natural modes.

Let us now analyze a few of the simpler problems illustrated in Art. 4.2.

(A) LONGITUDINAL VIBRATION OF A SLENDER BAR OF UNIFORM CROSS SECTIONS WITH A CONCENTRATED MASS M ATTACHED TO ONE END WHILE BEING HELD AT THE OTHER END (FIG. 87).

The differential equation and its boundary conditions are

$$\frac{E}{\rho}\frac{\partial^2 u}{\partial x^2} - \frac{\partial^2 u}{\partial t^2} = 0$$

At $x = 0$,

$$u = 0$$

At $x = L$,

$$\frac{\partial^2 u}{\partial t^2} + \frac{EA}{M}\frac{\partial u}{\partial x} = 0 \tag{20}$$

Let μ be the ratio of the attached mass to the mass of the bar. Then

$$M = \mu\rho AL \qquad \frac{EA}{M} = \frac{E}{\mu L\rho}$$

The eigenvalue problem results from letting $u(x, t) = p(t)r(x)$:

$$\frac{d^2r}{dx^2} + \frac{\omega^2\rho}{E}r = 0 \tag{21}$$

and

$$r(0) = 0$$

$$r'(L) - \mu L\frac{\omega^2\rho}{E}r(L) = 0 \tag{22}$$

For simplicity let

$$\beta^2 = \frac{\omega^2\rho}{E}$$

The solution of (21) is evidently

$$r = D\cos\beta x + B\sin\beta x \tag{23}$$

To satisfy $r(0) = 0$, D must vanish and β (or ω) must be real. To satisfy the remaining boundary condition, we must have

$$B(\beta \cos \beta L - \mu L \beta^2 \sin \beta L) = 0$$

or

$$\mu \beta L = \cot \beta L \tag{24}$$

This equation in β (or ω) is the *frequency* or *characteristic equation* of the system. It is equivalent to the determinant equation in the matrix eigenvalue problem. The coefficient B in (23) is indeterminate. Without losing generality, it may be taken as unity.

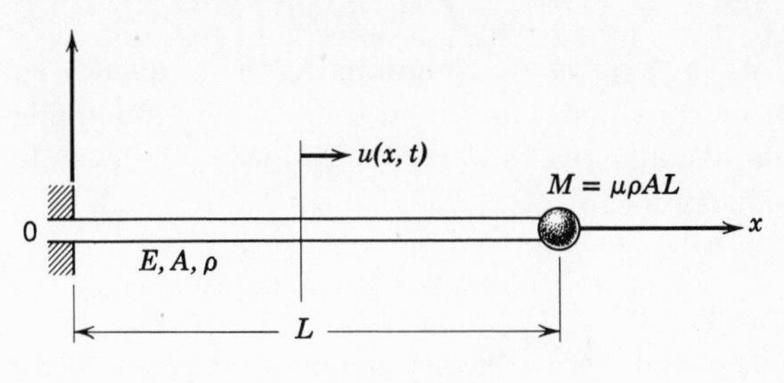

Figure 87

The equation (24), being transcendental in nature, has an infinite number of roots. The first few positive roots[10] for four values of μ are shown in the following tabulation:

	$\beta_1 L$	$\beta_2 L$	$\beta_3 L$	$\beta_4 L$	$\beta_5 L$	$\beta_6 L$
$\mu = 0$	$\pi/2$	$3\pi/2$	$5\pi/2$	$7\pi/2$	$9\pi/2$	$11\pi/2$
$\mu = \frac{1}{2}$	1.0769	3.6435	6.5789	9.6295	12.7223	15.8198
$\mu = 1$	0.9604	3.4348	6.4373	9.4258	12.6453	15.7712
$\mu = \infty$	0	π	2π	3π	4π	5π

The condition $\mu = 0$ corresponds to a free end at $x = L$. In this case $\beta_i = (2i - 1)\pi/2L$. The condition $\mu = \infty$ corresponds to a fixed end at $x = L$; there $\beta_i = (i - 1)\pi/L$. With the exception of these two extreme cases, the eigenvalues are not spaced regularly apart. But, for all $\mu > 0$, β_i approaches $(i - 1)\pi/L$ rather quickly. This is understandable, since the inertia force goes up with the square of frequency and at high frequencies the end mass becomes nearly immobile.

[10] The negative roots represent nothing new when put into (23).

Returning to the function p, we see that

$$\ddot{p} + \omega^2 p = 0$$

$$\omega^2 = \frac{\beta^2 E}{\rho}$$

Hence

$$p = C \cos (\omega t - \alpha)$$
$$= C \cos [\sqrt{(E/\rho)}\beta t - \alpha]$$

A typical solution to the boundary-value problem (20) is then

$$u(x, t) = r(x)p(t) = C \sin \beta x \cos [\sqrt{(E/\rho)}\beta t - \alpha]$$

in which β is any one of the solutions to the frequency equation (24). Since the problem is linear and homogeneous, by the application of the superposition theorem we obtain the following series solution to the boundary-value problem:

$$u(x, t) = \sum_{i=1}^{\infty} C_i \sin \beta_i x \cos [\sqrt{(E/\rho)}\beta_i t - \alpha_i] \tag{25}$$

The constants C and α are arbitrary as long as they produce a convergent series, and the function $u(x, t)$, so defined, is at least twice differentiable with respect to both x and t in the ranges[11] $0 < x < L$ and $t > 0$. With the freedom of choice in the C's and α's, we hope to be able to match the initial conditions of a given problem and to arrive at a particular solution.

Let the initial conditions be given by

$$u(x, 0) = f(x) \qquad \text{and} \qquad \left(\frac{\partial u}{\partial t}\right)_{t=0} = g(x)$$

If we know how to expand these two functions into two infinite series of eigenfunctions

$$\begin{aligned} u(x, 0) = f(x) &= \sum_{i=1}^{\infty} f_i \sin \beta_i x \\ \left(\frac{\partial u}{\partial t}\right)_{t=0} = g(x) &= \sum_{i=1}^{\infty} g_i \sin \beta_i x \end{aligned} \tag{26}$$

we can determine the constants in (25) by the coefficients f_i and g_i. By putting $t = 0$ in (25) and its derivative and comparing the results with (26), we have

$$\begin{aligned} C_i \cos \alpha_i &= f_i \\ \sqrt{(E/\rho)}\, \beta_i C_i \sin \alpha_i &= g_i \end{aligned} \tag{27}$$

[11] This differentiability requirement is a little more stringent than mathematically necessary.

For the special cases of $\mu = 0$ and $\mu = \infty$ the eigenvalues are spaced regularly apart; the two series in (26) are Fourier sine series and they can be obtained in the standard way. For other values of μ the series in (26) are no longer Fourier series in the ordinary sense of the term. The method of expanding given functions into infinite series of eigenfunctions is discussed in Art. 4.4.

(B) LATERAL VIBRATIONS OF BARS HAVING UNIFORM CROSS SECTIONS

The differential equation of motion as derived in the last article is

$$-\frac{\partial^2 v}{\partial t^2} = \frac{EI}{\rho A}\frac{\partial^4 v}{\partial x^4} \tag{28}$$

To separate the time variable from the space variable, we look again for solutions of the type

$$v(x, t) = p(t)r(x)$$

The substitution of pr for v results in two ordinary equations:

$$\ddot{p} + \omega^2 p = 0 \tag{29}$$

$$\frac{d^4 r}{dx^4} - \beta^4 r = 0 \tag{30}$$

in which

$$\beta^4 = \frac{\rho A \omega^2}{EI} \tag{31}$$

The solution for (30) is

$$r = A \sin \beta x + B \cos \beta x + C \sinh \beta x + D \cosh \beta x \tag{32}$$

The eigenvalue problem is now as follows:

Given a set of end conditions, determine the set of eigenvalues[12] of β so that the constants A, B, C, and D will not vanish together, and find the ratios $A:B:C:D$ corresponding to the eigenvalues.

Consider a cantilever beam which is fixed at one end and free at the other. The boundary values are (Fig. 88)

$$r(0) = 0 \qquad r'(0) = 0 \qquad r''(L) = 0 \qquad \text{and} \qquad r'''(L) = 0$$

in which L is the length of the beam. From the first two of these conditions we have

$$B + D = 0 \qquad \text{and} \qquad A + C = 0 \tag{33}$$

---

[12] It is immaterial whether we call β or ω the eigenvalue, since they are definitely related by (31).

From the last two conditions we have

$$-A \sin \beta L - B \cos \beta L + C \sinh \beta L + D \cosh \beta L = 0$$
$$-A \cos \beta L + B \sin \beta L + C \cosh \beta L + D \sinh \beta L = 0$$

or

$$\begin{aligned} C(\sin \beta L + \sinh \beta L) + D(\cos \beta L + \cosh \beta L) &= 0 \\ C(\cos \beta L + \cosh \beta L) + D(\sinh \beta L - \sin \beta L) &= 0 \end{aligned} \tag{34}$$

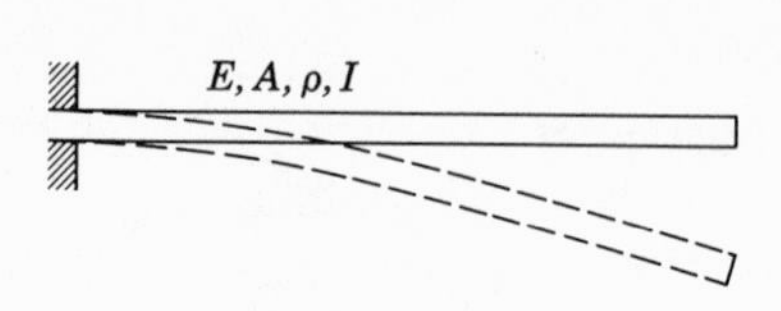

Figure 88

For nontrivial solutions the determinant formed by the coefficients of C and D must vanish. Hence

$$\begin{vmatrix} \sin \beta L + \sinh \beta L & \cos \beta L + \cosh \beta L \\ \cos \beta L + \cosh \beta L & \sinh \beta L - \sin \beta L \end{vmatrix} = 0$$

or

$$\cos \beta L \cosh \beta L = -1 \tag{35}$$

This is then the *characteristic or frequency* equation of the problem. It has an infinite number of solutions. The first six are

$\beta_1 L$	$\beta_2 L$	$\beta_3 L$	$\beta_4 L$	$\beta_5 L$	$\beta_6 L$
1.875	4.694	7.855	10.996	14.137	17.279

To each value of β there is an ω given by (31).

The eigenfunctions are obtained by substituting (33) and (34) into (32),

$$r(x) = \sinh \beta x - \sin \beta x + \gamma(\cosh \beta x - \cos \beta x) \tag{36}$$

where

$$\gamma = \frac{D}{C} = -\frac{\sinh \beta L + \sin \beta L}{\cosh \beta L + \cos \beta L}$$

We thus have a set of eigenvalues and eigenfunctions representing the frequencies and the shapes of the deformed bar of the natural modes.

Mathematically, because the boundary-value problem is linear and homogeneous, its general solution can be represented by an infinite series of the eigenfunctions that is convergent in the interval $0 < x < L$.

$$v(x, t) = \sum_{i=1}^{\infty} C_i \cos(\omega_i t - \alpha_i) r_i(x) \tag{37}$$

To find the particular solution under a given set of initial conditions,

$$v(x, 0) = f(x) \qquad \text{and} \qquad \dot{v}(x, 0) = g(x)$$

we first expand $f(x)$ and $g(x)$ into two infinite series of eigenfunctions.

$$f(x) = \sum_{i=1}^{\infty} f_i r_i(x)$$

$$g(x) = \sum_{i=1}^{\infty} g_i r_i(x) \tag{38}$$

Upon putting $t = 0$ in (37) and its derivative with respect to t, we have

$$f_i = C_i \cos \alpha_i$$
$$g_i = C_i \omega_i \sin \alpha_i \tag{39}$$

The solution for other end conditions can be obtained in the same manner. The reader should try his hand at verifying the following results:

(i) *Bars with hinged ends.*

$$r(0) = 0 \qquad r''(0) = 0 \qquad r(L) = 0 \qquad \text{and} \qquad r''(L) = 0$$

Frequency equation and eigenvalues:

$$\sin \beta L = 0 \qquad \beta L = \pi, 2\pi, 3\pi, \cdots$$

Eigenfunctions:

$$r(x) = \sin \beta x$$

(ii) *Bars with free ends.*

$$r''(0) = 0 \qquad r'''(0) = 0 \qquad r''(L) = 0 \qquad \text{and} \qquad r'''(L) = 0$$

Frequency equation and eigenvalues:

$$\cos \beta L \cosh \beta L = 1$$

$$\beta L = 0, 4.730, 7.853, 10.996, 14.137, 17.279$$

Eigenfunctions:

$$r(x) = \sinh \beta x + \sin \beta x + \gamma(\cosh \beta x + \cos \beta x)$$

$$\gamma = \frac{\sin \beta L - \sinh \beta L}{\cosh \beta L - \cos \beta L}$$

(iii) *Bars with fixed or built-in ends.*

$$r(0) = 0 \qquad r'(0) = 0 \qquad r(L) = 0 \qquad \text{and} \qquad r'(L) = 0$$

Frequency equation and eigenvalues: Same as (ii), except that $\beta L = 0$ has no physical significance.

Eigenfunctions:

$$r(x) = \sinh \beta x - \sin \beta x + \gamma(\cosh \beta x - \cos \beta x)$$

$$\gamma = \frac{\sinh \beta L - \sin \beta L}{\cos \beta L - \cosh \beta L}$$

(iv) *Bars with one built-in end and one hinged end.*

$$r(0) = 0 \qquad r'(0) = 0 \qquad r(L) = 0 \qquad \text{and} \qquad r''(L) = 0$$

Frequency equation and eigenvalues:

$$\tan \beta L = \tanh \beta L$$

$$\beta L = 3.927, 7.069, 10.210, 13.352, 16.493$$

Eigenfunctions:

$$r(x) = \sinh \beta x - \sin \beta x + \gamma(\cosh \beta x - \cos \beta x)$$

$$\gamma = \frac{\sinh \beta L - \sin \beta L}{\cos \beta L - \cosh \beta L}$$

(C) FREE VIBRATION OF A STRETCHED MEMBRANE

The differential equation of motion is given by (13) to be

$$\frac{\partial^2 w}{\partial^2 t} = \frac{S}{\rho h} \nabla^2 w$$

To separate the time-variable, we let

$$w = p(t) \cdot r(x, y)$$

$$= C \cos(\omega t - \alpha) r(x, y)$$

and obtain the partial differential equation for the eigenfunction

$$\nabla^2 r + \beta^2 r = 0 \tag{40}$$

where

$$\beta^2 = \frac{\rho h \omega^2}{S} \tag{41}$$

The original boundary condition $w = 0$ becomes $r = 0$ for (40).

This time, after t is separated, we are still left with a partial differential equation containing two space-variables. Except for numerical methods, there is no general way of solving a partial differential equation. Only when the boundary conditions are simple can the solution be expressed in terms of familiar functions—trigonometrical functions, exponential functions, or Bessel functions.[13] But whether or not a solution can be expressed simply, it has certain analytical properties. These we like to

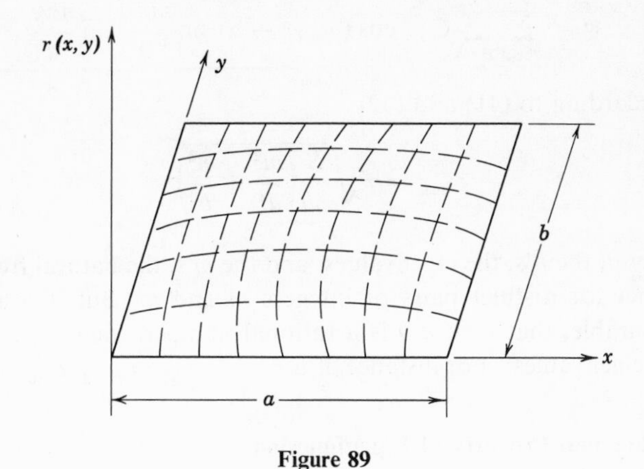

Figure 89

emphasize. To give an example of a solution to the boundary-value problem

$$\frac{\partial^2 r}{\partial x^2} + \frac{\partial^2 r}{\partial y^2} + \beta^2 r^2 = 0$$

with

$$r = 0 \text{ on the boundary}$$

let us consider the case of a rectangular membrane bounded by sides (Fig. 89).

$$x = 0 \qquad y = 0 \qquad x = a \qquad \text{and} \qquad y = b$$

For this problem we may again use the method of separation of the variable by trying to find a solution of the type

$$r(x, y) = X(x) \cdot Y(y)$$

Following a procedure similar to that used to separate t, we obtain

$$r(x, y) = \sin \frac{m\pi x}{a} \sin \frac{n\pi y}{b}$$

[13] This is understandable. After all, nature is capable of infinite varieties, whereas we have only a limited number of familiar functions.

and

$$\left(\frac{m}{a}\right)^2 + \left(\frac{n}{b}\right)^2 = \frac{\beta^2}{\pi^2} \tag{42}$$

in which m and n are positive integers. The eigenvalues for the problem are therefore *all* values of β that can be obtained from (42) by using *integers* for m and n. The complete solution is then the double series

$$w = \sum_{m=1}^{\infty} \sum_{n=1}^{\infty} C_{mn} \cos(\omega_{mn}t - \alpha) \sin\frac{m\pi x}{a} \sin\frac{n\pi y}{a}$$

where, according to (41) and (42)

$$\omega_{mn} = \pi\sqrt{\frac{S}{\rho h}\left(\frac{m^2}{a^2} + \frac{n^2}{b^2}\right)}$$

In general, the β's, the eigenvalues, and the ω's, the natural frequencies, are distinct for distinct pairs of integers m and n. But if a and b are commeasurable, that is, if a/b is a rational number, then there are some repeated eigenvalues, For instance, if $a/b = \frac{3}{2}$, $\omega_{34} = \omega_{62}$, $\omega_{36} = \omega_{92}$, etc.

4.4 Orthogonal Property of Eigenfunctions

We have seen in Art. 4.3 that in seeking a particular solution to a free vibration problem it is necessary to expand a given function that describes an initial condition into an infinite series of eigenfunctions. For this expansion process to be carried out in a simple way it is desirable that the eigenfunctions form an orthogonal set. For instance, it can be shown that the eigenfunctions of a vibrating cantilever beam obtained in Art. 4.3(B) satisfy

$$\int_0^L r_i r_j \, dx = 0 \qquad i \neq j \tag{43}$$

where $r(x)$ is defined by (36). With this established, the coefficients f_i and g_i in (38) and (39) can be obtained by the well-known procedure for the determination of the coefficients in a Fourier series. The principle is as follows: if $f(x)$ can be expanded into

$$f(x) = \sum_{j=1}^{n} f_j r_j(x)$$

then

$$r_i(x) f(x) = \sum_{j=1}^{n} f_j r_i(x) r_j(x)$$

By integrating both sides over the interval 0 to L and utilizing (43), we have

$$\int_0^L f(x) r_i(x)\, dx = f_i \int_0^L [r_i(x)]^2\, dx$$

In this way f_i is found. By finding g_i in the same way, the coefficient C_i and the angle α_i in (37) can be determined through (39).

On the other hand, the eigenfunctions in Art. 4.3(A) are not orthogonal in the sense of (43), except when $\mu = 0$ or ∞. Thus the same procedure cannot be used without alteration to find the constants in (25) and (26). The treatment of this case is taken up later.

Although it is possible to investigate the orthogonality of the eigenfunctions for each case, it is much better to begin with a general discussion. For this purpose let us return to Chapter 3, where we were dealing with eigenvalue problems of the matrix equation:

$$\mathbf{C}\,\mathbf{r} = \lambda \mathbf{A}\,\mathbf{r}$$

We showed in Art. 3.5(B) that the eigenvectors have the property that

$$\left.\begin{aligned} \bar{\mathbf{r}}^{(i)}\, \mathbf{C}\, \mathbf{r}^{(j)} &= 0 \\ \bar{\mathbf{r}}^{(i)}\, \mathbf{A}\, \mathbf{r}^{(j)} &= 0 \end{aligned}\right\} \text{ when } \lambda_i \neq \lambda_j$$

In the special case in which $\mathbf{A}$ or $\mathbf{C}$ is a scalar matrix we have [see Art. 3.12(B)]

$$\bar{\mathbf{r}}^{(i)}\, \mathbf{r}^{(j)} = 0$$

Here we are dealing with differential equations of the form

$$\mathsf{L}(r) = \lambda \mathsf{M}(r) \tag{44}$$

The corresponding orthogonal relations to be investigated are

$$\left.\begin{aligned} \int_\Sigma r_i \mathsf{L}(r_j)\, d\sigma &= 0 \\ \int_\Sigma r_i \mathsf{M}(r_j)\, d\sigma &= 0 \end{aligned}\right\} \text{ when } \lambda_i \neq \lambda_j \tag{45}$$

where the integration is over the domain Σ occupied by the elastic body. Note that the orthogonal relation for vectors involves a finite summation process, whereas for functions it involves an integration process.

Let us recall that in Art. 3.5(B) the orthogonal relation for eigenvectors is established upon the facts that the eigenvalues are distinct and that for any two vectors $\mathbf{u}$ and $\mathbf{v}$ the symmetry of the matrices $\mathbf{A}$ and $\mathbf{C}$ leads to

$$\bar{\mathbf{u}}\,(\mathbf{A}\mathbf{v}) = \bar{\mathbf{v}}\,(\mathbf{A}\,\mathbf{u})$$

and

$$\bar{\mathbf{u}}\,(\mathbf{C}\,\mathbf{v}) = \bar{\mathbf{v}}\,(\mathbf{C}\,\mathbf{u})$$

For our present problem we have a similar situation. Two eigenfunctions having different eigenvalues will satisfy (45) if the differential operators L and M, together with the boundary conditions, are such that for *any* two functions u and v *satisfying the boundary conditions* and certain continuity and differentiability requirements the following relationships hold:

$$\begin{aligned}\int_\Sigma u\mathsf{L}(v)\,d\sigma &= \int_\Sigma v\mathsf{L}(u)\,d\sigma\\ \int_\Sigma u\mathsf{M}(v)\,d\sigma &= \int_\Sigma v\mathsf{M}(u)\,d\sigma\end{aligned} \tag{46}$$

In mathematical terminology we call a boundary-value problem *self-adjoint* when the foregoing relations are satisfied. To prove that the eigenfunctions of a self-adjoint boundary-value problem satisfy the orthogonal relations, as defined by (45), we need only to follow the same steps displayed in Art. 3.5(B). Since eigenfunctions satisfy (44),

$$\mathsf{L}r_i = \lambda_i\mathsf{M}r_i \qquad \text{or} \qquad r_j\mathsf{L}r_i = \lambda_i r_j\mathsf{M}r_i$$

and

$$\mathsf{L}r_j = \lambda_j\mathsf{M}r_j \qquad \text{or} \qquad r_i\mathsf{L}r_j = \lambda_j r_i\mathsf{M}r_j$$

Hence

$$\int_\Sigma (r_j\mathsf{L}r_i - r_i\mathsf{L}r_j)\,d\sigma = \int_\Sigma (\lambda_i r_j\mathsf{M}r_i - \lambda_j r_i\mathsf{M}r_j)\,d\sigma$$

Because of (46), the left-hand side is zero and the right-hand side can be simplified by factoring. The result is

$$0 = (\lambda_i - \lambda_j)\int_\Sigma r_i\,\mathsf{M}r_j\,d\sigma$$

If $\lambda_i \neq \lambda_j$ whenever $i \neq j$,

$$\int_\Sigma r_i\mathsf{M}r_j\,d\sigma = \int_\Sigma r_j\mathsf{M}r_i\,d\sigma = 0$$

and

$$\int_\Sigma r_i\mathsf{L}r_j\,d\sigma = \int_\Sigma r_j\mathsf{L}r_i\,d\sigma = 0$$

The validity of (46) depends upon the nature of the operators L and M, as well as the boundary conditions of the problem. In the remaining part of this article we shall examine the existence of orthogonality among the eigenfunctions for the systems analyzed in Art. 4.3 by investigating the validity of (46) when applied to the differential operators in these problems.

The differential equations studied in (A) and (B) of Art. 4.3 can be put into the general form of

$$\frac{d^n}{dx^n}\left(k\frac{d^n}{dx^n}r\right) = (-1)^n m\omega^2 r$$

where (47)

$$m(x) = \rho(x)A(x)$$

When $n = 1$, this equation governs the eigenfunction for longitudinal vibrations of bars, lateral vibrations of a stretched string, and torsional vibrations of shafts. When $n = 2$, it governs lateral vibrations of slender bars. The parameters k and m represent the stiffness distribution and the mass distribution, respectively, along the bar, the shaft, or the beam. In general, these parameters are functions of x, but frequently they are constants. In the latter case the equation simplifies into

$$\frac{d^{2n}}{dx^{2n}}r = (-1)^n\beta^{2n}r \tag{48}$$

where

$$\beta^{2n} = \frac{m\omega^2}{k}$$

Referring to our previous notation, we see that the two differential operators L and M are

$$\mathsf{L} = \frac{d^n}{dx^n}\left[k\frac{d^n}{dx^n}\right] = \mathsf{D}^n[k(x)\mathsf{D}^n] \tag{49}$$

and

$$\mathsf{M} = m(x)$$

where D stands for d/dx.

Since the operation by M is merely a multiplication by a function $m(x)$, it is obvious that the second of the two equations in (46) is automatically satisfied. We must concentrate now only on establishing the first equation. Let us take the boundary of the system to be at $x = 0$ and $x = L$.

Case 1. $\mathsf{L} = \mathsf{D}(k\mathsf{D})$

For this case (47) becomes

$$\frac{d}{dx}\left(k\frac{dr}{dx}\right) = -m\omega^2 r$$

Or more simply

$$(kr')' = -m\omega^2 r$$

The group of vibrational phenomena governed by this equation is discussed in Art. 4.2(A). The difference between the two sides of the equations in (46) is then

$$\int_0^L [u\mathsf{L}(v) - v\mathsf{L}(u)]\, dx = \int_0^L [u(kv')' - v(ku')']\, dx$$

Through integration by parts, we obtain

$$\int_0^L [u\mathsf{L}(v) - v\mathsf{L}(u)]\, dx = [ukv' - vku']_0^L \tag{50}$$

If the boundary conditions are such that any two continuous and differentiable functions u and v satisfying them will make the right-hand side of (50) vanish, then the problem is self-adjoint, and its eigenfunctions are *mutually orthogonal in the sense of* (45), provided that the eigenvalues are distinct. In other words, if

$$[r_i(kr_j') - r_j(kr_i')]_0^L = 0 \tag{51}$$

it follows that

$$\int_0^L r_i\mathsf{L}(r_j)\, dx = \int_0^L r_i(x)[k(x)r_j'(x)]'\, dx = 0 \qquad i \neq j$$

and

$$\int_0^L r_i\,\mathsf{M}(r_j)\, dx = \int_0^L -m(x)r_i(x)r_j(x)\, dx = 0 \qquad i \neq j \tag{52}$$

The second of the two conditions is the one we need for the expansion of a given function into an infinite series of eigenfunctions.

Let us now examine the boundary conditions for which (51) is valid. It can be shown by simple substitution that if the two boundary conditions are both of the linear homogeneous form

$$ar + br' = 0 \tag{53}$$

then (51) is always satisfied. In (53) the coefficients a and b may have different values at different boundary points but they must not depend on the eigenvalues of the problem. Take the case of longitudinal vibrations of bars as an illustration. The general form (53) includes such common end conditions as

(i) fixed end $r = 0$
(ii) free end $r' = 0$
(iii) end terminating in an elastic spring, K,

$$EA\frac{\partial u}{\partial x} = Ku$$

or

$$r' - \frac{K}{EA}r = 0$$

When the condition at each end of a bar belongs to one of the three kinds described, the eigenfunctions are orthogonal to one another *with respect to the weighting function* $m(x)$.

$$\int_0^L m(x) r_i(x) r_j(x)\, dx = 0 \qquad i \neq j \tag{54}$$

The weighting function $m(x)$ is the mass distribution along the bar

$$m(x) = \rho(x) A(x)$$

For homogeneous bars with uniform cross sections m is a constant, and we have the ordinary orthogonal relation

$$\int_0^L r_i(x) r_j(x)\, dx = 0 \qquad i \neq j \tag{55}$$

Let the expansion of a given function $f(x)$ into a series of eigenfunctions satisfying (54) be

$$f(x) = \sum_{i=1}^{\infty} f_i r_i(x)$$

The coefficients f can be found by

$$\int_0^L m(x) r_i(x) f(x)\, dx = f_i \int_0^L m(x)[r_i(x)]^2\, dx \tag{56}$$

or

$$f_i = \frac{\displaystyle\int_0^L m(x) r_i(x) f(x)\, dx}{\displaystyle\int_0^L m(x)[r_i(x)]^2\, dx} \tag{57}$$

Let us now return to problem of Art. 4.3(A), in which one end of the bar terminates in a concentrated mass M. The boundary condition at such an end is given by (22) as

$$r' - \frac{\mu L \rho}{E} \omega^2 r = 0$$

Even though this boundary condition is linear and homogeneous, it does not belong to the type described by (53) because the second coefficient contains ω, which is not the same for all eigenfunctions. Therefore, the eigenfunctions in this problem $\sin \beta_i x$, in which β_i are the roots of (24), do not satisfy (55). In other words,

$$\int_0^L \sin \beta_i x \sin \beta_j x\, dx \neq 0$$

This lack of orthogonality not only causes difficulty in the finding of the coefficients f_i and g_i in (26) but also invalidates a number of important analytical results based on the orthogonality or eigenfunctions. Fortunately, by interpreting the problem in a different way, the desired property of orthogonality can be preserved. Let us observe that in the initial formulation of the problem a bar of uniform mass distribution is *the* vibrating elastic body under consideration, whereas the existence of an attached concentrated mass M enters into the problem only as a boundary

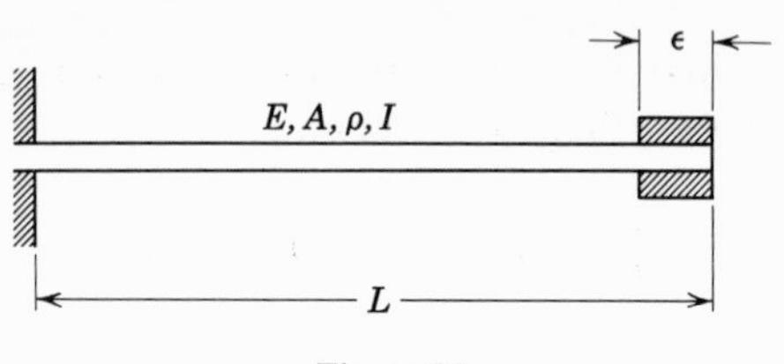

Figure 90

condition. The mass distribution of the system is therefore considered uniform as given by

$$m(x) = \rho A = \text{constant}$$

We can, however, reformulate the problem by considering the concentrated mass as a part of the vibrating bar, which will then have a free end. Suppose at first we redistribute the concentrated mass uniformly along a small portion of the bar near the right end of length ϵ. The right end is then free (Fig. 90). Let the eigenfunctions for this mass distribution be denoted by

$$\phi_i(\epsilon, x) \qquad i = 1, 2, \cdots$$

in which ϵ serves as a parameter. By physical reasoning,

$$\lim_{\epsilon \to 0} \phi_i(\epsilon, x) = \sin \beta_i x$$

since a concentrated mass is the limiting case of a finite mass distributed over an infinitesimal region. In the meantime the eigenfunctions are orthogonal with respect to the modified mass distribution function $m(\epsilon, x)$

$$\int_0^L m(\epsilon, x)\phi_i(\epsilon, x)\phi_j(\epsilon, x)\, dx = 0 \qquad i \neq j \tag{58}$$

where

$$m(\epsilon, x) = \rho A \qquad 0 < x < L - \epsilon$$

$$m(\epsilon, x) = \rho A + \mu\rho AL/\epsilon \qquad (L - \epsilon) \leq x < L$$

Because of (58), we can apply (57) and take the limit as $\epsilon \to 0$. Consider the numerator of (57) first.

$$\int_0^L m(\epsilon, x)\phi_i(\epsilon, x) f(x)\, dx$$
$$= \rho A\left[\int_0^{L-\epsilon} \phi_i(\epsilon, x) f(x)\, dx + \left(1 + \frac{\mu L}{\epsilon}\right)\int_{L-\epsilon}^{L} \phi_i(\epsilon, x) f(x)\, dx\right]$$

For sufficiently small ϵ the integrand in the second integral must be continuous. Hence we may use mean-value theorem to obtain

$$\int_0^L m(\epsilon, x)\phi_i(\epsilon, x) f(x)\, dx$$
$$= \rho A\left[\int_0^{L-\epsilon} \phi_i(\epsilon, x) f(x)\, dx + (\epsilon + \mu L)\phi_i(\epsilon, \xi) f(\xi)\right]$$

where $L - \epsilon \leq \xi \leq L$.

Hence[14]

$$\lim_{\epsilon \to 0} \int_0^L m(\epsilon, x)\phi_i(\epsilon, x) f(x)\, dx$$
$$= \rho A\left[\int_0^L \sin \beta_i x\, f(x)\, dx + \mu L \sin \beta_i L\, f(L)\right]$$

Similarly

$$\lim_{\epsilon \to 0} \int_0^L m(\epsilon, x)[\phi_i(\epsilon, x)]^2\, dx$$
$$= \rho A\left(\int_0^L \sin^2 \beta_i x\, dx + \mu L \sin^2 \beta_i L\right)$$

The result is

$$f_i = \frac{\displaystyle\int_0^L \sin \beta_i x\, f(x)\, dx + \mu L \sin \beta_i L\, f(L)}{\displaystyle\int_0^L \sin^2 \beta_i x\, dx + \mu L \sin^2 \beta_i L}$$

Although the formula just derived is for a concentrated mass at one end of a uniform bar, the principle behind the derivation is applicable whenever concentrated masses produce eigenfunctions not orthogonal in the ordinary sense. Mathematically speaking, the mass distribution function $m(x)$ in the general formulation of the problem described by (2) is allowed to behave like Dirac's δ-function, with singularities at a finite number of points, yet bounded elsewhere and integrable over the domain occupied

[14] We are using a convergence theorem, attributed to Lesbeque, which permits the passing of the limit sign from the outside to the inside of the integral.

by the system. When the existence of concentrated masses is treated in this way the eigenfunctions are again mutually orthogonal with respect to this modified density function.

Another broad implication of the example studied is that, although in a differential equation formulation of a dynamics problem we may be forced to define the boundary of our systems in such a way that no concentrated forces may appear at the interior points in formulations by integral equations or energy equations, such restrictions may not be needed. This aspect of the problem is to be amplified later.

Case 2. $\mathsf{L} = \mathsf{D}^2 (k\mathsf{D}^2)$

Having studied the case of $n = 1$ in (49), we can now follow the same procedure for $n = 2$. This case pertains to the lateral vibration of bars or beams. The eigenvalue problem is embodied in the differential equation

$$\frac{d^2}{dx^2}\left(k\,\frac{d^2}{dx^2}r\right) = m\omega^2 r$$

or

$$(kr'')'' = m\omega^2 r$$

where $k(x) = EI =$ bending stiffness of cross sections
$m(x) = \rho A =$ mass distribution along the bar

The parameters E, I, A, and ρ may be constants or variables. The next thing is to investigate the conditions under which the first equation of (46) is valid. The second one is obviously valid. Again, through integration by parts, we have

$$\begin{aligned}\int_0^L u\mathsf{L}(v)\,dx &= \int_0^L u(kv'')''\,dx = [u(kv'')']_0^L - \int_0^L u'(kv'')'\,dx \\ &= [u(kv'')' - u'(kv'')]_0^L + \int_0^L u''kv''\,dx \end{aligned} \tag{59}$$

Similarly,

$$\int_0^L v\mathsf{L}(u)\,dx = [v(ku'')' - v'(ku'')]_0^L + \int_0^L v''ku''\,dx$$

Since the integrals at the right-hand sides of the two equations are the same, the difference between the left-hand sides is

$$\int_0^L [u\mathsf{L}(v) - v\mathsf{L}(u)]\,dx = [u(kv'')' - v(ku'')' - u'kv'' + v'ku'']_0^L \tag{60}$$

Again the boundary conditions of the problem will determine whether it is self-adjoint and its eigenfunctions, mutually orthogonal. The physical meaning of the terms at the right-hand side of (60) should now be reviewed.

It is seen that

$$
\begin{aligned}
u, v &= \text{deflections at the ends} \\
u', v' &= \text{slopes at the ends} \\
ku'', kv'' &= \text{bending moments at the ends} \\
(ku'')', (kv'') &= \text{shear forces at the ends}
\end{aligned}
$$

Therefore, for any of the following simple end conditions each of the four terms at the right-hand side of (60) vanishes individually. (See Fig. 86.)

$$
\begin{array}{lcc}
\text{At built-in ends} & r = 0 & r' = 0 \\
\text{At pinned ends} & r = 0 & kr'' = 0 \\
\text{At free ends} & kr'' = 0 & (kr'')' = 0
\end{array}
\tag{61}
$$

A more general way whereby (60) will vanish is that each end condition is a linear homogeneous relationship either between the deflection and the shear or between the slope and moment. Analytically, it means that at each end there is a set of constants a, b, c, and d such that the boundary conditions may be expressed by

$$
ar + b(kr'')' = 0
$$

and

$$
cr' + d(kr'') = 0 \tag{62}
$$

The conditions stated by (61) are special cases of (62). The reader can verify that if u and v satisfy (62), then (60) vanishes. Physically, in the most general case (62) represents the end conditions when the ends are elastically supported. The stiffness of the support may be zero or infinite.

Sometimes a bar terminates in a concentrated mass. At such an end the linear relationship between the deflection and shear depends upon frequency. The orthogonal relation among the eigenfunctions will then have to be modified in the manner already discussed. The result is

$$
\int_0^L m(x)r_i(x)r_j(x)\,dx + Mr_i(L)r_j(L) = 0 \qquad i \neq j
$$

where M is the concentrated mass at $x = L$.

Case 3. $\mathsf{L} = \nabla^2$

The two-dimensional wave equation (13), after separation of time variable t, reduces into

$$
\nabla^2 r = -\omega^2 kr
$$

where

$$
k(x, y) = \rho h/S
$$

The integral to be examined this time is

$$\int_A (u\,\nabla^2 v - v\,\nabla^2 u)\,dA \tag{63}$$

This integral is over a *two-dimensional* region A. Our previous technique of integration by parts cannot be used here, but there is a procedure that is entirely equivalent. This procedure is best described with notations in vector analysis. It is known that the Laplacian operator ∇^2 is the divergence of a gradient

$$\nabla^2 = \text{div}\,(\text{grad}) = \nabla \cdot \nabla$$

Hence

$$u\,\nabla^2 v = u\nabla \cdot (\nabla v) = \nabla \cdot [u(\nabla v)] - (\nabla u) \cdot (\nabla v)$$

Similarly,

$$v\,\nabla^2 u = \nabla \cdot [v(\nabla u)] - (\nabla v) \cdot (\nabla u)$$

Substituting into (63), we have

$$\int_A (u\,\nabla^2 v - v\,\nabla^2 u)\,dA = \int_A \nabla \cdot [u(\nabla v) - v(\nabla u)]\,dA$$

Now we apply *divergence theorem* to the right-hand side and obtain the statement of *Green's theorem.*

$$\int_A (u\,\nabla^2 v - v\,\nabla^2 u)\,dA = \oint_C [u(\nabla v) - v(\nabla u)] \cdot d\vec{s}$$

The right-hand side is a contour integral around C, which is the boundary of A. It can also be written as

$$\int_A (u\,\nabla^2 v - v\,\nabla^2 u)\,dA = \oint_C \left(u\frac{\partial v}{\partial n} - v\frac{\partial u}{\partial n}\right) ds \tag{64}$$

in which $\partial/\partial n$ stands for "the normal derivative of" at the boundary. Hence, if the boundary condition of the problem is either

$$r = 0 \text{ on } C$$

or

$$\frac{\partial r}{\partial n} = 0 \text{ on } C$$

then (64) vanishes and the eigenfunctions with distinct eigenvalues are orthogonal in the sense that

$$\iint_A k(x, y) r_i(x, y) r_j(x, y)\,dx\,dy = 0 \tag{65}$$

$$\omega_i \neq \omega_j$$

The special case of two different eigenfunctions with the same eigenvalue can be handled by a principle similar to that used in Art. 3.10. If r_i and r_j are two independent eigenfunctions with the same eigenvalue and they are not orthogonal to each other in the sense of (65), it is possible to replace one of the two functions by a certain linear combination of the two functions, which is also an eigenfunction and satisfies (65). We shall not go into the details of finding this combination. After all, the situation is highly pathological because a very small change in the system will separate the eigenvalues and result in two orthogonal eigenfunctions.

Case 4. $\mathsf{L} = \nabla^2(k\nabla^2)$

Having gone through three similar cases and a general discussion, we shall simply give a key derivation for this case. The reader can easily fill in the rest of the details if he wishes.

By formulas in vector analysis

$$u\nabla^2(k\,\nabla^2 v) = \nabla\cdot[u\nabla(k\,\nabla^2 v)] - \nabla u\cdot\nabla(k\,\nabla^2 v)$$

and

$$\nabla u\cdot\nabla(k\,\nabla^2 v) = \nabla\cdot[k\,\nabla^2 v(\nabla u)] - k\,\nabla^2 v\,\nabla^2 u$$

Hence

$$\int_A [u\nabla^2(k\,\nabla^2 v) - v\nabla^2(k\,\nabla^2 u)]\,dA$$

$$= \int_A \nabla\cdot[u\nabla(k\,\nabla^2 v) - k\,\nabla^2 v(\nabla u) - v\nabla(k\,\nabla^2 u) + k\,\nabla^2 u(\nabla v)]\,dA$$

$$= \oint_C \left[u\frac{\partial}{\partial n}(k\,\nabla^2 v) - k\,\nabla^2 v\frac{\partial u}{\partial n} - v\frac{\partial}{\partial n}(k\,\nabla^2 u) + k\,\nabla^2 u\frac{\partial v}{\partial n}\right] ds$$

The problem is self-adjoint if this integral around the boundary vanishes.

4.5 Formulation by Integral Equation

In Chapter 3 we showed that equations of motion can be written with either the elastic constants or the influence coefficients for positive-definite systems. The matrix operators formed by the influence coefficient is the inverse of that formed by the elastic constants, and vice versa. Hence from

$$\mathbf{C}\,\mathbf{r} = \omega^2\mathbf{A}\,\mathbf{r}$$

we can obtain the equations by influence coefficients with an inverse operation.

$$\mathbf{C}^{-1}\,\mathbf{A}\,\mathbf{r} = \frac{1}{\omega^2}\,\mathbf{r}$$

We expect that similar inverse operations may exist for the differential operators being studied. That is, for

$$\mathsf{L}r = \omega^2 \mathsf{M}r \tag{66}$$

there is an equivalent relation written as

$$\mathsf{L}^{-1}\ \mathsf{M}r = \frac{1}{\omega^2}\, r$$

Since L is a differential operator, L^{-1} must denote an operation involving an integration process. To find the nature of this inverse operation, we have chosen to approach it on the basis of the physics of the problem rather than to discuss it as a purely mathematical theorem. (See Exercise 4.16.)

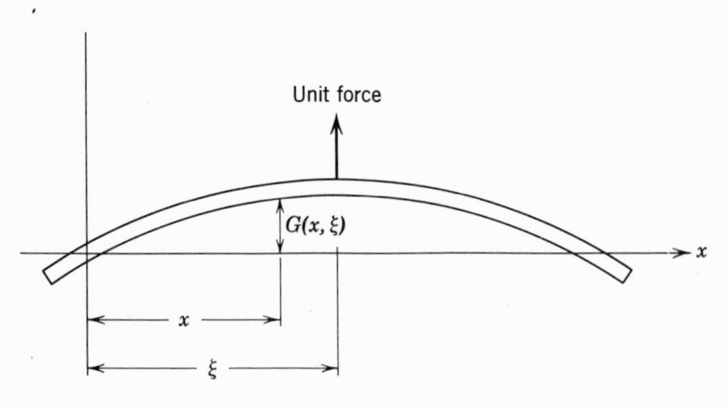

Figure 91

Consider for example the lateral vibration of a bar supported in some way. (Fig. 91). From the way the bar is supported (boundary conditions) and from its dimensions and make-up (operator L) we can find the influence coefficient between any pair of interior points in the bar. The influence coefficient for a given system is therefore a function of two points, which in the case of a slender bar are designated by two variables, say, the distances of the two points from the left end, x and ξ. In mathematics this function is called *Green's function* and is denoted by the symbol $G(x, \xi)$. For linear systems Maxwell's reciprocal theorem states that

$$G(x, \xi) = G(\xi, x)$$

or that Green's function for a linear system is symmetrical.

Let us now assume that the bar is vibrating in one of its natural modes. The displacement along the bar is then described by

$$v(x, t) = Cr(x) \cos(\omega t - \alpha)$$

The inertia forces acting on the bar have the distribution

$$-m(x)\frac{\partial^2 v}{\partial t^2} = C\omega^2 r(x)\cos(\omega t - \alpha)\cdot m(x) \tag{67}$$

where

$$m(x) = \rho(x)A(x)$$

The relation between the inertia forces on the bar and the displacement at a generic section x is then

$$v(x, t) = \int_0^L -G(x, \xi)m(\xi)\frac{\partial^2}{\partial t^2}v(\xi, t)\,d\xi$$

Or, after elimination of $\cos(\omega t - \alpha)$,

$$\int_0^L G(x, \xi)m(\xi)r(\xi)\,d\xi = \frac{1}{\omega^2}r(x) \tag{68}$$

Symbolically, this equation can be expressed by

$$\mathsf{L}^{-1}(\mathsf{M}r) = \frac{1}{\omega^2}r \tag{69}$$

where $\mathsf{M} = m$, and L^{-1} represents an integration operation.

The integral equation (68) is called a *linear homogeneous integral equation of the second kind.* It states a typical eigenvalue problem: "Given an operation characterized by G and m, find a function r which remains unchanged by this operation except for a multiplication factor." Stated in another way the problem is to find the values of ω^2 for which (68) can have nontrivial solution, the trivial solution being

$$r(x) \equiv 0$$

Let us note the fact that in this formulation no boundary conditions are mentioned. This is because the information concerning boundary conditions is already included in Green's function of the problem G. It is a simple matter to show that if $G(x, \xi)$ satisfies a linear homogeneous boundary condition

$$G + aG' + bG'' \cdots = 0 \tag{70}$$

in which the prime denotes differentiation with respect to x, then any function r satisfying (68) must also satisfy the same boundary condition. It should also be borne in mind that unless the boundary condition is linear homogeneous the superposition principle on which the formulation is based will no longer be valid.

Although the lateral vibration of bars was chosen initially for this discussion, the formulation presented is quite general. The integral equation (68) represents all linear eigenvalue problems having one space variable. For multidimensional problems (68) is generalized into

$$\int_{\Sigma} G(P, Q) r(Q)\, d\sigma_Q = \frac{1}{\omega^2} r(P) \tag{71}$$

in which P and Q represent the coordinates of two generic points in the elastic body. If the displacement r is not unidirectional, we shall have more than one equation of the form (71).

The usual analytical method of solving an integral equation, such as (68), is to find the associated differential equation, such as (66), and solve it. In this way, there is no advantage in formulating a problem by integral equation as long as we can always formulate the same physical problems by differential equations. However, the integral equation formulation has great heuristical value in numerical analysis. For instance, the form

$$\mathsf{L}^{-1}\mathsf{M} r = \frac{1}{\omega^2} r$$

immediately suggests an iteration procedure for the determination of the eigenfunction with the lowest ω^2. The scheme will be the same as that described in Art. 3.11(B). The numerical method for solving this integral equation is discussed in Art. 4.11.

4.6 Rayleigh's Quotient and Its Stationary Values

(A) RAYLEIGH'S QUOTIENT FOR FREE VIBRATION OF AN ELASTIC BODY[15]

In Chapter 3 we showed that the eigenvalue problem of the matrix equation

$$\mathbf{C}\,\mathbf{r} = \omega^2 \mathbf{A}\,\mathbf{r}$$

is related to the finding of stationary values of the associated Rayleigh's quotient

$$Q(\mathbf{u}) = \frac{\bar{\mathbf{u}}\,\mathbf{C}\,\mathbf{u}}{\bar{\mathbf{u}}\,\mathbf{A}\,\mathbf{u}}$$

Briefly we found that

(i) $Q(\mathbf{u})$ is greater or equal to the lowest eigenvalue. Or

$$Q(\mathbf{u}) \geq \omega_1^2 \qquad \text{if} \qquad \omega_1^2 \leq \omega_2^2, \cdots, \leq \omega_n^2$$

[15] To gain a better understanding of this discussion the reader is advised to review Arts. 2.6 and 3.6.

(ii) If $\mathbf{u}$ is an eigenvector, $Q(\mathbf{u})$ is the associated eigenvalue.

$$Q(\mathbf{r}^{(i)}) = \omega_i^2$$

(iii) If $\mathbf{u}$ is only slightly different from a modal vector, then Rayleigh's quotient of $\mathbf{u}$ differs from the corresponding eigenvalue by a second-order small amount. In other words, Rayleigh's quotient achieves a stationary value when $\mathbf{u}$ is one of the modal vectors.

It is also important to remember that one essential premise for these conclusions is that

$$\bar{\mathbf{u}}\,\mathbf{A}\,\mathbf{u} \geq 0 \qquad \bar{\mathbf{u}}\,\mathbf{C}\,\mathbf{u} \geq 0$$

The analysis in Art. 3.6 suggests heuristically that for the eigenvalue problem in this chapter

$$\mathsf{L}(r) = \omega^2\,\mathsf{M}(r)$$

We may form Rayleigh's quotient of a function $u(x, y, z)$

$$Q((u)) = \frac{\displaystyle\int_\Sigma u\mathsf{L}(u)\,d\sigma}{\displaystyle\int_\Sigma u\,\mathsf{M}(u)\,d\sigma} \tag{72}$$

which perhaps will have similar properties.

This time the value of the quotient Q depends on the form of a function u instead of a vector $\mathbf{u}$, hence it is a "function of a function" or a *functional*, denoted here by a double parenthesis as used in (72).

Having noted the similarity we shall now mention the obvious difference between the two cases. In forming $Q(\mathbf{u})$, the vector u is completely arbitrary, whereas the function u in $Q((u))$ is subjected to some restriction. In the first place, the function u must be sufficiently regular in its continuity and differentiability so that $\mathsf{L}(u)$ and $\mathsf{M}(u)$ can be defined and the two integrals in (72) have meanings. In the second place, since the boundary conditions of the problem as well as the differential equation describe the physical nature of the vibrating system, these conditions must somehow enter into consideration.

Let us consider a class of functions called *admissible functions*.[16] which satisfy *all* the boundary conditions of an eigenvalue problem and for which $\mathsf{L}(u)$ and $\mathsf{M}(u)$ are continuous functions inside Σ. Obviously, the eigenfunctions themselves must belong to this class. Any function u belonging to this class can be expanded into an infinite series of eigenfunctions,

[16] There is no universally accepted meaning for this term. It is thus necessary to examine the conditions of admissibility whenever one sees the term used.

which can be differentiated termwise to yield series representing $\mathsf{L}(u)$ and $\mathsf{M}(u)$; and all of the series thus obtained are uniformly convergent. Accepting this statement without proof, we may write

$$u = v_1 r_1 + v_2 r_2 + \cdots = \sum_{i=1}^{\infty} v_i r_i \tag{73}$$

where the coefficients v_i for self-adjoint problems are evaluated by methods in Art. 4.4. By termwise differentiation, we have

$$\mathsf{L}(u) = \sum_{i=1}^{\infty} v_i \mathsf{L} r_i = \sum_{i=1}^{\infty} v_i \omega_i^2 \, \mathsf{M}(r_i) \tag{74}$$

and

$$\mathsf{M}(u) = \mathsf{M}\left(\sum_{i=1}^{\infty} v_i r_i \right) = \sum_{i=1}^{\infty} v_i \, \mathsf{M}(r_i) \tag{75}$$

Let us assume that the boundary conditions are such that the problem is self-adjoint. The eigenfunctions are then mutually orthogonal with respect to both L and M. This orthogonality, together with the uniform convergence of (73) and (74), enables us to write

$$\int_\Sigma u \mathsf{L}(u) \, d\sigma = \sum_{i=1}^{\infty} \sum_{j=1}^{\infty} \int_\Sigma v_i v_j \omega_j^2 r_i M(r_j) \, d\sigma$$

$$= \sum_{i=1}^{\infty} v_i^2 \omega_i^2 \int_\Sigma r_i \mathsf{M}(r_i) \, d\sigma$$

Similarly,[17]

$$\int_\Sigma u \mathsf{M}(u) \, d\sigma = \sum_{i=1}^{\infty} v_i^2 \int_\Sigma r_i \mathsf{M}(r_i) \, d\sigma$$

For simplicity let us write

$$m_{ii} = \int_\Sigma r_i \mathsf{M}(r_i) \, d\sigma \tag{76}$$

Rayleigh's quotient (72) for an admissible function u can thus be written

$$Q((u)) = \frac{m_{11} v_1^2 \omega_1^2 + m_{22} v_2^2 \omega^2{}_2 + \cdots}{m_{11} v_1^2 + m_{22} v_2^2 + \cdots}$$

$$= \frac{\sum_{i=1}^{\infty} m_{ii} v_i^2 \omega_i^2}{\sum_{i=1}^{\infty} m_{ii} v_i^2} \tag{77}$$

[17] If (74) is uniformly convergent, so (75) will be.

Except for its infinite character, this expression resembles (39) of Art. 3.6 in every other way. Inasmuch as both the numerator and the denominator are convergent series, we can use the same reasoning employed in Art. 3.6 and conclude the following:

(i) Rayleigh's quotient for any admissible function must be at least equal to the lowest eigenvalue of the system. (This conclusion is contingent upon the fact that m_{ii} is nonnegative, a fact which will become clear later. See also Exercise 3.11.) To show this, we need only to observe that (77) can be written

$$Q((u)) = \omega_1^2 + \frac{m_{22}v_2^2(\omega_2^2 - \omega_1^2) + m_{33}v_3^2(\omega_3^2 - \omega_1^2)\cdots}{\sum_{i=1}^{\infty} m_{ii}v_i^2}$$

(ii) If $u = r_i$, from the orthogonal property of eigenfunctions

$$v_1 = v_2 = \cdots = v_{i-1} = v_{i+1} = \cdots = 0$$

Hence

$$Q((r_i)) = \omega_1^2$$

(iii) In the "neighborhood" of an eigenfunction Rayleigh's quotient is stationary. That is to say, if an admissible function is only slightly different from an eigenfunction, its Rayleigh's quotient differs from an eigenvalue by a "higher-order" small amount. Although this statement is not mathematically precise, it is intuitively useful. To justify this statement, we observe that since every admissible function u is supposed to have an infinite-series expansion consisting of eigenfunctions whose coefficients determine collectively the original function we may consider $Q((u))$ as a function of these coefficients as given by (76):

$$Q((u)) = Q(v_1, v_2, \cdots, v_i \cdots)$$

A small change in the function u corresponds to a set of small changes in the coefficients $v_1, v_2, \ldots, v_i, \ldots$. The corresponding change in Q, denoted by the symbol δQ and called the *variation of* Q, is given by

$$\begin{aligned} \delta Q &= \frac{\partial Q}{\partial v_1}\,\delta v_1 + \frac{\partial Q}{\partial v_2}\,\delta v_2 + \cdots \\ &= \sum_{i=1}^{\infty} \frac{\partial Q}{\partial v_i}\,\delta v_i \end{aligned}$$

Accepting the fact that here we can treat a function of (countable) infinite number of variables by the usual rules of calculus, we may easily show

$$\frac{\partial Q}{\partial v_i} = 0 \qquad \text{when} \qquad u = r_j$$

for *all* i and j. By $u = r_j$, we mean that

$$v_1 = v_2 = \cdots = v_{j-1} = v_{j+1} = \cdots = 0$$

and

$$v_j \neq 0$$

In other words

$$\delta Q = 0$$

when u is one of the eigenfunctions, say r_j.

(B) MINIMUM CHARACTERIZATION OF EIGENVALUES

A better and more precise way of characterizing the stationary property of Rayleigh's quotient is as follows. Arrange the eigenfunctions in a sequence with ascending eigenvalues:

$$r_1, r_2, \cdots, r_i, \cdots$$
$$\omega_1^2 \leq \omega_2^2 \leq, \cdots, \omega_i^2, \cdots$$

Suppose that we remove from the class of admissible functions all those which are *not* orthogonal to the first $(k - 1)$ eigenfunctions of the system. In other words, we select from the original class of admissible functions a subclass in which all the functions are orthogonal to $r_1, r_2, \ldots, r_{k-1}$. In this smaller class the function that has the minimum Q is r_k. Rayleigh's quotient of any other functions in this subclass will be greater than ω_k^2. The reader is left with the proof of this statement. In proving it one needs only (77) and the orthogonal relation of eigenfunctions.

(C) MAXIMUM-MINIMUM CHARACTERIZATION OF EIGENVALUES

Let

$$\phi_1, \phi_2, \cdots, \phi_{k-1}$$

be a set of $(k - 1)$ functions, which are *completely arbitrary* except that they are integrable in Σ. We remove from the class of admissible functions all those which do not satisfy the relation[18]

$$\int_\Sigma \phi_j \mathsf{M}(u)\, d\sigma = 0 \qquad j = 1, 2, \cdots, k - 1 \tag{78}$$

In other words, we retain only those admissible functions satisfying (78). Again we end up with a smaller subclass. This subclass will be the same as that in (B) if the ϕ's are the first $(k - 1)$ eigenfunctions; otherwise they

[18] This relation will mean orthogonality between ϕ_j and u if the operator M is such that (46) is satisfied.

will be different. We now have the following theorem: the minimum value of Q formed by functions in this subclass is not greater than the kth eigenvalue, or

$$[Q((u))]_{\min} \leq \omega_k^2$$

in which u is an admissible function satisfying (78). To prove this theorem, we show first that there is a function u_0 belonging to this subclass, which can be represented by a linear combination of the first k eigenfunctions:

$$u_0 = v_1 r_1 + v_2 r_2, \cdots, v_k r_k \tag{79}$$

where $v_1, v_2, \ldots, v_k$ are the coefficients. If there is a u_0, then according to (77)

$$Q((u_0)) = \frac{m_{11}\omega_1^2 v_1^2 + m_{22}\omega_2^2 v_2^2 + \cdots + m_{kk}\omega_k^2 v_k^2}{m_{11}v_1^2 + m_{22}v_2^2 + \cdots + m_{kk}v_k^2} \leq \omega_k^2$$

To prove that indeed there is such a function we must show that it is possible to find $v_1, v_2, \ldots, v_k$ for (79) so that (78) will be valid. It is not difficult to show that by substituting (79) into (78) we can obtain $(k - 1)$ linear homogeneous equations with k unknowns, namely, $v_1, v_2, \ldots, v_k$.

$$\begin{aligned} f_{11}v_1 + f_{12}v_2 + \cdots + f_{1k}v_k &= 0 \\ f_{21}v_1 + f_{22}v_2 + \cdots + f_{2k}v_k &= 0 \\ \cdots\cdots\cdots\cdots\cdots\cdots\cdots \\ f_{(k-1)1}v_1 + f_{(k-1)2}v_2, \cdots, f_{(k-1)k}v_k &= 0 \end{aligned} \tag{80}$$

where

$$f_{ji} = \int_{\Sigma} \phi_j M(r_i)\, d\sigma \tag{81}$$

$$j = 1, 2, \cdots, (k - 1)$$
$$i = 1, 2, \cdots, k$$

This set of equations (80), having more unknowns than equations, evidently has a solution, though not a unique solution. This completes the proof.

4.7 Rayleigh-Ritz Method

(A) MATHEMATICAL PRINCIPLE

The discussion in Art. 4.6 reveals that if we have a way of finding in a class of functions the one that gives the least value for Q we shall either have the solution to the eigenvalue problem or establish the lower or upper bound of the eigenvalues. To perform this minimization process to a class of all admissible functions is equivalent to solving the original problem in differential equation, which cannot always be carried out. In the Rayleigh-Ritz Method we apply the minimization process to a smaller class of admissible functions and thereby obtain an approximate solution to the problem.

We begin by selecting a set of n linearly independent admissible functions:

$$\phi_1, \phi_2, \cdots, \phi_n$$

Except for the requirement of linear independence and the condition of admissibility previously defined, the selection of these functions can be done in an arbitrary manner. From this set of ϕ's and by taking linear combinations of ϕ's, we can form a class of functions, which have the general form

$$u = q_1\phi_1 + q_2\phi_2, \cdots + q_n\phi_n \tag{82}$$

in which the q's are a set of arbitrary coefficients. It is obvious that every function belonging to this class is an admissible function but not all admissible functions are in this class. The set of functions ϕ is called a *generating set*. It generates a class of functions u defined by (82).

Let us define

$$\begin{aligned} a_{ij} &= \int_\Sigma \phi_i \mathsf{M}\phi_j \, d\sigma \\ c_{ij} &= \int_\Sigma \phi_i \mathsf{L}\phi_j \, d\sigma \end{aligned} \tag{83}$$

For self-adjoint problems

$$a_{ij} = a_{ji} \qquad \text{and} \qquad c_{ij} = c_{ji}$$

Rayleigh's quotient for any function u representable by (82) can be obtained by substituting (82) and (83) into (72). The result is

$$Q((u)) = \frac{\sum_{i=1}^{n}\sum_{j=1}^{n} c_{ij}q_iq_j}{\sum_{i=1}^{n}\sum_{j=1}^{n} a_{ij}q_iq_j}$$

Or, by the summation convention used in Chapter 3, we have simply

$$Q = \frac{c_{ij}q_iq_j}{a_{ij}q_iq_j} = \frac{\bar{\mathbf{q}}\,\mathbf{C}\,\mathbf{q}}{\bar{\mathbf{q}}\,\mathbf{A}\,\mathbf{q}} \tag{84}$$

In this expression a_{ij} and c_{ij} are predetermined by the initial choice of ϕ, the generating set. The q's, however, are still free to vary. The amount of freedom is thus equivalent to that of n-degree-freedom systems. To minimize Q, with respect to all possible combinations of q's, we set

$$\frac{\partial Q}{\partial q_1} = 0, \frac{\partial Q}{\partial q_2} = 0, \cdots, \frac{\partial Q}{\partial q_n} = 0 \tag{85}$$

and

$$Q = \tilde{\omega}^2 \tag{86}$$

The procedure for combining (84), (85), and (86) is exactly the same as that leading from (26) to (31) in Art. 2.6. The result is the familiar equation

$$|a_{ij}\tilde{\omega}^2 - c_{ij}| = 0 \tag{87}$$

In general, this equation will have n roots: $\tilde{\omega}_1^2, \tilde{\omega}_2^2, \ldots, \tilde{\omega}_n^2$, *arranged in the ascending order of magnitude*. To each of these roots there associates a modal vector $(\tilde{q}_1, \tilde{q}_2, \ldots, \tilde{q}_n)$, which in turn yields a function $\tilde{r}$ through (82):

$$\tilde{r} = \tilde{q}_1\phi_1 + \tilde{q}_2\phi_2 + \cdots + \tilde{q}_n\phi_n$$

In total we have n such functions, $\tilde{r}_1, \tilde{r}_2, \ldots, \tilde{r}_n$.

The essence of this method is that by limiting the admissible functions to a class representable by (82), we are approximating a system having an infinite number of degrees of freedom by one having n degrees of freedom. The n frequencies and modal vectors of the latter are then considered as giving an approximate description of the first n modes of vibration of the original system. To amplify this statement, let us observe that $\tilde{r}_1$ is the function with the smallest Q in the class of functions represented by (82). If this class is "sufficiently representative" of the original admissible class, $\tilde{r}_1$ is an approximation of r_1, which is characterized by having the smallest Q of *all* admissible functions. In the meantime $\tilde{\omega}_1^2$ is a better approximation to ω_1^2 than $\tilde{r}_1$ is to r_1 because of the stationary property of Q. In any event, $\tilde{r}_1$ and $\tilde{\omega}_1^2$ are the best approximations available within the freedom of choice allowed by (82).

There is, of course, no guarantee that the approximation will be good. For instance, it can conceivably happen that all of the ϕ's in the generating set will be orthogonal to r_1. In that case, $\tilde{r}_1$ must also be orthogonal to r_1 and can never be considered as an approximation. In practice, this does not happen because we generally have some idea of what r_1 should be like and choose the generating set accordingly. Now in the approximating system it can be verified readily that $\tilde{r}_2$ is orthogonal to $\tilde{r}_1$ with respect to M.

$$\int_\Sigma \tilde{r}_1 \mathsf{M} \tilde{r}_2 \, d\sigma = 0$$

Hence $\tilde{r}_2$ is the function with the smallest Rayleigh's quotient among all functions orthogonal to $\tilde{r}_1$ and representable by (82). This description parallels the minimum characterization of r_2, except that there we consider a larger class of admissible functions. It is clear then that, if $\tilde{r}_1$ were exactly r_1, $\tilde{\omega}_2$ and $\tilde{r}_2$ would be only approximations for ω_2 and r_2, respectively. Since $\tilde{r}_1$ is only an approximation for r_1, $\tilde{\omega}_2$ and $\tilde{r}_2$ in general can be only rougher approximations of ω_2 and r_2. Similar things can be said for the rest of eigenvalue-eigenfunction pairs.

Because we use a smaller class of admissible functions in the Rayleigh-Ritz method we know immediately that

$$\omega_1^2 = R((r_1)) \leq R((\tilde{r}_1)) = \tilde{\omega}_1^2$$

It is also true that

$$\omega_2^2 \leq \tilde{\omega}_2^2, \omega_3^2 \leq \tilde{\omega}_3^2, \cdots, \omega_n^2 \leq \tilde{\omega}_n^2$$

but the proof of these inequalities is not within our reach at the moment. To avoid excessive digression we shall put the matter aside and return to it later in Art. 4.8(B).

(B) LIBERALIZATION OF REQUIREMENTS FOR ADMISSIBILITY BY ENERGY CONSIDERATION—AN EXAMPLE

Up till now an admissible function u eligible for consideration in the minimization process had to satisfy *all* the boundary conditions of the problem. Besides, $\mathsf{L}(u)$ and $\mathsf{M}(u)$ had to be defined and to be continuous everywhere. Both of these requirements can be liberalized. For instance, the continuity requirement for $\mathsf{L}(u)$ and $\mathsf{M}(u)$ can certainly be relaxed somewhat. In other words, to be valid, we can have a larger class of admissible functions and still have all the conclusions arrived at in Art. 4.6. To carry out this liberalization by a general and strictly mathematical approach is neither feasible here nor conducive to a clear understanding of the physical problem. Therefore, this time we choose to develop the theory by the use of an example.

Consider the problem of lateral vibrations of a bar with a built-in left end and a right end fastened to an elastic support (Fig. 92). The separation of time-variable t from the partial differential equation (10) results in

$$(kr'')'' = \omega^2 mr \tag{88}$$

where

$$k(x) = EI \qquad \text{and} \qquad m(x) = \rho A$$

The boundary conditions to be satisfied by r are

$$r(0) = 0, \qquad r'(0) = 0 \tag{89}$$

$$k(L)r''(L) = -K_1 r'(L) \qquad \text{and} \qquad [k(L)r''(L)]' = K_2 r(L) \tag{90}$$

in which K_1 and K_2 represent the rotational and the lateral stiffness of the right-end support. Note the proper signs for the right-hand side of (86) in order for K_1 and K_2 to be positive.

The problem is self-adjoint, since the boundary conditions are in the form of (62).

When k and m are constants, this eigenvalue problem can be solved without much difficulty. But, if there are variations in the stiffness and mass distribution along the bar, the problem is usually solved only by an

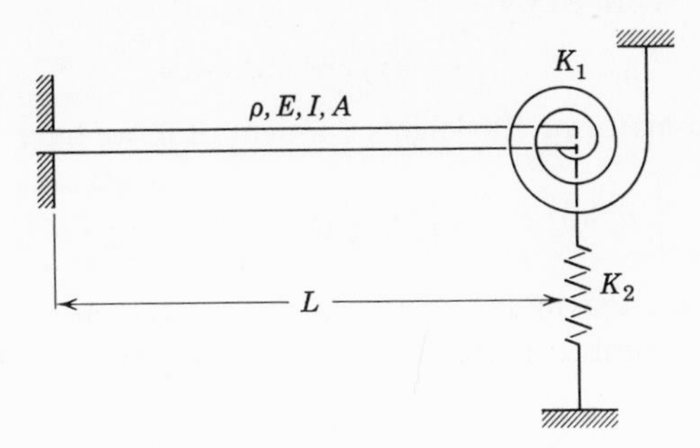

Figure 92

approximate method based on the Rayleigh-Ritz principle. According to our previous discussion, we shall have to choose a set of admissible functions $\phi_1, \phi_2, \ldots, \phi_n$, which satisfy the boundary conditions (89) and (90). Although it is not too difficult to find a set of these functions, they may make the subsequent computation algebraically complicated. Hence the relaxation of boundary conditions is of practical interest.

Let us suppose for the time being that we are still dealing with functions satisfying our original requirements of admissibility. The numerator of Rayleigh's quotient for an admissible function u is

$$\int_\Sigma u\mathsf{L}(u)\,d\sigma = \int_0^L u(x)[k(x)u''(x)]''\,dx$$

According to (59), integration by parts yields

$$\int_\Sigma u\mathsf{L}(u)\,d\sigma = \int_0^L k(u'')^2\,dx + [u(ku'')' - u'(ku'')]_0^L \tag{91}$$

Since u satisfies (89) and (90), we have finally

$$\int_\Sigma u\mathsf{L}(u)\,d\sigma = \int_0^L k(u'')^2\,dx + K_2[u(L)]^2 + K_1[u'(L)]^2 \tag{92}$$

As we examine the three terms at the right-hand side of (92), we see that, except for a factor of $\frac{1}{2}$, the first term represents the strain energy in the bar and the last two terms represent the strain energy in the two supporting springs. Hence

$$\int_{\Sigma} u\mathsf{L}(u)\, d\sigma = 2V_m \tag{93}$$

if u satisfies all the boundary conditions. The physical meaning of the symbol V_m is the maximum potential energy the system would have if its vibration were described by

$$v(x, t) = u(x) \cos(\omega t - \alpha) \tag{94}$$

As the denominator of Rayleigh's quotient of u, we have

$$\int_{\Sigma} u\mathsf{M}(u)\, d\sigma = \int_0^L m(x)[u(x)]^2\, dx = \frac{2}{\omega^2} T_m \tag{95}$$

in which T_m is the maximum kinetic energy the system would have if its vibration were described by (94). Therefore, Rayleigh's quotient can be expressed as

$$Q = \frac{\omega^2 V_m}{T_m} \tag{96}$$

The quantity ω^2 actually does not appear because it is also contained in T_m and will be canceled out when the energy expressions are written explicitly. It was also shown in Art. 2.6 that the minimization of (96) is equivalent to the minimization of the expression $(T_m - V_m)$; or $\delta Q = 0$ implies

$$\delta(T_m - V_m) = 0 \tag{97}$$

Thus we can characterize the natural frequencies of a vibrating system as the stationary values of the ratio in (96). This is true regardless of the number of degrees of freedom the system may have.

Now we must realize that in deriving (96) from (91) we were actually reasoning backward. Without going into topics in advanced dynamics, we somehow feel that (96) is a more basic expression of Rayleigh's quotient than (72), since, unlike (72), it contains well-defined physical quantities and its definition does not contain explicitly such mathematical operations as differentiation and integration. Accepting as a fundamental physical fact that[19]

$$\delta\left(\frac{\omega^2 V_m}{T_m}\right) = 0$$

[19] Note also that the orthogonal property of eigenfunctions needed to arrive at (77) also becomes unnecessary if (97) is accepted as a basic physical law.

with T_m and V_m as the maximum energies in a natural mode of vibration, we realize that many of the requirements are imposed on the admissible functions simply to make the left-hand sides of (93) and (95) become the energy expressions. For instance, the function u must satisfy the boundary condition (90), so that (93) will then be valid. But, on the other hand, we can obtain directly through formulas in strength of material

$$2V_m = \int_0^L k(u'')^2\,dx + K_1[u(L)]^2 + K_2[u(L)]^2 \tag{98}$$

without the benefit of (92).

Looking at (98), we see now that the admissibility requirements for the present problem are simplified:

(i) An admissible function u must be at least twice differentiable and u'' must be integrable between the limits 0 and L. This is in contrast to the four-time differentiability needed in defining $\mathsf{L}(u)$, although this relaxation of requirement is of little practical significance, since in picking a set of ϕ's for the Rayleigh-Ritz method we generally choose functions with regular behavior.

(ii) An admissible function u for the problem on hand must satisfy the two boundary conditions in (89), but not necessarily those in (90), if Rayleigh's quotient is defined by (96) instead of (72). The difference in the two types of boundary conditions lies with the fact that the use of potential energy expressions automatically takes care of the conditions at the right-end elastic support, whereas they cannot take care of the fixed support at the left end. This is because we can include the two springs in our vibrating system. We cannot do the same for the fixed support without introducing ambiguity in the energy expression, for whenever a boundary point is immovably constrained the presence of an infinitely rigid and infinitely large external body is implied. If this body is considered part of the system, the energy expressions become indeterminate. If this body is considered external to the system, the boundary conditions it imposes must be obeyed by the functions eligible for consideration in minimizing (96). Generally speaking, if

$$\mathsf{L} = \frac{d^n}{dx^n}\left(k\,\frac{d^n}{dx^n}(\cdots)\right)$$

all boundary conditions containing *no derivatives higher than the* $(n-1)$*th order* must always be satisfied. Such boundary conditions are thus called *imposed* boundary conditions. They usually describe constraints on the system that are purely geometrical; hence they are also called *geometrical* boundary conditions. On the other hand, boundary conditions containing[20] derivatives of the nth order or higher are called *natural* or *dynamical.* These boundary conditions do not have to be satisfied by the admissible functions in minimizing (96), since they describe dynamical conditions at the boundary that will automatically be satisfied by the function obtained from the minimization process. Functions satisfying all of the imposed boundary conditions and having the differentiability described in (i) are called *essentially admissible functions.*[21]

Returning to our example of a bar with a built-in end and an elastically supported end, we see that the following functions are examples of essentially admissible functions:

$$\phi_n = 1 - \cos \frac{n\pi x}{2L} \qquad n = 1, 2, \cdots$$

$$\phi_n = x^{n+2} \qquad n = 1, 2, \cdots$$

$$\phi_n = \sinh^2 \frac{nx}{L} \qquad n = 1, 2, \cdots$$

To apply the Rayleigh-Ritz method, let us choose as the generating set the following four functions:

$$\left(1 - \cos \frac{\pi x}{2L}\right) \quad \left(1 - \cos \frac{3\pi x}{2L}\right) \quad \left(1 - \cos \frac{5\pi x}{2L}\right) \quad \text{and} \quad \left(1 - \cos \frac{7\pi x}{2L}\right)$$

The system is thus approximated by one having four degrees of freedom. The functions generated by this set are representable by

$$u = \sum_{n=1}^{4} q_n \left[1 - \cos \left(n - \frac{1}{2}\right) \frac{\pi x}{L}\right]$$

$$u' = \sum_{n=1}^{4} \left(n - \frac{1}{2}\right) \frac{\pi}{L} q_n \sin \left(n - \frac{1}{2}\right) \frac{\pi x}{L}$$

$$u'' = \sum_{n=1}^{4} \left(n - \frac{1}{2}\right)^2 \frac{\pi^2}{L^2} q_n \cos \left(n - \frac{1}{2}\right) \frac{\pi x}{L}$$

For the purpose of illustration let us assume

$$k = \text{constant} \qquad m = \text{constant}$$

---

[20] It is assumed that these high-order derivatives cannot be eliminated in the set of boundary conditions of the problem.

[21] L. Collatz, a German author who writes a great deal on the subject, calls such functions simply *zulässige* (admissible) functions and uses the term *Vergleichsfunktionen* (compatible functions) for those satisfying all the boundary conditions. He also uses the adjectives *wesentliche* (essential) and *restliche* (remaining) for imposed and natural boundary conditions, respectively.

The strain energy due to the bending of the bar is thus

$$\frac{1}{2}k\int_0^L (u'')^2\,dx = \frac{kL}{4}\left(\frac{\pi}{2L}\right)^4 \sum_{n=1}^{4}(2n-1)^4 q_n{}^2$$

$$= \frac{\pi^4 k}{64L^3}(q_1{}^2 + 3^4 q_2{}^2 + 5^4 q_3{}^2 + 7^4 q_4{}^2)$$

The strain energy in the two supporting springs is

$$\frac{1}{2}K_1[u(L)]^2 + \frac{1}{2}K_2[u'(L)]^2$$

$$= \frac{1}{2}K_1(q_1 + q_2 + q_3 + q_4)^2 + \frac{1}{2}K_2\left(\frac{\pi}{2L}\right)^2(q_1 - 3q_2 + 5q_3 - 7q_4)^2$$

By putting the two together, we have a strain energy expression that is a quadratic form in q's:

$$V_m = \tfrac{1}{2}c_{ij}q_iq_j$$

in which the repeated indices i and j are summed over the range 1 to 4.

Similarly, the maximum kinetic energy expression T_m is

$$T_m = \tfrac{1}{2}m\omega^2\int_0^L u^2\,dx = \tfrac{1}{2}\omega^2 a_{ij}q_iq_j$$

where

$$a_{ij} = m\int_0^L\left[1 - \cos\,(2i-1)\frac{\pi x}{2L}\right]\left[1 - \cos\,(2j-1)\frac{\pi x}{2L}\right]dx$$

$$a_{ij} = \frac{2mL}{\pi}\left(\frac{\pi}{2} - \frac{(-1)^i}{2i-1} - \frac{(-1)^j}{2j-1} + \delta_{ij}\frac{\pi}{4}\right)$$

in which δ_{ij} is the Kronecker delta ($\delta_{ij} = 1$, when $i = j$; $\delta_{ij} = 0$, when $i \neq j$).

With a_{ij} and c_{ij} computed, the problem can then be solved by methods in Chapter 3. We solve a problem of similar nature in Art. 4.8.

4.8 Formulation of Problem by Infinite-Series Expansions of Energy Expressions—Rayleigh-Ritz Method Re-examined

(A) SOLUTION BY INFINITE SERIES

In Art. 4.1 we mentioned the alternate method of specifying the configuration of a vibrating elastic body by infinite series. We now show that this method leads directly to an approximate solution of the free vibration problem, which resembles the Rayleigh-Ritz method in detail.

Consider first the simple case of longitudinal vibrations of a slender bar of length L. The motion of the system is described by the displacement function $u(x, t)$, which is the unknown to be determined. At any instant t the shape (or the configuration) of the bar is described by a function of x. As a function of x for a fixed t, u is known to be (i) continuous for $0 \leq x \leq L$, since the bar would otherwise be broken, and (ii) $E(\partial u/\partial x) = \sigma_x$ exists and is continuous in $0 \leq x \leq L$, except possibly at a few points along the bar where concentrated external forces are acting on it.

It is known that all functions having the regular behavior described above can be expanded into an infinite series formed by a set of "suitably chosen" functions of x: $\phi_1, \phi_2, \ldots, \phi_i, \ldots$.

$$u = q_1\phi_1 + q_2\phi_2, \cdots, q_i\phi_i, \cdots$$

so that the series converges uniformly in $0 \leq x \leq L$ and is termwise differentiable, except possibly at a few points. The same set of functions ϕ can be used for different values of t. As u varies with t, the q's vary also. Therefore,

$$u(x, t) = \sum_{i=1}^{\infty} q_i(t)\phi_i(x) \tag{99}$$

The unknown of the problem now becomes a set of functions of t: q_1, $q_2, \ldots, q_i, \ldots$ which now becomes the generalized coordinates of the system, since by specifying their values one specifies uniquely the configuration of the system.

To study what constitutes a suitable set of ϕ's, we must consider among other things the boundary conditions of the bar. Let us assume that the bar is held fixed at the left end where $x = 0$. Hence

$$u(0, t) = q_1(t)\phi_1(0) + q_2(t)\phi_2(0) \cdots = 0$$

for all t. If the q's, the generalized coordinates, are supposed to be linearly independent, it becomes necessary that

$$\phi_i(0) = 0 \tag{100}$$

for all i.

We know that a continuous function in $0 \leq x \leq L$ can be expanded into a Fourier series with the fundamental interval $-2L \leq x \leq 2L$. We choose a fundamental interval of expansion longer than the length of the bar L so that we will have more selections of the functions to be used.[22] To satisfy (100), only the sine functions are retained.

$$\sin \frac{n\pi x}{2L} \qquad n = 1, 2, 3, \cdots$$

[22] Also, by making $x = 0$ and $x = L$ inside the fundamental interval of Fourier-series expansion, it is easier to make the series converge to the function u at these two points.

Furthermore, we can delete from this set either those with odd n or those with even n, depending upon the boundary condition at the right end. If the right end is also held fixed, that is,

$$u(L) = 0$$

to satisfy this imposed boundary condition, we must choose n as even. If the right end is allowed to move (not necessarily free), we must choose n as odd, so that the sine series can converge at $x = L$ to a value other than zero.

Let us suppose that at the right end a concentrated mass M is attached. The boundary condition there is

$$k \frac{\partial u}{\partial x} = -M \frac{\partial^2 u}{\partial t^2} \qquad \text{at } x = L \tag{101}$$

in which $k = EA$. Evidently this condition is not satisfied by

$$\sin \frac{n\pi x}{2L} \qquad n = 1, 3, 5, \cdots$$

But this is not important for reasons to be seen later.

The kinetic energy T and potential energy V for this system are given by

$$\begin{aligned} T &= \frac{1}{2}\int_0^L m\left(\frac{\partial u}{\partial t}\right)^2 dx + \frac{1}{2} M\left(\frac{\partial u}{\partial t}\right)^2_{x=L} \\ V &= \frac{1}{2}\int_0^L k\left(\frac{\partial u}{\partial x}\right)^2 dx \end{aligned} \tag{102}$$

If we represent $u(x, t)$ by

$$u = \sum_{i=1}^{\infty} q_i(t) \sin \frac{(2i-1)\pi x}{2L} \tag{103}$$

we can obtain $\partial u/\partial x$ by termwise differentiation,

$$\frac{\partial u}{\partial x} = \sum_{i=1}^{\infty} q_i(t) \frac{(2i-1)\pi}{2L} \cos \frac{(2i-1)\pi x}{2L} \tag{104}$$

which is valid for all $0 \leq x \leq L$. We can also obtain $\partial u/\partial t$ by termwise differentiation,

$$\frac{\partial u}{\partial t} = \sum_{i=1}^{\infty} \dot{q}_i(t) \sin \frac{(2i-1)\pi x}{2L} \tag{105}$$

assuming that the resulting series is uniformly convergent with respect to t. By substituting (104) and (105) into (102), we obtain

$$T = \frac{1}{2}\sum_{i=1}^{\infty}\sum_{j=1}^{\infty} a_{ij}\dot{q}_i\dot{q}_j$$

$$V = \frac{1}{2}\sum_{i=1}^{\infty}\sum_{j=1}^{\infty} c_{ij}q_iq_j \tag{106}$$

where

$$a_{ij} = \int_0^L m(x)\sin\frac{(2i-1)\pi x}{2L}\sin\frac{(2j-1)\pi x}{2L}\,dx + (-1)^{i+j}M$$

$$c_{ij} = \int_0^L k(x)\frac{\pi^2}{4L^2}(2i-1)(2j-1)\cos\frac{(2i-1)\pi x}{2L}\cos\frac{(2j-1)\pi x}{2L}\,dx$$

Now the conservation of energy requires that

$$\frac{d}{dt}(T+V) = 0$$

$$\sum_{i=1}^{\infty}\sum_{j=1}^{\infty}(a_{ij}\ddot{q}_j + c_{ij}q_j)\dot{q}_i = 0$$

Since $\dot{q}$'s are supposed to be independent,

$$\sum_{j=1}^{\infty} a_{ij}\ddot{q}_j + c_{ij}q_j = 0 \qquad i = 1, 2, 3, \cdots \tag{107}$$

Thus we have an infinite set of linear differential equations of an infinite number of unknowns.

Whether or not such infinite formulation is always mathematically legitimate is too involved a question to be discussed here. For a given problem this question may be answered when the solution is obtained and each step is retraced to examine its legitimacy. Even that task is difficult. Fortunately, as subsequently demonstrated, the reasoning used here leads in practice to the same result as the Rayleigh-Ritz method, of which the mathematical foundation is more secure.

We note that each of the function ϕ_i in (99) satisfies the imposed boundary conditions, hence can be used as a generating function in the Rayleigh-Ritz method. If we terminate (99) at the nth term, the energy expressions (106) will be that of an n-degree-freedom system. The frequency equation obtained from (107) with $i, j = 1, 2, \ldots, n$, is exactly that for minimizing (96).

As an example, let us take the simple case in which m and k are constants in (102). The resulting problem was solved exactly in Art. 4.3(A); therefore, we can evaluate the accuracy of the method. Let

$$n = 4 \qquad \text{and} \qquad M = \tfrac{1}{2}mL$$

$$u(x, t) = q_1 \sin \frac{\pi x}{2L} + q_2 \sin \frac{3\pi x}{2L} + q_3 \sin \frac{5\pi x}{2L} + q_4 \sin \frac{7\pi x}{L}$$

By putting this into (106), we obtain

$$\begin{aligned} T &= \tfrac{1}{4}mL[\dot{q}_1^2 + \dot{q}_2^2 + \dot{q}_3^2 + \dot{q}_4^2 + (\dot{q}_1 - \dot{q}_2 + \dot{q}_3 - \dot{q}_4)^2] \\ &= \tfrac{1}{4}mL(2\dot{q}_1^2 + 2\dot{q}_2^2 + 2\dot{q}_3^2 + 2\dot{q}_4^2 - 2\dot{q}_1\dot{q}_2 + 2\dot{q}_1\dot{q}_3 \\ &\quad - 2\dot{q}_1\dot{q}_4 - 2\dot{q}_2\dot{q}_3 + 2\dot{q}_2\dot{q}_4 - 2\dot{q}_3\dot{q}_4) \end{aligned}$$

$$V = \frac{1}{2} k \frac{\pi^2}{8L}(q_1^2 + 9q_2^2 + 25q_3^2 + 49q_4^2)$$

Hence

$$\mathbf{A} = \begin{bmatrix} 2 & -1 & 1 & -1 \\ -1 & 2 & -1 & 1 \\ 1 & -1 & 2 & -1 \\ -1 & 1 & -1 & 2 \end{bmatrix} \frac{mL}{2} \qquad \mathbf{C} = \begin{bmatrix} 1 & 0 & 0 & 0 \\ 0 & 9 & 0 & 0 \\ 0 & 0 & 25 & 0 \\ 0 & 0 & 0 & 49 \end{bmatrix} \frac{k\pi^2}{8L}$$

$$\mathbf{C}^{-1}\mathbf{A} = \begin{bmatrix} 2.0000 & -1.0000 & 1.0000 & -1.0000 \\ -0.1111 & 0.2222 & -0.1111 & 0.1111 \\ 0.0400 & -0.0400 & 0.0800 & -0.0400 \\ -0.0204 & 0.0204 & -0.0204 & 0.0408 \end{bmatrix} \frac{4mL^2}{k\pi^2}$$

By the matrix iteration method described in Chapter 3, we obtain

$$\tilde{\omega} = 1.086\sqrt{(k/m)}L = 1.086\sqrt{(E/\rho)}L$$

and

$$\tilde{r}_1 = 92.8 \sin \frac{\pi x}{2L} - 5.68 \sin \frac{3\pi x}{2L} + 1.99 \sin \frac{5\pi x}{2L} - \sin \frac{7\pi x}{2L}$$

The exact solution of (24) for $\mu = \frac{1}{2}$ is

$$\omega_1 = 1.0769\sqrt{(E/\rho)}L$$

and

$$r_1 = B \sin 1.0769 \frac{x}{L}$$

in which B is an arbitrary multiplication constant. The comparison between r_1 and $\tilde{r}_1$ is shown in Fig. 93.

Note that the approximate function $\tilde{r}_1$ does not satisfy the boundary condition (101). This is reasonable, since that boundary condition describes an equilibrium relationship that supplements the differential equation of motion. In other words, both the differential equation (5) and the dynamical boundary condition (101) originate from Newton's law. In the infinite-series formulation they are replaced by (107). An approximate solution of (107) is not expected to satisfy (101) any more than it is expected to satisfy the differential equation of motion.[23] However, by

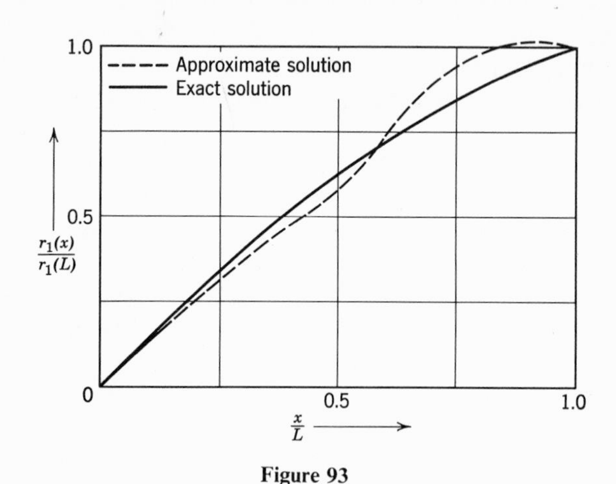

Figure 93

taking a sufficient number of terms in (103), the two sides of (101) can be made arbitrarily close to each other at $x = L - \epsilon$, where ϵ is arbitrarily small.

(B) EFFECTS OF CONSTRAINTS ON NATURAL FREQUENCIES

A very important concept in vibration analysis is that the introduction of additional constraints into a system will raise all the natural frequencies of the system (or at least will not lower them). For instance, in the lateral vibration of bars all the natural frequencies will be raised if a free end is made into a hinged end, and they will be raised again if the hinged end becomes a built-in end.

To prove this statement in a general way, we utilize the maximum-minimum characterization of eigenvalues discussed in Art. 4.6(C). Before we proceed, let us point out that an imposed boundary condition, being geometrical in nature, constitutes a constraint, whereas a natural boundary

[23] In this particular example the approximate solution does satisfy the differential equation of motion. This is an exception rather than a rule.

condition is not considered as a constraint, since it originates from consideration of forces. A constraint may also be any interdependence relation imposed upon the coordinates of a system; for instance, such imposition as

$$u(0, t) = 3u(L/2, t) = u(L, t)$$

or in (99)

$$q_1 = q_3 = q_5 = \cdots = 0$$

Let S be a vibrating system and $\tilde{S}$ be another vibrating system, which can be obtained by imposing additional constraints on S. The two systems therefore share the same differential operators L and M, and their energy expressions derived from an (essentially) admissible function will also look the same. Hence Rayleigh's quotients for the two systems are computed in the same way. We note also that since any constraint of system S is also a constraint of $\tilde{S}$, but not vice versa, any admissible or essentially admissible function of $\tilde{S}$ is also admissible for S, but not vice versa.

Let $r_1, r_2, \ldots, r_{k-1}$ be the first $k - 1$ eigenfunctions of S. Let C_k be the class of functions that is admissible to S and orthogonal to $r_1, r_2, \ldots, r_{k-1}$, with respect to M. Let $\tilde{C}_k$ be the class of functions that is admissible to $\tilde{S}$ and orthogonal to $r_1, r_2, \ldots, r_{k-1}$. It is clear that every function in $\tilde{C}_k$ must also belong to C_k, but not vice versa. According to the minimum characterization of eigenvalues, the function in C_k having the least Rayleigh's quotient is the kth eigenfunction of S, namely r_k, and

$$Q((r_k)) = \omega_k^2$$

Since C_k contains all the functions in $\tilde{C}_k$, the minimum value of Rayleigh's quotient formed by a function u in $\tilde{C}_k$ is no less than $Q((r_k))$.

$$[Q((u))]_{\min} \geq Q((r_k)) = \omega_k^2$$

In the meantime, if $\tilde{\omega}_k^2$ is the kth eigenvalue of $\tilde{S}$, according to Art. 4.6(c),

$$\tilde{\omega}_k^2 \geq [Q((u))]_{\min}$$

because $\tilde{C}_k$ is formed by removing from functions admissible to $\tilde{S}$ all those which do not satisfy

$$\int_\Sigma r_j \mathsf{M}(u)\, d\sigma = 0 \qquad j = 1, 2, \cdots, (k-1)$$

and, insofar as $\tilde{S}$ is concerned, $r_1, r_2, \ldots, r_{k-1}$ is a set of arbitrary functions. Hence

$$\tilde{\omega}_k^2 \geq \omega_k^2 \tag{108}$$

The natural frequencies obtained by the Rayleigh-Ritz method can also be considered as the true natural frequencies of a hypothetical system, which is obtained by imposing additional constraints to the actual system. By terminating the infinite series (99) at the nth term, we introduce the constraints

$$q_{n+1}(t) = q_{n+2}(t) \cdots = 0$$

We note also that in proving (108) all we needed was the fact that the class of admissible functions of $\tilde{S}$ is a smaller class than that for S. It is therefore clear that the n natural frequencies obtained by the Rayleigh-Ritz method, interpreted in the light of either Art. 4.7 or Art. 4.8, must be equal to or greater than the first n frequencies of the actual system. Hence

$$\omega_1 \leq \tilde{\omega}_1, \omega_2 \leq \tilde{\omega}_2, \cdots, \omega_n \leq \tilde{\omega}_n$$

and by retaining more terms in (99) or by adding more functions to the generating set for (82) the answers tend to be improved. In other words, *the Rayleigh-Ritz method approximates the natural frequencies from above* and can always be used to establish their upper bounds.

(C) ADDITIONAL REMARKS ABOUT ENERGY METHOD

(i) From the simple example worked out in (A) it is seen that the energy method can give usable engineering answers for the lowest natural frequency with a relatively small, well-chosen generating set. The eigenfunction obtained from the approximate method is, however, not quite so reliable, especially at places near a boundary point at which a natural boundary condition is not satisfied by the functions in the generating set. A look at Fig. 93 will reveal this fact.

(ii) If n lowest natural frequencies are to be found, a generating set larger than n functions is needed. How much larger the generating set has to be depends on the nature of the functions chosen. If they have close analytical resemblance to the eigenfunctions of the problem, only a few more than n functions are needed. The existence of such resemblance can be assured if the diagonal elements of both $\mathbf{A}$ and $\mathbf{C}$ for the approximating system are much larger than their off-diagonal elements. Although this condition is not mathematically necessary for the generating set to generate functions closely approximating eigenfunctions, in practice we always aim to achieve this condition.

(iii) It must be pointed out that in practical problems we are seldom interested in knowing more than the first few natural modes of the system. Furthermore, although the energy method combined with a digital computer can determine accurately the higher eigenvalues and their associated eigenfunctions, they may not describe the actual modes of vibration. This is because the mathematical formulation often loses its physical validity for these modes. For instance, the first few modes of the lateral vibration of a round bar having a length-to-diameter ratio of 10 can be described accurately by the equations or energy expressions obtained from the elementary theory of beams. But these same equations and energy expressions are grossly in error when applied to, say, the tenth or higher modes.

(iv) The labor required as well as the accuracy obtainable in solving problems approximately by the energy method depends upon the choice of generating functions $\phi_1, \phi_2, \ldots, \phi_n$. A desirable choice is one which facilitates the evaluation of the integral in (83) and yields a pair of matrices **A** and **C**, whose diagonal terms are much larger than the off-diagonal terms. In other words, we aim to make the ϕ's and the true eigenfunctions as nearly alike as possible, without excessive computational labor.

There are no hard and fast rules to be followed in achieving these results. The following observations, however, may serve as a rough guide.

(i) Polynomials are often conveniently chosen as generating functions because they can be easily differentiated, integrated, and made to satisfy the boundary conditions. For instance, in analyzing a nonuniform beam with a built-in end at $x = 0$ and a free end at $x = L$ the generating set can be simply

$$x^2, x^3, x^4, \cdots, x^n$$

which satisfy the imposed boundary condition at $x = 0$ but not the natural boundary condition at $x = L$. Or we may use as the generating set

$$\begin{aligned} \phi_1 &= x^4 - 4Lx^3 + 6L^2x^2 \\ \phi_2 &= x^5 - 10L^2x^3 + 20L^3x^2 \\ \phi_3 &= x^6 - 20L^3x^3 + 45L^4x^2 \\ \phi_4 &= x^7 - 35L^4x^3 + 84L^5x^2 \\ &\cdots\cdots\cdots \end{aligned}$$

which satisfy all the boundary conditions.

It is to be expected that for a given accuracy we need fewer functions of the second set than will be needed if the first set is used. The matrix problem resulting from the second generating set will be smaller but it will take longer to compute a_{ij} and c_{ij} defined by (83).

(ii) It is always desirable to take advantage of any known orthogonal properties relative to the differential operators M and L. For instance, if M is merely a simple multiplication constant, then the generating set can be simple sine and cosine functions satisfying the imposed boundary conditions. In that way, $a_{ij} = 0$, when $i \neq j$; or, if $\mathsf{M} = x$, we may choose Bessel functions of the appropriate order satisfying the imposed boundary conditions.

(iii) If by changing the natural boundary conditions of a problem the eigenfunctions are known, these eigenfunctions can be advantageously chosen to be the generating functions of the original problem. For example, the eigenfunctions (36) of the cantilever beam shown in Fig. 88 are good generating functions for the system in Fig. 92, especially when the right-end spring supports are soft. Similarly, if by a slight change of the differential equation the eigenfunctions of the problem are known, they can be used as the generating functions of the original problem.

4.9 Forced Vibration of Elastic Bodies

(A) CONCENTRATED FORCE APPLIED AT A FIXED POINT

In Chapter 3 we discussed a method of solving forced-vibration problems by a transformation of coordinates that results in a set of differential equations, each of which contains only a single unknown, namely, one of the principal coordinates. The same approach has proved to be a convenient one for the problem at hand.

The essence of the discussions in Arts. 4.7 and 4.8 is that the distribution of elastic force and that of the inertia force in a vibrating elastic body can be characterized either by two differential operators L and M, together with a set of boundary conditions, or by two energy expressions V and T. Furthermore, if u is the *actual* displacement function during vibration, the energy expressions and the differential operators are related by

$$T = \tfrac{1}{2}\int_{\Sigma} \dot{u}\,\mathsf{M}(\dot{u})\,d\sigma$$
$$V = \tfrac{1}{2}\int_{\Sigma} u\mathsf{L}(u)\,d\sigma \tag{109}$$

where $\dot{u}$ stands for $\partial u/\partial t$.

In free vibrations the principle of conservation of energy

$$\frac{d}{dt}(T + V) = 0$$

leads to the equations of motion. Similarly, we may derive the equations of motion for forced vibrations from

$$\frac{d}{dt}(T + V) = \text{rate of doing work by external forces}$$

For a given elastic system the energy expressions V and T, as well as the operators L and M, are the same regardless of whether the vibration is forced or free.

Let u be the displacement function describing the forced vibration of an elastic body. Let the eigenfunctions for the free vibration of this elastic body be $r_1, r_2, \ldots, r_i, \ldots$. The function u can be expanded into an infinite series of r's.

$$u(x, t) = \sum_{i=1}^{\infty} p_i(t) r_i(x) \tag{110}$$

We assume here that there is only one space variable, x. However, the generalization to cases with more than one space variable is immediate.

As the eigenfunctions in free vibration, the r's have the property

$$\left.\begin{aligned} \int_0^L r_i \mathsf{M}(r_j)\, dx &= 0 \\ \int_0^L r_i \mathsf{L}(r_j)\, dx &= 0 \end{aligned}\right\} \quad i \neq j \tag{111}$$

and

$$\mathsf{L}(r_i) = \omega_i^2 \mathsf{M}(r_i) \tag{112}$$

Now let us call for simplicity

$$\int_\Sigma r_i \mathsf{M}(r_i)\, d\sigma = m_{ii} \tag{113}$$

By substituting (110) into (109) and utilizing (111), (112), and (113), we have

$$T = \tfrac{1}{2} \sum_{i=1}^{\infty} m_{ii} \dot{p}_i^2 \qquad V = \tfrac{1}{2} \sum_{i=1}^{\infty} m_{ii} \omega_i^2 p_i^2$$

Hence

$$\frac{d}{dt}(T + V) = \sum_{i=1}^{\infty} m_{ii}(\ddot{p}_i + \omega_i^2 p_i)\dot{p}_i$$

Let a force $f(t)$ in the direction of u be applied at a fixed point in the body at $x = \xi$. The rate of doing work by this force is

$$f(t)\dot{u}(\xi, t) = f(t) \sum_{i=1}^{\infty} \dot{p}_i r_i(\xi)$$

Therefore, the energy equation leads to

$$\sum_{i=1}^{\infty} [m_{ii}(\ddot{p}_i + \omega_i^2 p_i) - f(t) r_i(\xi)]\dot{p}_i = 0 \tag{114}$$

Since $\dot{p}_i$'s are not dynamically related to p_i or $\ddot{p}_i$, being dependent upon initial conditions which are quite arbitrary, the vanishing of (113) demands that

$$m_{ii}(\ddot{p}_i + \omega_i^2 p_i) = f(t) r_i(\xi) \qquad i = 1, 2, 3, \cdots \tag{115}$$

There is an infinite number of equations in (115), but each contains only one unknown, which can be found separately by the methods discussed in Chapter 1. The initial conditions for p_i are derived from those for u.

$$u(x, t_0) = \sum_{i=1}^{\infty} p_i(0) r_i(x)$$

$$\left(\frac{\partial u}{\partial t}\right)_{t=t_0} = \sum_{i=1}^{\infty} \dot{p}_i(0) r_i(x)$$

After the p's are obtained, they are put into (110) to get the solution for u.

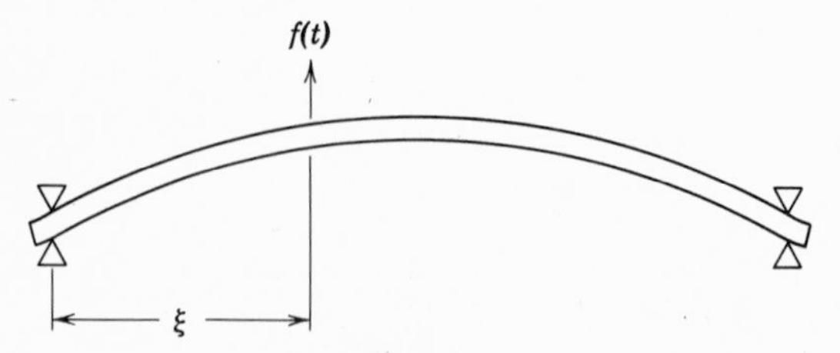

Figure 94

The solution is in the form of an infinite series. This series must be convergent and termwise differentiable in order that the operations leading to (114) legitimate. Such is usually the case.

To illustrate the procedure, let us take the case of a simply supported beam, having uniform cross sections and subjected to a concentrated force $f(t)$ at $x = \xi$, as shown in Fig. 94. According to the results on p. 257 the eigenfunctions for this case are the sine functions

$$r_i = \sin \frac{i\pi x}{L}$$

and the eigenvalues are given by

$$\omega_i^2 = \frac{EI\beta_i^4}{\rho A} = \frac{EI}{\rho A}\left(\frac{\pi i}{L}\right)^4$$

and

$$m_{ii} = \int_0^L \sin^2 \frac{i\pi x}{2}\, dx = \frac{L}{2} \qquad \text{for all } i$$

By substituting these into (115), we have

$$\ddot{p}_i + \frac{EI}{\rho A}\left(\frac{\pi}{L}\right)^4 i^4 p_i = \frac{2}{L} \sin \frac{i\pi\xi}{L} f(t)$$

(B) DISTRIBUTED EXTERNAL FORCE, MOVING EXTERNAL FORCE, AND GENERALIZED EXTERNAL FORCE

The results given in (A) can now be generalized in the following three ways:

(i) If the external force is distributed over the elastic body with the distribution described by

$$f = f(x, t)$$

(115) is modified into

$$m_{ii}(\ddot{p}_i + \omega_i^2 p_i) = \int_0^L f(\xi, t) r_i(\xi)\, d\xi \tag{116}$$

by the principle of superposition.

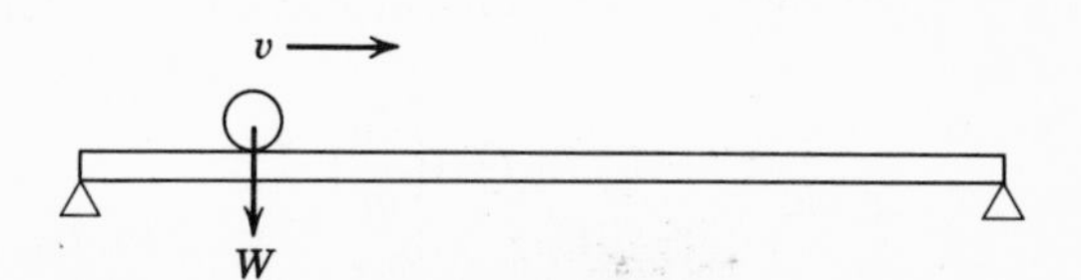

Figure 95

(ii) If a concentrated external force changes its point of application, then $\xi = \xi(t)$, and (115) is changed into

$$m_{ii}(\ddot{p}_i + \omega_i^2 p_i) = f(t) r_i[\xi(t)]$$

This is true because there is nothing in the derivation of (115) that implies ξ is fixed. This generalization is of practical interest in studying vibrations of a structure under a moving load. For example, in Fig. 95 a weight W moves across the simply supported horizontal beam with a uniform velocity v, and the force exerted on the beam is of magnitude

$$-W - \frac{W}{g} a_w = f(t) \tag{117}$$

in which a_w is the vertical acceleration of W. If $a_w \ll g$, (115) is modified into

$$m_{ii}(\ddot{p}_i + \omega_i^2 p_i) = -W r_i[(vt + \xi_0)]$$

in which ξ_0 is the location of W at $t = t_0$. Otherwise

$$a_w = \left(\frac{\partial^2 u}{\partial t^2} + 2v\frac{\partial^2 u}{\partial x\, \partial t} + v^2\frac{\partial^2 u}{\partial x^2}\right)_{x=\xi}$$

$$= \sum_{j=1}^{\infty}[r_j(\xi)\ddot{p}_j + 2vr_j'(\xi)\dot{p}_j + v^2 r_j''(\xi)p_j]$$

By substituting this expression for a_w in (117) and (115) and replacing ξ by $(vt + \xi_0)$, we obtain a set of linear differential equations for p's in which the coefficients vary with time. Furthermore, all the unknowns appear in all the equations. Such equations are not readily solvable. They are mentioned here merely to illustrate the fact than when additional inertia force due to W exists the original set of eigenfunctions is no longer that of the new system, and since this additional inertia force changes its location the system is no longer time-invariant.

(iii) *Generalized forces.* In the preceding examples we assume that work is done by external forces applied in the direction of the displacement u, and for a single concentrated force at $x = \xi$ the rate of doing work is

$$\frac{d}{dt}(T + V) = f(t)\left(\frac{\partial u}{\partial t}\right)_{x=\xi}$$

But there are other ways in which external forces may do work. Taking the lateral vibrations of bars as an example, we know that work can be performed by a couple or moment in the plane of bending of the bar. In that case

$$\frac{d}{dt}(T + V) = M(t)\left(\frac{\partial^2 u}{\partial t\, \partial x}\right)_{x=\xi} = \sum_{i=1}^{\infty} M(t)r_i'(\xi)\dot{p}(t)$$

Thus (115) is modified into

$$m_{ii}(\ddot{p}_i + \omega_i^2 p_i) = M(t)r_1'(\xi)$$

Work can also be performed by a pair of equal and opposite axial forces acting on two ends of the bar, as shown in Fig. 96. Let the force be $P(t)$; then

$$\frac{d}{dt}(T + V) = P(t)\dot{X}(t)$$

where $X(t)$ is the displacement relative between the two ends. To compute $X(t)$, we observe that two points on the neutral axis a distance dx apart are separated in the axial direction during vibration by a distance $dx \cos\theta$, where θ is the slope of the deflected bar.[24] Hence

$$\dot{X}(t) = \frac{d}{dt}\int_0^L dx\,(1 - \cos\theta) \doteq \frac{d}{dt}\int_0^L dx\,\frac{\theta^2}{2}$$

$$\doteq \frac{d}{dt}\int_0^L \frac{1}{2}\left(\frac{\partial u}{\partial x}\right)^2 dx$$

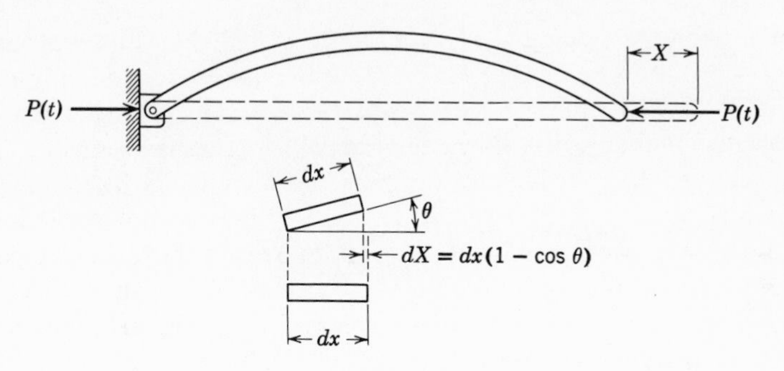

Figure 96

By utilizing (110), we have

$$\dot{X}(t) = \sum_{i=1}^{\infty}\sum_{j=1}^{\infty} \dot{p}_i p_j \int_0^L r_i'(x) r_j'(x)\,dx$$

This modifies (115) to read

$$m_{ii}(\ddot{p}_i + \omega_i^2 p_i) = P(t)\sum_{j=1}^{\infty} p_j \int_0^L r_i'(x) r_j'(x)\,dx$$

The introduction of axial forces is similar to a change in the elastic property of the system. As a result, the r's are no longer the eigenfunctions and the p's no longer appear separately in the equations. In the particular case of a uniform bar with two hinged ends

$$r_i(x) = \sin\frac{i\pi x}{L}$$

$$r_i'(x) = \frac{i\pi}{L}\cos\frac{i\pi x}{L}$$

it so happens that

$$\int_0^L r_i'(x) r_j'(x)\,dx = 0 \qquad i \neq j$$

$$\int_0^L [r_i'(x)]^2\,dx = \frac{i^2\pi^2}{2L}$$

[24] The effects of the direct compressive stress produced by $P(t)$ are neglected.

Here again we have a set of equations with variables separated:

$$m_{ii}(\ddot{p}_i + \omega_i^2 p_i) = \frac{i^2\pi^2}{2L} P(t)p_i(t)$$

or

$$m_{ii}\ddot{p}_i + \left(m_{ii}\omega_i^2 - \frac{i^2\pi^2}{2L} P(t)\right) p_i = 0$$

Since for this particular case

$$m_{ii} = \rho A \int_0^L \sin^2 \frac{i\pi x}{L}\, dx = \frac{\rho AL}{2}$$

$$\omega_i^2 = \beta^4 \frac{EI}{\rho A} = \frac{i^4\pi^4 EI}{\rho AL^4}$$

we have

$$\frac{\rho AL}{2} \ddot{p}_i + \frac{i^2\pi^2}{2L}\left(\frac{i^2\pi^2 EI}{L^2} - P(t)\right) p_i = 0$$

If P is a constant, the foregoing equation can be considered as the standard form for systems in free vibration.

$$\ddot{p}_i + \tilde{\omega}_i^2 p_i = 0$$

where

$$\tilde{\omega}_i^2 = \frac{i^2\pi^2}{\rho AL^2}\left(\frac{i^2\pi^2 EI}{L^2} - P\right)$$

In other words the existence of an axial force merely modifies the elastic force of the system; hence it changes the natural frequencies. It is interesting to note that if P is equal to Euler's critical load for column buckling

$$P = \frac{\pi^2 EI}{L^2}$$

then $\tilde{\omega}_1 = 0$, and the system is in a neutral equilibrium. If P is *less* than Euler's critical load, all the natural frequencies will be real and positive, and the system is stable. If P is *greater* than Euler's critical load, one or more of the natural frequencies will be imaginary, and the system is capable of a spontaneous motion in which the displacements will grow without limit. The system is therefore unstable. The fact that a column subjected to axial forces greater than Euler's buckling load is an unstable column is thus explained by theory of vibration, whereas it cannot be explained by elementary column theory. We can therefore state that the criterion for the stability of an elastic system is *the absence of negative eigenvalues or imaginary frequencies* in the free vibration problem of the system.

(C) INDICIAL RESPONSE, IMPULSE RESPONSE, AND IMPACT—GENERAL SOLUTION OF FORCED VIBRATION PROBLEMS

The indicial response of an elastic system can be defined as the vibration caused by a concentrated unit step force applied at a fixed point in the system and at a time when the system is at rest.

Let this indicial response be denoted by the function $U(\xi, x, t)$ for a one-dimensional elastic system. If its eigenfunction-series expansion is

$$U(\xi, x, t) = \sum_{i=1}^{\infty} p_i(t) r_i(x)$$

then p_i is the solution to

$$m_{ii}(\ddot{p}_i + \omega_i^2 p_i) = \mathcal{J}(t) r_i(\xi) \qquad i = 1, 2, 3, \cdots$$

under the initial conditions that

$$p_i(0) = 0 \qquad \dot{p}_i(0) = 0$$

According to (75) of Chapter 1,

$$p_i(t) = \frac{r_i(\xi)}{m_{ii}\omega_i^2}(1 - \cos \omega_i t)$$

Hence

$$U(\xi, x, t) = \sum_{i=1}^{\infty} \frac{r_i(\xi) r_i(x)}{m_{ii}\omega_i^2}(1 - \cos \omega_i t)$$

The impulse response, which describes the free vibration caused by an impact, is obtained by differentiating U with respect to t.

$$U'(\xi, x, t) = \sum_{i=1}^{\infty} \frac{r_i(\xi) r_i(x)}{m_{ii}\omega_i} \sin \omega_i t$$

Thus, if the system is initially at rest and is subsequently set into motion by a force $f(t)$ applied at $x = \xi$, the solution is

$$u(x, t) = \sum_{i=1}^{\infty} \frac{r_i(\xi) r_i(x)}{m_{ii}\omega_i} \int_0^t f(\tau) \sin \omega_i(t - \tau)\, d\tau \tag{118}$$

And, if we are dealing with distributed force of distribution $g(\xi, t)$, the solution is

$$u(x, t) = \sum_{i=1}^{\infty} \int_0^L \int_0^t \frac{g(\xi, \tau) r_i(\xi) r_i(x)}{m_{ii}\omega_i} \sin \omega_i(t - \tau)\, d\tau\, d\xi \tag{119}$$

This is the general solution of forced vibration of a one-dimensional elastic body which is initially at rest.

4.10 Vibration of an Infinite or Semi-Infinite Elastic Body—Wave Phenomenon

(A) CONTINUOUS FREQUENCY SPECTRUM

The systems we have dealt with so far are finite in extent. A system of this kind was found to possess a set of distinct natural modes, and its natural frequencies form a discrete set of values. As a result, any free vibration it may have is representable by an infinite series

$$u = \sum_{i=1}^{\infty} C_i \cos(\omega_i t - \alpha_i) r_i \tag{120}$$

The total energy possessed by the system in a given vibratory motion is

$$\begin{aligned} T + V &= \tfrac{1}{2}\int_{\Sigma} [\dot{u}\,\mathsf{M}(\dot{u}) + u\mathsf{L}(u)]\, d\sigma \\ &= \tfrac{1}{2}\sum_{i=1}^{\infty} m_{ii} C_i^2 \omega_i^2 \end{aligned} \tag{121}$$

where m_{ii} is defined in (113). The total energy expression (121) indicates that a unique and definite amount of energy is associated with each natural frequency or that between different natural modes there is no energy transfer. Because the natural frequencies are discrete the free vibrations of a finite body are said to have *discrete frequency spectra.*

To examine the changes when an elastic body becomes infinite or semi-infinite in extent, let us reflect that for a finite body the eigenvalues or the natural frequencies are determined by the conditions at the boundary. When a system becomes infinite or semi-infinite, all or part of its boundary is located at infinity, where the prevailing conditions are hardly expected to have an effect on the motion of the interior mass elements of the system. Take, for example, the longitudinal vibration of a uniform bar with a fixed end at $x = 0$. The eigenfunction is

$$r(x) = \sin \beta x$$

The allowable values for β, or the eigenvalues, are determined by a linear homogeneous boundary condition at $x = L$.

$$ar + br' = a \sin \beta L + b\beta \cos \beta L = 0 \tag{122}$$

This becomes the characteristic equation of the problem. Now, as L becomes infinitely large, this equation can be satisfied by any arbitrary real value[25] of β. Looking at the problem in another way, we see that the

[25] To state it correctly, we should say that given an arbitrarily small $\epsilon > 0$, with a sufficiently large L we can find for every real positive β a $\tilde{\beta}$ such that $\tilde{\beta}$ satisfies (122) and $|\beta - \tilde{\beta}| < \epsilon$.

characteristic equation for a one-dimensional continuum is satisfied by $\beta L =$ (one of a set of dimensionless numbers). The difference between two consecutive numbers is always finite.

$$\beta_{i+1}L - \beta_i L \le N < \infty \qquad \text{for all } i$$

Hence

$$\lim_{L \to \infty} (\beta_{i+1} - \beta_i) = 0 \qquad \text{for all } i$$

All this means that when an elastic body is infinite in extent *its frequency spectrum becomes continuous.*

(B) A PHENOMENON OF WAVE PROPAGATION

The concept of the natural mode of vibration loses its physical significance in dealing with an infinite or semi-infinite body, not only because the natural frequencies are no longer distinct, but also because the vibration represented by an eigenfunction cannot be excited without an infinite amount of energy input. For instance, a longitudinal vibration represented by

$$u(x, t) = C \sin \beta x \cos (\omega t - \alpha)$$

$$\beta = \omega \sqrt{E/\rho} \qquad C > 0$$

is mathematically possible for a uniform bar of infinite length. But such vibration is of little physical interest, since its energy content is infinite as

$$(T + V) = \frac{1}{2}\int_0^\infty \omega^2 C^2 \sin^2 \beta x \, dx = \infty$$

A more realistic physical problem follows. An infinite elastic medium is initially at quiescent state. A finite disturbance is introduced at certain parts of the medium. What is the resulting motion of the medium?

Consider again the longitudinal vibration of a uniform bar, which is governed by the one-dimensional wave equation:

$$\frac{\partial^2 u}{\partial t^2} = c^2 \frac{\partial^2 u}{\partial x^2} \tag{123}$$

where

$$c = +\sqrt{E/\rho}$$

The general solution to this second-order, partial differential equation is

$$u = \phi(x - ct) + \psi(x + ct) \tag{124}$$

in which ϕ and ψ are two arbitrary, twice-differentiable functions. The way x and t enter into the arguments of ϕ and ψ indicates that a propagation phenomenon is involved. Obviously,

$$\phi(x_1 - ct_1) = \phi(x_2 - ct_2)$$

if

$$x_2 - x_1 = c(t_2 - t_1)$$

Stated in words, these equations say that whatever exists at x_1 will exist at x_2 at an instant $(x_2 - x_1)/c$ *later*. The phenomenon represented by ϕ therefore propagates to the right. Similarly,

$$\psi(x_1 + ct_1) = \psi(x_2 + ct_2)$$

if

$$x_2 - x_1 = -c(t_2 - t_1)$$

which says that whatever exists at x_1 existed at x_2 at an instant $(x_2 - x_1)/c$ *earlier*. The phenomenon represented by ψ therefore propagates to the left. In either case the speed of propagation is the constant c.

Now let us suppose we have a very long bar extending from $x = a < 0$ to $x = b > 0$. A small external disturbance is introduced into the bar near $x = 0$ at $t = 0$. Let this disturbance be in the form of an initial displacement, which is restricted to a small interval containing the point $x = 0$. The initial conditions are thus

$$u(x, 0) = U(x)$$
$$\left(\frac{\partial u}{\partial t}\right)_{t=0} \equiv 0 \tag{125}$$

As shown in Fig. 97, the initial displacement function $U(x)$ is zero, outside of a small interval. It can be readily verified that both the differential equation (123) and the initial conditions (125) will be satisfied if we let

$$\phi = \psi = \tfrac{1}{2}U$$

in (124), or

$$u(x, t) = \tfrac{1}{2}U(x - ct) + \tfrac{1}{2}U(x + ct) \tag{126}$$

Hence the disturbance introduces splits into two equal waves and propagates in two opposite directions with a constant speed c. If the bar extends to infinity at both ends, then (126) is valid for all t's. If, on the other hand, the bar terminates at a finite point or points, the solution (126) is valid for a time interval $0 \leq t \leq t_1$, in which t_1 is time required for the disturbance to reach one or both ends of the bar. This is so, regardless

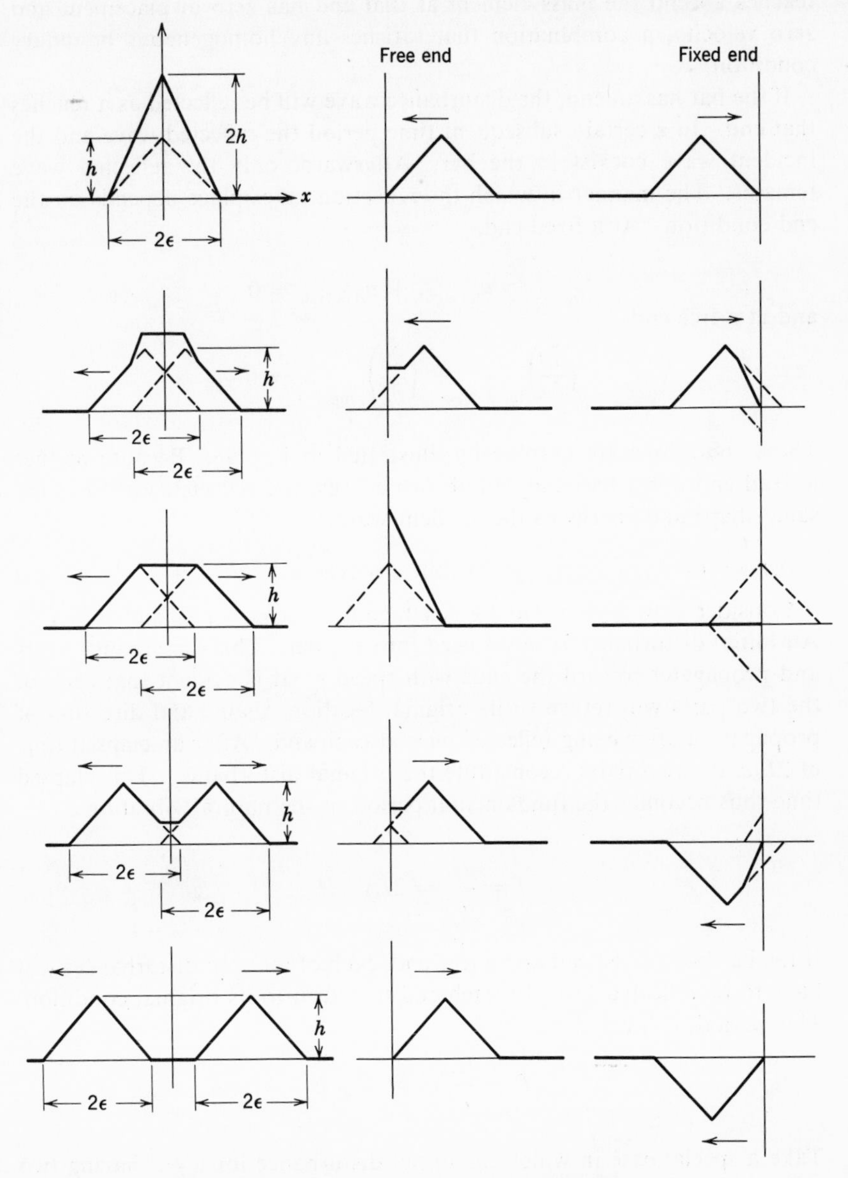

Figure 97

Figure 98

of the end conditions, because, according to (126), until the disturbance reaches an end the mass element at that end has zero displacement and zero velocity, a combination that satisfies any homogeneous boundary condition.

If the bar has an end, the disturbance wave will be reflected as it reaches that end. In a certain subsequent time period the reflected wave and the incident wave coexist in the bar. Afterward, only the reflected wave remains. The manner in which the reflection takes place depends on the end condition. At a fixed end

$$u_{\text{incident}} + u_{\text{reflected}} = 0$$

and at a free end

$$\left(\frac{\partial u}{\partial x}\right)_{\text{incident}} + \left(\frac{\partial u}{\partial x}\right)_{\text{reflected}} = 0$$

These conditions are graphically illustrated in Fig. 98. Because neither a fixed end nor a free end can absorb energy, the reflected wave has the same shape and energy as the incident wave.

(C) NATURAL MODES AND STANDING WAVES

Consider now a bar having fixed ends at $x = -L/2$ and $x = L/2$. An initial disturbance is introduced into the bar. This disturbance splits and propagates toward the ends with speed c. It is evident that each of the two parts will return to its original location, shape, and direction of propagation after being reflected *once* at each end. After an elapsed time of $2L/c$, the two parts reconstitute the original disturbance. This elapsed time thus becomes the fundamental period of the natural vibration

$$T = \frac{2L}{c} = 2L\sqrt{\rho/E}$$

If the bar has a fixed end and a free end, each of the split disturbances will have to be reflected twice by each end to return to its original condition. The period is then

$$T = \frac{4L}{c} = 4L\sqrt{\rho/E}$$

Take a special case in which the initial disturbance for a bar having two fixed ends is given by

$$U(x) = C \sin \frac{\pi x}{L}$$

Referring to Fig. 99, we see after the wave splits that the reflection from one part complements the incident wave of the other part to constitute a shifted half sine wave. Hence for this special case (126) is always valid. Therefore,

$$u(x, t) = \tfrac{1}{2}C\left[\sin\frac{\pi}{L}(x - ct) + \sin\frac{\pi}{L}(x + ct)\right]$$
$$= C \sin\frac{\pi x}{L} \cos\frac{\pi ct}{L}$$

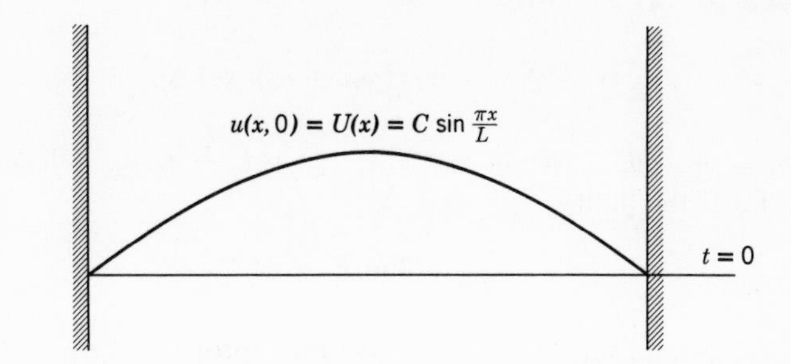

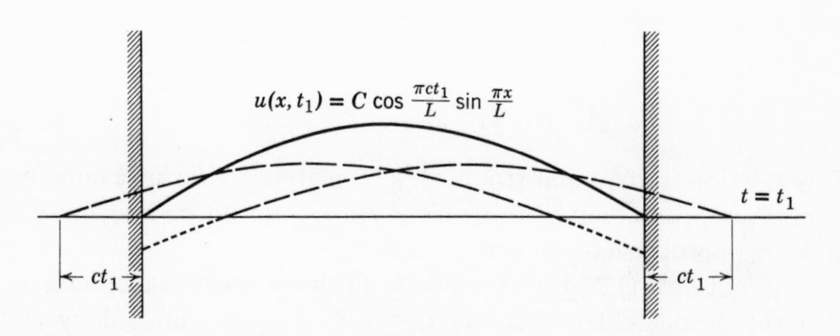

Figure 99

Since the shape of the displacement curve is now always a half sine wave, we call it a *standing wave*, and it represents the first natural mode of vibration. A standing wave can also be formed in this case by

$$U(x) = C \sin\frac{n\pi x}{L}$$

in which n is any integer.

(D) LATERAL VIBRATION OF AN INFINITE BAR

We now illustrate another approach to the analysis of vibrations of an infinite body. A mathematically rigorous development of the subject to be discussed must utilize the theory of Fourier transformation. Here we have to be satisfied with a version that is mathematically less rigorous but physically more informative.

Let us begin with a finite bar extending from $x = -L/2$ to $x = L/2$. According to (37), the free vibration of this bar can be described by

$$v(x, t) = \sum_{i=1}^{\infty} C_i \cos (\omega_i t - \alpha_i) r_i(x) \tag{37}$$

Since for each i there is a β_i, we may consider C, ω, α, and r as functions of a variable β. Let us rewrite (37) as

$$v(x, t) = \sum_{i=1}^{\infty} \frac{C_i}{\Delta\beta_i} \cos (\omega_i t - \alpha_i) r_i(x) \, \Delta\beta_i \tag{127}$$

where $\Delta\beta_i = \beta_i - \beta_{i-1}$. We noted in (A) that as $L \to \infty$, $\beta_1 \to 0$, $\Delta\beta_i \to 0$, and $C_i \to 0$. If the limit

$$\lim_{L\to\infty} \frac{C_i}{\Delta\beta_i} = \lim E_i < \infty$$

exists, the right-hand side of (127) becomes an improper integral as $L \to \infty$ or $\Delta\beta_i \to 0$.

$$v(x, t) = \int_0^{\infty} E(\beta) \cos (\omega t - \alpha) r(\beta, x) \, d\beta \tag{128}$$

where

$$\omega = \beta^2 \sqrt{EI/\rho A} \tag{129}$$

This solution is arrived at strictly in a formal way. We have no knowledge of the appearance of $E(\beta)$, $\alpha(\beta)$, and $r(\beta, x)$, nor do we know whether or not the improper integral converges.

To find out how (128) can be made to fit the problem, we observe first that if the partial differential equation (28) is to be satisfied by (128) $r(\beta, x)$ must satisfy (30). Hence from (32)

$$r(\beta, x) = A \sin \beta x + B \cos \beta x + C \sinh \beta x + D \cosh \beta x$$

in which A, B, C, and D may be functions of β but not of x. Since (128) must converge for all x and since hyperbolic functions grow without limit, the coefficients C and D must vanish. Thus

$$\begin{aligned} r(\beta, x) &= A \sin \beta x + B \cos \beta x \\ &= F(\beta) \cos (\beta x - \delta) \end{aligned}$$

By substituting this into (128) and combining E and F into a new function G, we have

$$v(x, t) = \int_0^{\infty} G(\beta) \cos (\omega t - \alpha) \cos (\beta x - \delta) \, d\beta \tag{130}$$

Now let us take a simple initial condition

$$v(x, 0) = V(x)$$
$$\left(\frac{\partial v}{\partial t}\right)_{t=0} = 0$$

Furthermore, let us assume that V is an even function, $V(x) = V(-x)$. It is not difficult to see that these conditions imply

$$\alpha(\beta) \equiv 0 \qquad \text{and} \qquad \delta(\beta) \equiv 0$$
$$V(x) = \int_0^\infty G(\beta) \cos \beta x \, d\beta \tag{131}$$

This is the formula for a Fourier cosine transform,[26] and the inverse is given by

$$G(\beta) = \frac{2}{\pi}\int_0^\infty V(x) \cos (\beta x) \, dx$$

The solution is then

$$v(x, t) = \int_0^\infty G(\beta) \cos \omega t \cos \beta x \, d\beta \tag{132}$$

where ω is given by (129). By an identical procedure, we can show that if the initial displacement is an odd function of x

$$v(x, 0) = V(x) = -V(-x)$$

then

$$\delta = -\pi/2$$

and

$$v(x, t) = \int_0^\infty G(\beta) \cos \omega t \sin \beta x \, d\beta \tag{133}$$

where

$$G(\beta) = \frac{2}{\pi}\int_0^\infty V(x) \sin \beta x \, dx$$

Since any arbitrary initial displacement function can be decomposed into an even function and an odd function by

$$V(x) \equiv \tfrac{1}{2}[V(x) + V(-x)] + \tfrac{1}{2}[V(x) - V(-x)]$$

by the principle of superposition, we can obtain the solution for any initial displacement $V(x)$. The result is

$$v(x, t) = \frac{1}{\pi}\int_0^\infty \int_{-\infty}^\infty V(\xi) \cos \beta(\xi - x) \cos \omega t \, d\xi \, d\beta \tag{134}$$

---

[26] See Sneddon, *Fourier Transforms*, McGraw-Hill, New York, 1951, p. 18.

4.11 Method of Finite Difference

A very straightforward way of solving an eigenvalue problem numerically is by the method of finite difference. The principle is simply that differential equations and integral equations can be approximated by algebraic equations. The technique, however, has many refinements and ramifications. In this article we shall illustrate the basic principle by simple examples.[27]

(A) FINITE DIFFERENCE APPROXIMATION FOR A DIFFERENTIAL EQUATION

Consider the eigenvalue problem in the lateral vibration of uniform bars. Formulation by differential equation leads to

$$\frac{d^4r}{dx^4} - \beta^4 r = 0 \tag{135}$$

Let $(n + 1)$ equally spaced points be chosen along the bar. These are called the *pivot points*: $x_0 = 0, x_1 = h, x_2 = 2h, \ldots, x_n = nh = L$. Let the corresponding values and the derivatives for r be designated by

$$r_0 = r(0), r_1 = r(h), r_2 = r(2h), \cdots, r_n = r(L)$$

$$r_0' = r'(0), r_1' = r'(h), \cdots, r_n' = r'(L)$$

For the purpose of deriving formulas we must also introduce the following intermediate pivot points:

$$x_{1/2} = \frac{h}{2} \qquad x_{1\,1/2} = \frac{3h}{2} \qquad \text{etc.}$$

The derivatives of r of various orders can then be approximated by the following difference formulas

$$hr_i' = (r_{i+1/2} - r_{i-1/2})$$

$$h^2 r_i'' = h(r'_{i+1/2} - r'_{i-1/2}) = (r_{i+1} - r_i - r_i + r_{i-1})$$

$$= r_{i+1} - 2r_i + r_{i-1}$$

$$h^3 r_i''' = h^2(r''_{i+1/2} - r''_{i+1/2})$$

$$= r_{i+3/2} - 2r_{i+1/2} + r_{i-1/2} - (r_{i+1/2} - 2r_{i-1/2} + r_{i-3/2})$$

$$= r_{i+3/2} - 3r_{i+1/2} + 3r_{i-1/2} - r_{i-3/2} \tag{136}$$

It is not difficult to show that the formulas resemble that of binomial expansion for

$$a^i(a^{1/2} - a^{-1/2})^j$$

---

[27] See also the example at the end of Art. 4.2(A).

in which the exponents of a become the subscripts for r and the coefficients in the expansions are the same. At any rate, the approximation for the fourth-order derivative needed for the present problem is

$$\frac{d^4r}{dx^4} = r_i'''' = \frac{1}{h^4}(r_{i+2} - 4r_{i+1} + 6r_i - 4r_{i-1} + r_{i-2})$$

$$i = 1, 2, \cdots, (n-1)$$

We can thus approximate (135) by

$$r_{i+2} - 4r_{i+1} + 6r_i - 4r_{i-1} + r_{i-2} = (h\beta)^4 r_i \qquad i = 1, 2, \cdots, (n-1) \tag{137}$$

There is one such equation for each *interior pivot point*.

Besides the interior pivot points, there are two boundary points. Moreover, to write the difference equation (137) for an interior pivot point near the boundary, we shall also need two *imaginary pivot points* lying outside the interval 0 to L. The values of r at these four points must either be known or be expressed in terms of those for the interior points by the use of the boundary conditions.

At a hinged end,

$$r(0) = 0 \qquad \text{thus} \qquad r_0 = 0$$

$$r''(0) = 0 \qquad \text{thus} \qquad r_{-1} - 2r_0 + r_1 = 0 \qquad \text{or} \qquad r_{-1} = -r_1$$

At a built-in end

$$r(0) = 0 \qquad \text{thus} \qquad r_0 = 0$$

$$r'(0) = 0 \qquad \text{thus} \qquad r_1 = r_{-1}$$

At a free end the situation is slightly complicated. There we try to write (137) differently for the nearby interior pivot points so that they will not include r_{-1} and/or r_0. This is done by the following scheme.

The fourth derivative of the first pivot point may be written

$$r_1'''' = (r_1'')'' = \frac{1}{h^2}(r_2'' - 2r_1'' + r_0'')$$

Since $r_0'' = 0$

$$\begin{aligned} r_1'''' &= \frac{1}{h^4}(r_3 - 2r_2 + r_1 - 2r_2 + 4r_1 - 2r_0) \\ &= \frac{1}{h^4}(r_3 - 4r_2 + 5r_1 - 2r_0) \end{aligned} \tag{138}$$

In the meantime, the same derivative can also be written

$$r_1'''' = \frac{1}{2h}(r_2''' - r_0''') = \frac{1}{2h} r_2''' \qquad \text{since } r_0''' = 0$$

where we may approximate r_2''' by

$$r_2''' = \tfrac{1}{2}(r_{2.5}''' + r_{1.5}''')$$

Utilizing (136), we obtain

$$r_1'''' = \frac{1}{4h^4}(r_4 - 2r_3 + 2r_1 - r_0) \tag{139}$$

Elimination of r_0 between (138) and (139) yields

$$r_1'''' = \frac{1}{h^4}(2r_4 - 5r_3 + 4r_2 - r_1) = \beta^4 r_1 \tag{140}$$

This equation now replaces the first equation in (137). Also by equating (138) and (139), we can express r_0 in terms of r_1, r_2, r_3, and r_4. The resulting expression can be used to eliminate r_0 in the second equation of (137).

Example: To find the natural frequency for the first mode of lateral vibration of a uniform bar with hinged ends.

Let the spacing of pivot points be

$$h = \frac{L}{6}$$

Because of the symmetry of the motion to be investigated and of the end conditions it is known that

$$r_0 = 0 \quad r_6 = 0 \quad r_{-1} = r_1 = r_5 = r_7 \quad \text{and} \quad r_2 = r_4 \tag{141}$$

By utilizing these conditions, we obtain the first three equations for (137):

$$\begin{aligned} 5r_1 - 4r_2 + r_3 &= \lambda r_1 \\ -4r_1 + 7r_2 - 4r_3 &= \lambda r_2 \\ 2r_1 - 8r_2 + 6r_3 &= \lambda r_3 \end{aligned} \tag{142}$$

where

$$\lambda = (h\beta)^4 = \left(\frac{\beta L}{6}\right)^4$$

The remaining two equations of (137) are duplicates of the first two. The lowest eigenvalue of (142) is found to be

$$\lambda = 0.0718$$

and the corresponding eigenvector is (1, 1.732, 2). Hence

$$\beta L = 6 \times 0.0718^{1/4} = 3.108$$

The true answers are known to be

$$\beta L = \pi = 3.1416$$

$$r_1 : r_2 : r_3 = \sin\frac{\pi}{6} : \sin\frac{\pi}{3} : \sin\frac{\pi}{2} = 1 : 1.732 : 2$$

This represents an error of about 1 per cent in β and 2 per cent in ω, since ω is proportional to β^2. The values for r at the pivot points happen to be exact.

It is interesting to note that this method of approximation results in a frequency value lower than the true value, whereas most other approximating methods give a value higher than the true value. This is because the two sides are not equal in the approximation (136), and

$$h^4 r_1'''' = (r_{i+2} - 4r_{i+1} - 6r_i - 4r_{i-1} + r_{i-2}) + \epsilon$$

The error ϵ is approximately[28]

$$\epsilon \doteq -\frac{h^6}{6} r_i^{(6)} = -\frac{h^6}{6} \beta^4 r_i''$$

In a problem in which r is of the opposite sign to r'' the error term makes the finite difference approximation to r'''' too small. Physically, it means that the restoring force based on the approximation is too small or the system is too soft. The result is a frequency lower than the actual.

(B) FINITE DIFFERENCE APPROXIMATION FOR INTEGRAL EQUATION

In Art. 4.5 it was shown that the eigenfunction $r(x)$ satisfies the integral equation

$$\frac{1}{\omega^2} r(x) = \int_0^L G(x, \xi) m(\xi) r(\xi)\, d\xi$$

If we choose a set of equally spaced pivot points and integrate the right-hand side by either the trapezoid rule or Simpson's rule, we obtain a set of algebraic equations in r-values at the pivot points. Let us take again the vibration of a uniform bar with hinged ends and divide the interval into six segments. For a generic pivot point i the trapezoid rule yields

$$\frac{r_i}{\rho A \omega^2} = h\left(\frac{1}{2} G_{i0} r_0 + G_{i1} r_1 + G_{i2} r_2 + G_{i3} r_3 + G_{i4} r_4 + G_{i5} r_5 + \frac{1}{2} G_{i6} r_6\right)$$

For the first mode we can utilize (141) to obtain

$$\frac{r_i}{h\rho A \omega^2} = 2(G_{i1} + G_{i5}) r_1 + 2(G_{i2} + G_{i4}) r_2 + G_{i3} r_3 \qquad (143)$$

[28] Salvadori and Baron, *Numerical Methods in Engineering*, Prentice-Hall, New York, 1952, p. 67.

It can be shown by theorems in strength of materials that for a simply supported beam divided into sixths the influence coefficients are given by

$$G_{ij} = \frac{h^3}{36EI}(6 - i)j(12i - i^2 - j^2) \qquad \text{if } i \geq j$$

Since $G_{ij} = G_{ji}$, this formula is sufficient for computing all G's. Let

$$b = \frac{h^3}{36EI}$$

$$G_{11} = 50b \qquad G_{22} = 128b \qquad G_{33} = 162b$$

$$G_{12} = G_{21} = G_{45} = G_{54} = 76b$$
$$G_{13} = G_{31} = G_{35} = G_{53} = 78b$$
$$G_{23} = G_{32} = G_{34} = G_{43} = 138b$$
$$G_{14} = G_{41} = G_{25} = G_{52} = 62b$$

$$G_{24} = G_{42} = 120b \qquad G_{15} = G_{51} = 34b$$

Substitute the values for the influence coefficient into (143) and simplify

$$\begin{aligned} 42r_1 + 69r_2 + 39r_3 &= \lambda r_1 \\ 69r_1 + 124r_2 + 69r_3 &= \lambda r_2 \\ 78r_1 + 138r_2 + 81r_3 &= \lambda r_3 \end{aligned}$$

where

$$\lambda = \frac{18EI}{h^4 \rho A \omega^2} = \frac{18}{(\beta h)^4}$$

This time, since we are looking for the highest λ so we can use the matrix iteration method, we find

$$\begin{bmatrix} 42 & 69 & 39 \\ 69 & 124 & 69 \\ 78 & 138 & 81 \end{bmatrix} \begin{bmatrix} 1.00 \\ 1.76 \\ 2.00 \end{bmatrix} = \begin{bmatrix} 241.7 \\ 425.1 \\ 483.0 \end{bmatrix} = 241.7 \times \begin{bmatrix} 1.000 \\ 1.759 \\ 1.998 \end{bmatrix}$$

Hence

$$\lambda = \frac{18}{(\beta h)^4} = 241.7$$

or

$$\beta L = 6\left(\frac{18}{241.7}\right)^{1/4} = 3.135$$

The error in the natural frequency is thus very small.

(C) COMPARISON OF THE DIFFERENT APPROXIMATE METHODS

Although the examples we have chosen do not include many complexities that appear in practical problems solved by numerical methods, they do give an idea of the algebraic and arithmetic processes required. When handled properly, all numerical methods presented are capable of giving good answers. They differ, however, in convenience for different problems. The following general observations can be made regarding the relative merits of the two methods presented.

(i) Difference equations derived from the differential equation formulation of an eigenvalue problem have the advantage of being easy to set up. This is especially true when the boundary conditions are simple and when there are no abrupt changes in mass distribution and elastic properties in the system. When the number of pivot points is increased for accuracy, the number of unknowns in each equation does not increase, although there will be more unknowns and more equations to solve. The use of nonuniformly spaced pivot points is possible, but it is usually not convenient. The smallest eigenvalue of the set of difference equations derived from the differential equation corresponds to the lowest natural frequency of the system. This is an undesirable feature because it is necessary to compute the inverse matrix in order to use the matrix iteration method described in Chapter 3.

(ii) The setting up of difference equations approximating the integral equation requires extensive preliminary computation of the influence coefficients or the values of Green's function. On the other hand, this could be an advantage: (1) when a model of the system is available the coefficients can be determined experimentally; (2) the treatment of boundary conditions causes few special problems. The integration operation is a "smoothing" operation. It is particularly suited for taking care of abrupt changes in the interior of the system. For instance, if there is a concentrated mass M attached to the midpoint of the bar, its existence can be taken care of quickly by adding the term

$$\frac{M}{h\rho A} G_{i3} r_3$$

to the right-hand side of (143). The difference equation (137) cannot be modified so easily. The use of pivot points not evenly spaced requires very little modification of the trapezoid rule. When there are abrupt changes in cross section, the convenience with which the integral equation can be approximated with nonuniformly spaced pivot points becomes a distinct advantage. The matrix equation representing the integral equation is already in the inverse form. That is to say, the largest eigenvalue corresponds to the lowest natural frequency so that the matrix iteration method previously discussed can be immediately applied to determine the lower modes of vibration.

(iii) In comparing these two methods with the energy method described in preceding articles, we can say that in general the energy method is capable of much more accurate results if we choose as many generating functions as there are pivot points. In the study of two-dimensional or three-dimensional systems the number of pivot points required to set up difference equations is often too large even for machine computation. In that case, the energy method becomes the only feasible one.

Exercises

4.1. Set up the differential equations of motion and the boundary conditions for the following vibratory systems:

(*a*) The longitudinal vibration of a uniform bar, whose two ends are connected to a stationary frame by two identical springs which exert axial forces on the bar proportional to the end displacements.
(*b*) The lateral vibration of a cantilever beam having uniform cross sections and carrying a concentrated mass at its unsupported end.
(*c*) The swinging of a heavy flexible chain hung by one end from the ceiling. The other end is free.
(*d*) The longitudinal vibration of a tapered round bar, whose end diameters are d_0 and d_L. The end with the larger diameter d_0 is built into a rigid wall.

4.2. The formulation by differential equation of each of the following vibration problems consists of two boundary value problems with interrelated boundary conditions. Write the differential equations and specify the boundary conditions.

(*a*) The lateral vibration of a flexible elastic string initially stretched to a tension S. A coil spring of constant $K = S/3L$ connects the point $x = L/3$ to a stationary point to one side of the string, L being the length of the string.
(*b*) The lateral vibration of a uniform beam of length L simply supported at $x = 0$ and $x = L/3$.
(*c*) The lateral vibration of a round bar with a built-in end and a free end. The bar has a hole which extends from the free end to a depth of $L/2$ and has a diameter of $3d/4$, where L and d are the length and the outside diameter of the bar, respectively.

4.3. Obtain by separation of variables the differential equations and the boundary conditions governing the eigenfunctions belonging to the systems described in Exercise 4.1.

4.4. A uniform bar with a fixed end and a free end is set into longitudinal vibration in the following manner. A constant axial force P initially exists at the free end of the bar, which is stationary. At $t = 0$ this force is suddenly removed. Determine the coefficient C_i in (25). (Note that $\alpha_i = 0$.)

4.5. Verify the characteristic equations and the eigenfunctions, given in Art. 4.3(B) for lateral vibrations of uniform bars having various end conditions.

4.6. The vibration of each of the prongs of a tuning fork is approximately the same as that of a cantilever beam. Design a tuning fork for the note C (512 cps), which is to be made of steel weighing 0.286 lb per cu in. and having Young's modulus of 29.5×10^6 lb per sq in. The effective prong length is 6 in., and the prongs are to have a rectangular cross section. What is the frequency of the next highest note the fork may put out?

4.7. A vibrating steel reed having a natural frequency of 60 cps is commonly used for the calibration of a stroboscope. If the reed is 2 in. long, what is its thickness? Assume that the steel used has the properties given in Exercise 4.6.

4.8. A simply supported uniform beam of length L carries a concentrated mass at its mid-point.

(*a*) Show that the characteristic equation for symmetrical modes of vibration is

$$\mu\theta(\tan\theta - \tanh\theta) = 2$$

where μ = ratio of the concentrated mass to the mass of the beam

$$\theta = \frac{\beta L}{2}$$

(*b*) Find the lowest eigenvalue for $\mu = 2$.

(*c*) A given function $f(x)$ is to be expanded into an infinite series made up of the eigenfunctions of the system. Show how the coefficients of this series are determined.

4.9.

(*a*) Show that Green's function for a stretched string with $x(0) = 0$ and $x(L) = 0$ is

$$G(x, \xi) = \frac{(L - \xi)}{LS}x \qquad \text{for } 0 \le x \le \xi$$

and

$$G(x, \xi) = \frac{\xi}{LS}(L - x) \qquad \text{for } \xi \le x \le L$$

(*b*) Formulate by integral equation the vibration of a string with a mass distribution given by

$$m(x) = \rho A(x) = m_0\left(1 - \sin\frac{\pi x}{L}\right)$$

4.10.

(*a*) Obtain Green's function for a uniform bar of length L, which has a built-in end at $x = 0$ and a free end at $x = L$.

(*b*) If the right end of the bar is connected to a stationary frame by a linear spring K so that

$$EI\,r'''(L) - Kr(L) = 0$$

Green's function, different from that in (*a*), must be used in (68). However, the same Green's function can still be used if we modify (68) to read

$$\frac{1}{\omega^2}r(x) = \int_0^L G(x, \xi)r(\xi)\,d\xi + f(x)$$

What is the function $f(x)$?

4.11. The static deflection curve of a cantilever beam under a uniformly distributed load is

$$u(x) = C(x^2 + 6L^2 - 4Lx)$$

in which C is a constant. The function $u(x)$, which is an admissible function, can be used to approximate the first mode of lateral vibration of the beam. Compute $Q((u))$ according to (72) and compare it with ω_1^2 determined by (35).

4.12. The frequency of the first mode of vibration of the beam in Exercise 4.8 can also be approximated by Rayleigh's quotient for the static deflection curve due to a concentrated force at the middle. Show that by the use of (96) and this deflection curve we can obtain

$$Q((u)) \doteq \omega_1^2 = \frac{48EI}{\rho AL^4} \frac{1}{(\mu + 17/35)}$$

Compare this approximation with the answer to Exercise 4.8(b) for $\mu = 2$.

4.13. Use a three-term Fourier sine series approximation to find the approximate answer to Exercise 4.8(b).

4.14. It has been pointed out that the eigenfunctions for a uniform cantilever beam, as given by (36), can be used as the generating functions in the Rayleigh-Ritz method for the system shown in Fig. 92. In this procedure it is necessary to evaluate

$$\int_0^L [r_i(x)]^2 \, dx$$

(a) Evaluate the foregoing integral for $i = 1$, 2, and 3, by the numerical method. Note that although these integrals can be evaluated analytically, a numerical method appears to be less time-consuming, especially since tables have been prepared for values of $r_i(x)$ by Dana Young and R. P. Edgar, University of Texas Publications No. 4913, 1949.

(b) Use r_1, r_2, and r_3 of (36) as the generating set to find the approximate lowest natural frequency of the system in Fig. 92, assuming that

$$K_1 = 0 \qquad \text{and} \qquad K_2 = \frac{EI}{2L^3}$$

4.15. Utilize the results from (a) to find the approximate amplitude of steady-state vibration of a uniform cantilever beam at $x = L$, when a sinusoidal concentrated force

$$f(t) = \rho ALg \cos \omega_f t$$

is acting on the beam at $x = L$. Assume that $2\omega_f = \omega_1 =$ the lowest natural frequency.

4.16. Given a differential equation,

$$\mathsf{L}(r) = \lambda r$$

and a set of boundary conditions. Green's function associated with this boundary-value problem $G(x, \xi)$ can be defined as a function satisfying the equation

$$\mathsf{L}(G) = 0$$

and the original boundary conditions *when* $x \neq \xi$ and

$$\mathsf{L}(G) = \infty \qquad \text{when } x = \xi$$

Furthermore,

$$\int_0^L \mathsf{L}(G)\, dx = 1$$

Show that

$$r(x) = \int_0^L \lambda G(x, \xi) r(\xi)\, d\xi$$

satisfies the original boundary-value problem.

4.17. If the variables in polar coordinates are denoted by s and θ, the Laplacian operator ∇^2 is known to be

$$\nabla^2 = \frac{\partial^2}{\partial s^2} + \frac{1}{s}\frac{\partial}{\partial s} + \frac{1}{s^2}\frac{\partial^2}{\partial \theta^2}$$

(*a*) Write the differential equation of motion for the vibration of a uniform thin circular membrane.

(*b*) Let the membrane be held fixed at its outer rim, where $s = s_0$, and let the vibration be symmetrical with respect to the center. Show that the eigenvalue problem associated with such vibrations is described by zero-order Bessel's differential equation

$$\frac{d^2 r}{ds^2} + \frac{1}{s}\frac{dr}{ds} + \beta^2 r = 0$$

where

$$\beta^2 = \omega^2 \frac{\rho h}{S}$$

The solution is zero-order Bessel's function

$$r(s) = J_0(\beta s)$$

(*c*) Show through the self-adjoint property of this eigenvalue problem that

$$\int_0^{s_0} s J_0(\beta_i s) J_0(\beta_j s)\, ds = 0 \qquad i \neq j$$

where β_i and β_j satisify

$$J_0(\beta s_0) = 0$$

(*d*) By separation of variables, derive the eigenvalue problem for vibrations that are not symmetrical with respect to the center of the membrane.

4.18. Show that the eigenvalue problem

$$\mathsf{D}^4 r = \beta^4 r$$

$$r(0) = 0 \qquad r'''(0) = 0 \qquad r(L) = 0 \qquad \text{and} \qquad r''(0) = 0$$

has no solution. Can you reason out physically that there is no solution?

4.19. Use the wave propagation concept to find the solution for Exercise 4.4 for $0 < t < L/c$. How can you relate this function with the indicial response function?

4.20. A uniform bar of length $4a$ is fixed at $x = 0$ and free at $x = 4a$. At $t = 0$, the initial conditions for a longitudinal vibration are given by

$$\begin{aligned} u(x, 0) &= x & 0 &\leq x \leq a \\ u(x, 0) &= 2a - x & a &\leq x \leq 2a \\ u(x, 0) &= 0 & 2a &\leq x \leq 4a \end{aligned}$$

and

$$\left(\frac{\partial u}{\partial t}\right)_{t=0} = 0$$

(*a*) Show by concept of wave propagation that at $t = 2a/c$ the displacement is given by

$$\begin{aligned} u &= -\tfrac{1}{2}x & 0 &\leq x \leq a \\ u &= (x - 2a) & a &\leq x \leq 3a \\ u &= (4a - x) & 3a &\leq x \leq 4a \end{aligned}$$

(*b*) How would you find $\partial u/\partial t$ at $t = 2a/c$?

4.21. A semi-infinite beam has a hinged end at $x = 0$ and extends to $x = +\infty$. Show that (133) is the solution for the lateral vibration of this beam under the initial condition

$$v(x, 0) = V(x)$$

$$\left(\frac{\partial v}{\partial t}\right)_{t=0} = 0$$

4.22. Find the approximate solution for the first mode of vibration of a beam with fixed ends:

(*a*) By finite difference equations approximating the differential equation.
(*b*) By finite difference equations approximating the integral equations.

4.23. Furnish the missing steps in the derivation of (134).

4.24. The boundary conditions for a uniform thin plate simply supported along its edge are

$$w = 0 \quad \text{and} \quad \nabla^2 w = 0 \quad \text{on} \quad C$$

Show that the eigenvalue problem for the vibration of this plate is the same as that for the vibration of a uniform membrane of the same contour.

Hint: The boundary-value problem associated with (14) may be written as

$$(\nabla^2 - \beta^2)[(\nabla^2 + \beta^2)r] = 0$$

in which $\beta^4 = \rho h/E'I'$.

APPENDIX

An Outline of Matrix Algebra in Linear Transformation of Vectors

1. Introduction

A matrix is an array of numbers taken together as a single mathematical entity. The dictionary meaning of the word matrix is "something in which other things are imbedded." In mathematics an array of numbers, which we call a matrix, also fits this description. Take for instance a set of linear simultaneous equations

$$\begin{aligned} 3x_1 + 4x_2 - 5x_3 &= 1 \\ x_1 - 3x_2 \qquad &= 4 \\ 2x_1 + 7x_2 - x_3 &= -3 \end{aligned} \tag{1}$$

The two things that characterize this set of equations or distinguish it from other sets of linear equations are

$$\text{the coefficients of the unknowns} \quad \begin{bmatrix} 3 & 4 & -5 \\ 1 & -3 & 0 \\ 2 & 7 & -1 \end{bmatrix}$$

$$\text{and the constant terms} \quad \begin{bmatrix} 1 \\ 4 \\ -3 \end{bmatrix}$$

Therefore, in these two arrays of numbers a set of linear simultaneous equations is imbedded.

If we wish to emphasize the fact that the unknowns are called x_1, x_2, and x_3 and that the constant terms appear at the right-hand side of the equations, we may write symbolically

$$\begin{bmatrix} 3 & 4 & -5 \\ 1 & -3 & 0 \\ 2 & 7 & -1 \end{bmatrix} \begin{bmatrix} x_1 \\ x_2 \\ x_3 \end{bmatrix} = \begin{bmatrix} 1 \\ 4 \\ -3 \end{bmatrix} \tag{2}$$

And if we wish to represent a set of simultaneous equations in general, we may write symbolically

$$\mathbf{A} \cdot \mathbf{x} = \mathbf{c} \tag{3}$$

in which the symbol $\mathbf{A}$ stands for a square array of numbers (coefficients), $\mathbf{x}$ for a column of numbers (unknowns), and $\mathbf{c}$ for a column of numbers (known constants).

Thus we have a shorthand notation of a set of linear simultaneous equations. This notation, called the matrix notation, achieves an economy of thought as well as an economy in writing.

Notations alone, of course, do not make an algebra, which also deals with rules of operation. In (3) we have more or less indicated that there is a relationship denoted by the equal sign "=" and an operation denoted by the multiplication sign "·". The question now is what other kinds of operations can be defined and what algebraic properties do they possess. For instance, is there a matrix $\mathbf{0}$ and an operation "−" such that the expression

$$\mathbf{A} \cdot \mathbf{x} - \mathbf{c} = \mathbf{0}$$

is equivalent to the one above? Or, is there a matrix $\mathbf{A}^{-1}$ such that equivalent to (3) we may have

$$\mathbf{A}^{-1}\,\mathbf{c} = \mathbf{x}$$

Matrix algebra deals with questions of this nature.

2. Vectors in n-Dimensional Space

Although, historically, matrix algebra evolved from the study of linear equations, for our present exposition we shall use geometrical models to illustrate matrix operations. Such models have the advantage of revealing at once both the computational aspects and the algebraic properties of matrix operations. Geometrical models with more than three dimensions are, of course, difficult to visualize. Fortunately, methods in analytical geometry allow us to extrapolate, so that we shall not have to visualize more than three dimensions.

It is well known that by a suitable choice of coordinate system we can represent any point in space by an *ordered* set of numbers, which we call the coordinates of the point. Also, by joining the origin of the coordinate system to a point in space, we define a free vector, and the set of numbers representing the coordinates of the point become the components of the vector. The three things, a point, a vector, and a set of numbers, therefore, are images of one another. We can thus use one kind of symbol, such as $\mathbf{p}$, to denote any one of these things, or we can use a set of n numbers arranged in a column to denote the same things.

$$\mathbf{p} = \begin{bmatrix} p_1 \\ p_2 \\ \cdot \\ \cdot \\ \cdot \\ p_n \end{bmatrix}$$

Such a column of numbers is called a *column matrix.*

3. Equality among Column Matrices

Two vectors are the same if and only if all their respective components are equal. Two points coincide if and only if their respective coordinates are equal. Hence we can define the equality between two column matrices as follows. Let

$$\mathbf{p} = \begin{bmatrix} p_1 \\ p_2 \\ \cdot \\ \cdot \\ \cdot \\ p_n \end{bmatrix} \quad \text{and} \quad \mathbf{q} = \begin{bmatrix} q_1 \\ q_2 \\ \cdot \\ \cdot \\ \cdot \\ q_n \end{bmatrix}$$

The equality relation

$$\mathbf{p} = \mathbf{q}$$

implies

$$p_1 = q_1 \qquad p_2 = q_2 \cdots p_n = q_n$$

or, in general

$$p_i = q_i \qquad i = 1, 2, \cdots, n$$

An equality relation among column matrices is like the equality among numbers in that it is *reflexive*, *symmetric*, and *transitive*.

4. Addition of Column Matrices

(A) ALGEBRAIC RULES

It is known in vector algebra that if $\mathbf{p}$ and $\mathbf{q}$ are two vectors there is an addition operation (parallelogram law) which yields another vector $\mathbf{r}$. Or, symbolically,

$$\mathbf{p} + \mathbf{q} = \mathbf{r} \tag{4}$$

Two column matrices can also be added together to yield a third column matrix. Furthermore, vectorial addition is known to be *commutative* and *associative*. That is,

$$\mathbf{p} + \mathbf{q} = \mathbf{q} + \mathbf{p} \tag{5}$$

$$(\mathbf{p} + \mathbf{q}) + \mathbf{r} = \mathbf{p} + (\mathbf{q} + \mathbf{r}) \tag{6}$$

(B) ARITHMETIC RULES—PARALLEL COORDINATES

We have shown that two column matrices can be added together and what the algebraic properties of the addition operation are. Now we may ask, "How is the sum to be determined?" The actual numbers that make up a column matrix, so that it represents a given vector, evidently depend on the coordinate system chosen. The same vector is represented by different columns of numbers in different coordinate systems. The question of how to obtain from given $\mathbf{p}$ and $\mathbf{q}$ the column of numbers making up $\mathbf{r}$ in (4) must also depend upon the choice of coordinate system.

The arithmetic rules of matrix operations are based upon the use of a *parallel coordinate system*, in which the coordinate axes are all straight lines. The scaling of each axis is uniform, but it can vary from axis to axis. A three-dimensional parallel coordinate system is illustrated in Fig. 100. The vector $\mathbf{p}$ shown is represented by the column matrix

$$\mathbf{p} = \begin{bmatrix} 3 \\ 4 \\ -2 \end{bmatrix}$$

A rectangular or Cartesian coordinate system is a special form of parallel coordinate system in which the coordinate axes are mutually orthogonal and the scaling is the same on all axes.

Vectorial addition in a parallel coordinate system is particularly simple. It can be shown that the parallelogram law of addition is equivalent to the following rule. If

$$\mathbf{p} = \begin{bmatrix} p_1 \\ p_2 \\ \cdot \\ \cdot \\ \cdot \\ p_n \end{bmatrix} \quad \text{and} \quad \mathbf{q} = \begin{bmatrix} q_1 \\ q_2 \\ \cdot \\ \cdot \\ \cdot \\ q_n \end{bmatrix}$$

then

$$\mathbf{p} + \mathbf{q} = \begin{bmatrix} (p_1 + q_1) \\ (p_2 + q_2) \\ \cdots \\ (p_n + q_n) \end{bmatrix} \tag{7}$$

In other words, each component of the vectorial sum is the sum of the respective components of the vectors making up the sum.

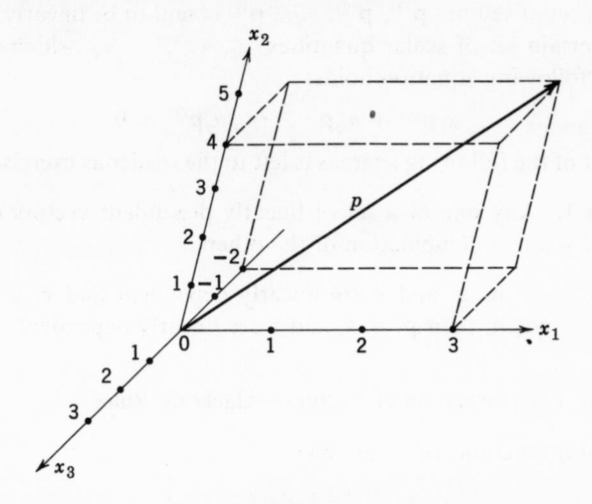

Figure 100

Let us remark that although one can deduce the algebraic property of addition, (5) and (6), from the arithmetic rule (7) the former has an independent existence of its own.

5. Multiplication by a Scalar and Linear Dependence

If

$$\mathbf{p} + \mathbf{p} = \mathbf{q}$$

we can write

$$2\mathbf{p} = \mathbf{q} \qquad \text{or} \qquad \mathbf{p} = \tfrac{1}{2}\mathbf{q}$$

Thus a column matrix can be multiplied by a scalar, and the equality

$$\mathbf{q} = \lambda \mathbf{p} \tag{8}$$

implies that in a parallel coordinate system

$$q_i = \lambda p_i \qquad \text{for all } i = 1, 2, \cdots, n$$

Geometrically, (8) implies that $\mathbf{q}$ and $\mathbf{p}$ have the same direction but differ in length.

A vector $\mathbf{r}$ is said to be a linear combination of $\mathbf{p}$ and $\mathbf{q}$ if

$$\mathbf{r} = \alpha\mathbf{p} + \beta\mathbf{q}$$

in which α and β are scalar quantities. Geometrically this means that the line segments representing the vectors $\mathbf{p}$, $\mathbf{q}$, and $\mathbf{r}$ are coplanar. The vectors $\mathbf{p}$, $\mathbf{q}$, and $\mathbf{r}$ are in the meantime said to be linearly dependent. In general, a set of vectors $\mathbf{p}^{(1)}, \mathbf{p}^{(2)}, \ldots, \mathbf{p}^{(i)}$ is said to be linearly dependent if for a certain set of scalar quantities, $\alpha_1, \alpha_2, \ldots, \alpha_i$, which are not all zero, the following equation holds:

$$\alpha_1\mathbf{p}^{(1)} + \alpha_2\mathbf{p}^{(2)}, \cdots, \alpha_i\mathbf{p}^{(i)} = \mathbf{0} \tag{9}$$

The proof of the following lemmas is left to the reader as exercises.

Lemma 1. Any one of a set of linearly dependent vectors can be expressed as a linear combination of the others.

Lemma 2. If $\mathbf{p}$, $\mathbf{q}$, and $\mathbf{r}$ are linearly dependent and $\mathbf{r}$, $\mathbf{s}$, and $\mathbf{t}$ are linearly dependent, then $\mathbf{p}$, $\mathbf{q}$, $\mathbf{s}$, and $\mathbf{t}$ are linearly dependent.

6. Linear Transformation of Vectors—Algebraic Rules

A set of n functions of n variables

$$\begin{aligned} y_1 &= F_1(x_1, x_2, \cdots, x_n) \\ y_2 &= F_2(x_1, x_2, \cdots, x_n) \\ &\cdots\cdots\cdots\cdots\cdots \\ y_n &= F_n(x_1, x_2, \cdots, x) \end{aligned}$$

can be considered as a functional relationship between two vectors

$$\mathbf{y} = F(\mathbf{x}) \tag{10}$$

since, given a column matrix $\mathbf{x}$, one can find a corresponding column matrix $\mathbf{y}$, and $\mathbf{y}$ may be considered as a vectorial function of a vector $\mathbf{x}$.

There are many physical and mathematical models for the relationship (10). We cite three such models for illustration.

(i) $\mathbf{x}$ is the location of a generic material point in a deformable body before deformation, and $\mathbf{y}$ is the location of the same material point after the body has deformed. In this case (10) describes how the body is deformed.

(ii) $\mathbf{x}$ is the location of a generic spatial point in a steady-state fluid flow. $\mathbf{y}$ is the velocity of the fluid particle occupying the point $\mathbf{x}$. In this case (10) describes the velocity distribution of the flow.

(iii) $\mathbf{x}$ is a column of numbers representing the coordinates of a fixed point, according to a certain coordinate system. $\mathbf{y}$ is another column of numbers representing the coordinates of the *same* point, according to another coordinate system. In this case (10) describes a *transformation of coordinates*.

In comparing (i) with (iii), we see that in one case the coordinate system is fixed, whereas the point moves, and in the other case the point is fixed, whereas the coordinate system changes. From a mathematical point of view the difference in the situations hardly matters. We can, therefore, always speak of (10) as representing a transformation of $\mathbf{x}$ into $\mathbf{y}$.

The simplest example of a transformation is that represented by (8), in which the vector $\mathbf{q}$ is obtained by "lengthening" $\mathbf{p}$ without a change in direction. Or we can consider (8) as representing a uniform change of scale factor of the coordinate system. Let us now conceive another class of transformations, which is rather simple and yet of great utility in analyzing physical and mathematical problem. These transformations are called *linear* and are denoted by bold sans serif letters such as A, B, L, and M.[1] A linear transformation is supposed to have the following properties:

(I) Every point in space has a transformation and the origin remains fixed. Or, $\mathsf{A}(\mathbf{x})$, $\mathsf{B}(\mathbf{x})$, etc., are uniquely defined for every $\mathbf{x}$ and $\mathsf{A}(\mathbf{0}) = \mathbf{0}$, $\mathsf{B}(\mathbf{0}) = \mathbf{0}$, etc.

(II) Points lying on a straight line remain colinear.

Without going into the method of carrying out this transformation, we can deduce the following lemmas successively from the properties postulated.

Lemma 1. Coplanar points remain coplanar because, unless a plane remains a plane, some straight lines on the plane will become curved.

Lemma 2. Two intersecting lines remain intersecting, and two coplanar parallel lines remain coplanar parallel. This follows if we take (i) to mean that ∞ remains at ∞ and no finite point goes to infinity.

Lemma 3. A parallelogram remains a parallelogram.

Lemma 4. Linear transformation is distributive; that is

$$\mathsf{A}(\mathbf{p} + \mathbf{q}) = \mathsf{A}(\mathbf{p}) + \mathsf{A}(\mathbf{q}) \tag{11}$$

Proof:

Let $\mathbf{p} + \mathbf{q} = \mathbf{r}$

[1] For the moment these symbols have not yet been tied in with the similar symbol in (3).

Then, before transformation, $\mathbf{p}$ and $\mathbf{q}$ are two adjacent sides of a parallelogram and $\mathbf{r}$ is the diagonal in between. After transformation, the parallelogram is still a parallelogram, with $\mathbf{A}(\mathbf{p})$ and $\mathbf{A}(\mathbf{q})$ forming its two adjacent sides and $\mathbf{A}(\mathbf{r})$ forming the diagonal in between. Hence

$$\mathbf{A}(\mathbf{p}) + \mathbf{A}(\mathbf{q}) = \mathbf{A}(\mathbf{r}) = \mathbf{A}(\mathbf{p} + \mathbf{q})$$

Lemma 5. Linear transformation preserves all linear dependence relationships.

First we see that

$$\mathbf{A}(2\mathbf{p}) = \mathbf{A}(\mathbf{p} + \mathbf{p}) = \mathbf{A}(\mathbf{p}) + \mathbf{A}(\mathbf{p}) = 2\mathbf{A}(\mathbf{p})$$

and, by similar reasoning,

$$\mathbf{A}(\lambda\mathbf{p}) = \lambda\mathbf{A}(\mathbf{p}) \tag{12}$$

Hence, if

$$\mathbf{r} = \alpha\mathbf{p} + \beta\mathbf{q}$$

$$\mathbf{A}(\mathbf{r}) = \alpha\mathbf{A}(\mathbf{p}) + \beta\mathbf{A}(\mathbf{q}) \tag{13}$$

Lemma 6. A linear transformation followed by a linear transformation is still a linear transformation. This is obvious from the postulated properties of linear transformation. Symbolically, if

$$\mathbf{A}(\mathbf{p}) = \mathbf{q} \qquad \text{and} \qquad \mathbf{B}(\mathbf{q}) = \mathbf{r}$$

$\mathbf{r}$ is related to $\mathbf{p}$ by a linear transformation

$$\mathbf{r} = \mathbf{C}(\mathbf{p}) = \mathbf{B}[\mathbf{A}(\mathbf{p})]$$

or

$$\mathbf{C} = (\mathbf{B}\ \mathbf{A}) \tag{14}$$

This is equivalent to a multiplication operation. We say by (14) that $\mathbf{C}$ is obtained by premultiplying $\mathbf{A}$ by $\mathbf{B}$.

Lemma 7. It follows from the foregoing that a succession of linear transformations is still a linear transformation. Symbolically, if $\mathbf{C} = \mathbf{B}\ \mathbf{A}$ and $\mathbf{E} = \mathbf{D}\ \mathbf{C}$, then

$$\mathbf{E} = [\mathbf{D}(\mathbf{B}\ \mathbf{A})] \tag{15}$$

Furthermore, the multiplication operation is *associative* or

$$[\mathbf{D}(\mathbf{B}\ \mathbf{A})] = [(\mathbf{D}\ \mathbf{B})\mathbf{A}]$$

because, by the definition of multiplication operation,

$$[\mathbf{D}(\mathbf{B}\ \mathbf{A})](\mathbf{p}) = \mathbf{D}[(\mathbf{B}\ \mathbf{A})(\mathbf{p})] = \mathbf{D}[\mathbf{B}\{\mathbf{A}(\mathbf{p})\}]$$

$$[(\mathbf{D}\ \mathbf{B})\mathbf{A}](\mathbf{p}) = [\mathbf{D}\ \mathbf{B}]\{\mathbf{A}(\mathbf{p})\} = \mathbf{D}[\mathbf{B}\{\mathbf{A}(\mathbf{p})\}]$$

Thus we can write (15) simply as

$$\mathbf{E} = \mathbf{D}\ \mathbf{B}\ \mathbf{A}$$

Lemma 8. The sum of the results from two separate linear transformations on the same vector is also a linear transformation. This is to say, if

$$\mathbf{A}(\mathbf{p}) + \mathbf{B}(\mathbf{p}) = \mathbf{u} \tag{16}$$

there is a linear transformation $\mathbf{C}$, such that

$$\mathbf{C}(\mathbf{p}) = \mathbf{u}$$

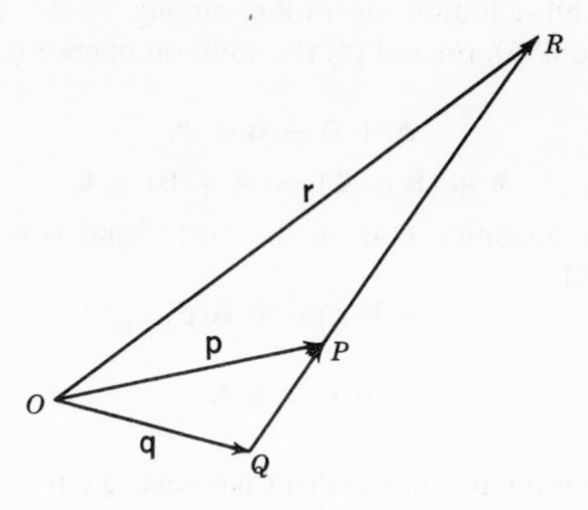

Figure 101

In other words, the relation between $\mathbf{p}$ and $\mathbf{u}$, as defined by (16), is also a linear transformation. To show this, we observe first that (16) satisfies the property (I). All is left now is to show that (16) also satisfies property (II). This can be done as follows:

The necessary and sufficient condition for three points $\mathbf{p}$, $\mathbf{q}$, and $\mathbf{r}$ to lie on a straight line is that (see Fig. 101) there is a scalar parameter α so that

$$\alpha\mathbf{p} + (1 - \alpha)\mathbf{q} = \mathbf{r}$$

Since $\mathbf{A}$ and $\mathbf{B}$ are linear transformations, according to (13),

$$\begin{aligned} \alpha\mathbf{A}(\mathbf{p}) + (1 - \alpha)\mathbf{A}(\mathbf{q}) &= \mathbf{A}(\mathbf{r}) \\ \alpha\mathbf{B}(\mathbf{p}) + (1 - \alpha)\mathbf{B}(\mathbf{q}) &= \mathbf{B}(\mathbf{r}) \end{aligned} \tag{17}$$

Now if

$$\mathbf{A}(\mathbf{p}) + \mathbf{B}(\mathbf{p}) = \mathbf{u}$$
$$\mathbf{A}(\mathbf{q}) + \mathbf{B}(\mathbf{q}) = \mathbf{v}$$
$$\mathbf{A}(\mathbf{r}) + \mathbf{B}(\mathbf{r}) = \mathbf{w}$$

then by adding the equations in (17) and utilizing the foregoing equations, we have

$$\alpha\mathbf{u} + (1 - \alpha)\mathbf{v} = \mathbf{w}$$

Hence the transformation (16) preserves the colinearity and is a linear transformation representable by a symbol $\mathbf{C}$. This completes the proof of this lemma.

If we define

$$(\mathbf{A} + \mathbf{B})\mathbf{p} = \mathbf{A}(\mathbf{p}) + \mathbf{B}(\mathbf{p}) \tag{18}$$

we may write

$$(\mathbf{A} + \mathbf{B}) = \mathbf{C} \tag{19}$$

Thus there is an addition operation among linear transformations. Furthermore, from (5), (6) and (8) the addition operation is commutative and associative.

$$\begin{aligned} \mathbf{A} + \mathbf{B} &= \mathbf{B} + \mathbf{A} \\ \mathbf{A} + (\mathbf{B} + \mathbf{C}) &= (\mathbf{A} + \mathbf{B}) + \mathbf{C} \end{aligned} \tag{20}$$

Note that the operation (14) on the other hand is not commutative. That is, in general,

$$\mathbf{A}\,\mathbf{B}(\mathbf{p}) \neq \mathbf{B}\,\mathbf{A}(\mathbf{p})$$

or

$$\mathbf{A}\,\mathbf{B} \neq \mathbf{B}\,\mathbf{A} \tag{21}$$

7. Linear Transformation in Parallel Coordinate Systems

In Art. 6 we made no mention of the method by which linear transformation can be carried out. The algebraic rules were deduced strictly from the geometrical properties of the transformation. To determine how a linear transformation can be carried out, we refer again to a parallel coordinate system.

Let

$$\mathbf{x} = \begin{bmatrix} x_1 \\ x_2 \\ \cdot \\ \cdot \\ \cdot \\ x_n \end{bmatrix} \quad \text{and} \quad \mathbf{y} = \begin{bmatrix} y_1 \\ y_2 \\ \cdot \\ \cdot \\ \cdot \\ y_n \end{bmatrix}$$

where the elements in the column matrices represent the coordinates of $\mathbf{x}$ and $\mathbf{y}$ in a parallel coordinate system. If $\mathbf{x}$ and $\mathbf{y}$ are related by a linear transformation,

$$\mathbf{y} = \mathbf{A}(\mathbf{x}) \tag{22}$$

then $y_1, y_2, \ldots, y_n$ are linear combinations of $x_1, x_2, \ldots, x_n$.

$$\begin{aligned} y_1 &= a_{11}x_1 + a_{12}x_2, \cdots, a_{1n}x_n \\ y_2 &= a_{21}x_1 + a_{22}x_2, \cdots, a_{2n}x_n \\ &\cdots\cdots\cdots\cdots\cdots\cdots \\ y_n &= a_{n1}x_1 + a_{n2}x_2, \cdots, a_{nn}x_n \end{aligned} \tag{23}$$

It is not possible to show here that a linear transformation in Euclidean geometry must take the form of (23). However, one can easily verify that (23) represents a transformation that satisfies all the requirements of being a linear transformation.

The linear transformation (22) therefore embodies a set of linear simultaneous equations relating the coordinates before to those after transformation. These equations are imbedded in the matrix equation

$$\mathbf{y} = \mathbf{A}(\mathbf{x}) = \mathbf{A} \cdot \mathbf{x} = \mathbf{A}\,\mathbf{x}$$

Or

$$\begin{bmatrix} y_1 \\ y_2 \\ \cdot \\ \cdot \\ \cdot \\ y_n \end{bmatrix} = \begin{bmatrix} a_{11} a_{12} \cdots a_{1n} \\ a_{21} a_{22} \cdots a_{2n} \\ \cdot \\ \cdot \\ \cdot \\ a_{n1} a_{n2} \cdots a_{nn} \end{bmatrix} \begin{bmatrix} x_1 \\ x_2 \\ \cdot \\ \cdot \\ \cdot \\ x_n \end{bmatrix}$$

The rule of premultiplying a column matrix by a square matrix is given by (23), or

$$y_i = \sum_{j=1}^{n} a_{ij} x_j \qquad i = 1, 2, \cdots, n \tag{23a}$$

where a_{ij} is the element in the ith row and jth column of the square matrix $\mathbf{A}$. We can now deduce the following rules:

(i) If, for all $\mathbf{x}$,

$$\mathbf{A}(\mathbf{x}) = \mathbf{B}(\mathbf{x})$$

we write

$$\mathbf{A} = \mathbf{B}$$

This equality implies that the transformations $\mathbf{A}$ and $\mathbf{B}$ yield identical results,

$$\sum_{j=1}^{n} a_{ij} x_j = \sum_{j=1}^{n} b_{ij} x_j \qquad i = 1, 2, \cdots, n$$

for all x_j. In order for this to be true, we must have

$$a_{ij} = b_{ij} \qquad \begin{matrix} i = 1, 2, \cdots, n \\ j = 1, 2, \cdots, n \end{matrix}$$

In other words, two $n \times n$ square matrices are said to be equal if and only if all the corresponding elements are equal.

(ii) If, for all $\mathbf{x}$, according to Lemma 8,

$$\mathbf{A}(\mathbf{x}) + \mathbf{B}(\mathbf{x}) = (\mathbf{A} + \mathbf{B})\mathbf{x} = \mathbf{C}(\mathbf{x})$$

we write

$$\mathbf{A} + \mathbf{B} = \mathbf{C}$$

This implies

$$\sum_{j=1}^{n} (a_{ij} + b_{ij})x_j = \sum_{j=1}^{n} c_{ij}x_j \qquad i = 1, 2, \cdots, n$$

or

$$a_{ij} + b_{ij} = c_{ij} \qquad \begin{matrix} i = 1, 2, \cdots, n \\ j = 1, 2, \cdots, n \end{matrix} \tag{24}$$

In other words, the sum of two $n \times n$ square matrices is also an $n \times n$ square matrix, whose elements are obtained by adding the corresponding elements of the original two matrices.

(iii) If for all $\mathbf{x}$, according to Lemma 6,

$$\mathbf{B}[\mathbf{A}(\mathbf{x})] = \mathbf{C}(\mathbf{x})$$

we write

$$\mathbf{B\,A} = \mathbf{C}$$

This implies

$$\sum_{j=1}^{n} \sum_{k=1}^{n} b_{ik}a_{kj}x_j = \sum_{j=1}^{n} c_{ij}x_j \qquad i = 1, 2, \cdots, n$$

or

$$\sum_{k=1}^{n} b_{ik}a_{kj} = c_{ij} \qquad \begin{matrix} i = 1, 2, \cdots, n \\ j = 1, 2, \cdots, n \end{matrix} \tag{25}$$

In other words, when two $n \times n$ square matrices form a product, which is also an $n \times n$ matrix, the element at the ith row and jth column of the product is determined by the entire ith row of the first matrix and the entire jth column of the second matrix, according to (25).

8. Summation Convention and a Summary

We note the following in all foregoing equations that describe the relationships among elements of matrices in matrix operations:

(i) All subscript indices that are to be summed from 1 to n appear precisely twice in a term.

(ii) All subscript indices that are not summed but are to take on any value from 1 to n appear precisely once in each term of the equation. Since this is always the case, we can simplify our notation by deleting all summation signs and omitting notations such as $i = 1, 2, \ldots, n$.

The convention then adopted is as follows:

(i) If an index appears twice in a given term, a summation process is understood to exist without the explicit use of a summation sign. The index is called a *dummy index*.

(ii) If an index appears only once in each term of an equation (except the term zero), it is understood that this index may take on any value from 1 to n. The index is called a *free index*.

An equation such as (25) can be written without ambiguity as

$$b_{ik}a_{kj} = c_{ij}$$

in which k is a dummy and i and j are free.

With this convention, we can summarize the result of the previous articles by the following table:

Matrix Relation*	Relation Among Elements
$\mathbf{x} = \mathbf{y}$	$x_i = y_i$
$\mathbf{x} + \mathbf{y} = \mathbf{z}$	$x_i + y_i = z_i$
$\lambda\mathbf{x} = \mathbf{y}$	$\lambda x_i = y_i$
$\mathbf{A}\,\mathbf{x} = \mathbf{y}$	$a_{ij}x_j = y_i$
$\mathbf{A} = \mathbf{B}$	$a_{ij} = b_{ij}$
$\mathbf{A} + \mathbf{B} = \mathbf{C}$	$a_{ij} + b_{ij} = c_{ij}$
$\lambda\mathbf{A} = \mathbf{B}$	$\lambda a_{ij} = b_{ij}$
$\mathbf{A}\,\mathbf{B} = \mathbf{C}$	$a_{ij}b_{jk} = c_{ik}$
$\mathbf{A}\,\mathbf{B}\,\mathbf{C} = \mathbf{D}$	$a_{ij}b_{jk}c_{km} = c_{im}$

* We have omitted parenthesis and dots in matrix products. Greek letters represent scalar quantities.

The operations among matrices shown have all the properties of arithmetic operation among numbers, except that multiplications are not commutative. Thus we can deduce relations as follows:

$$(\mathbf{A} + \mathbf{B})(\mathbf{x} + \mathbf{y}) = \mathbf{A}\,\mathbf{x} + \mathbf{B}\,\mathbf{x} + \mathbf{A}\,\mathbf{y} + \mathbf{B}\,\mathbf{y}$$
$$(\mathbf{A} + \mathbf{B})(\mathbf{A} + \mathbf{B}) = \mathbf{A}^2 + \mathbf{A}\,\mathbf{B} + \mathbf{B}\,\mathbf{A} + \mathbf{B}^2$$

where

$$\mathbf{A}^2 = \mathbf{A}\,\mathbf{A} \quad \text{and} \quad \mathbf{B}^2 = \mathbf{B}\,\mathbf{B}$$

Also, if the elements of the matrices are functions of a scalar variable such as time t, we may perform differentiation and integration processes with respect to t, since they are the limits of processes involving only additions and scalar multiplications. Hence

$$\frac{d}{dt}(\mathbf{A} + \mathbf{B}) = \frac{d}{dt}\mathbf{A} + \frac{d}{dt}\mathbf{B}$$

$$\frac{d}{dt}(\mathbf{A}\,\mathbf{B}) = \left(\frac{d}{dt}\mathbf{A}\right)\mathbf{B} + \mathbf{A}\frac{d}{dt}\mathbf{B}$$

Note that

$$\left(\frac{d}{dt}\mathbf{A}\right)\mathbf{B} \neq \mathbf{B}\frac{d}{dt}\mathbf{A}$$

Thus

$$\frac{d}{dt}(\mathbf{A}^2) = \left(\frac{d}{dt}\mathbf{A}\right)\mathbf{A} + \mathbf{A}\left(\frac{d}{dt}\mathbf{A}\right)$$

9. Inverse Operation

The linear transformation

$$\mathbf{A}\,\mathbf{x} = \mathbf{y}$$

is supposed to be unique only in the sense that for every $\mathbf{x}$ there is a unique $\mathbf{y}$. It is, however, not necessary that a unique $\mathbf{x}$ be transformed into every $\mathbf{y}$. In other words, although every point is transformed into only one point, two different points may be transformed into the same point. *If, however, a one-to-one correspondence exists* in the transformation, then the transformation has an inverse.

Let

$$\mathbf{A}\,\mathbf{x} = \mathbf{y} \tag{26}$$

If we are given $\mathbf{y}$, $\mathbf{x}$ is to be found by solving the set of simultaneous equations (23). Now, it is known that (23) will have a unique solution if and only if the determinant

$$|\mathbf{A}| = \begin{vmatrix} a_{11}a_{12} \cdots a_{1n} \\ a_{21}a_{22} \cdots a_{2n} \\ \cdots\cdots\cdots\cdots \\ a_{n1}a_{n2} \cdots a_{nn} \end{vmatrix} = |a_{ij}| \neq 0$$

Thus the condition for the existence of an inverse to $\mathbf{A}$ is that $|\mathbf{A}| \neq 0$. We say that $\mathbf{A}$ is *nonsingular* if it has an inverse. Let the inverse of $\mathbf{A}$ be denoted by the symbol $\mathbf{A}^{-1}$. The inverse transformation of (26) is then

$$\mathbf{A}^{-1}\,\mathbf{y} = \mathbf{x} \tag{27}$$

Evidently, if $\mathbf{A}^{-1}$ exists, it must also be a linear transformation.

The square matrix

$$\mathbf{I} = \begin{bmatrix} 1 & 0 & \cdots & 0 \\ 0 & 1 & \cdots & 0 \\ \cdot & \cdot & & \cdot \\ \cdot & \cdot & & \cdot \\ \cdot & \cdot & & \cdot \\ 0 & 0 & \cdots & 1 \end{bmatrix}$$

is called *an identity or unity matrix* because it represents the identity transformation

$$\mathbf{I}\,\mathbf{x} = \mathbf{x}$$

where every point remains fixed.

From (26) and (27) we see that

$$\mathbf{A}\,\mathbf{A}^{-1}\,\mathbf{y} = \mathbf{A}\,\mathbf{x} = \mathbf{y} = \mathbf{I}\,\mathbf{y}$$

$$\mathbf{A}^{-1}\,\mathbf{A}\,\mathbf{x} = \mathbf{A}^{-1}\,\mathbf{y} = \mathbf{x} = \mathbf{I}\,\mathbf{x}$$

or

$$\mathbf{A}\,\mathbf{A}^{-1} = \mathbf{A}^{-1}\,\mathbf{A} = \mathbf{I}$$

$$a_{ik}a_{kj}^{-1} = i_{ij} = \delta_{ij} \tag{28}$$

where δ_{ij} is called Kronecker's delta[2] defined by

$$\delta_{ij} = 1 \qquad \text{when } i = j$$

$$\delta_{ij} = 0 \qquad \text{when } i \neq j$$

In n-dimensional space (28) represent n sets of n simultaneous equations. A typical set is

$$\begin{aligned}
a_{11}a_{12}^{-1} + a_{12}a_{22}^{-1} + \cdots a_{1n}a_{n2}^{-1} &= 0 \\
a_{21}a_{12}^{-1} + a_{22}a_{22}^{-1} + \cdots a_{2n}a_{n2}^{-1} &= 1 \\
a_{31}a_{12}^{-1} + a_{32}a_{22}^{-1} + \cdots a_{3n}a_{n2}^{-1} &= 0 \\
\cdots\cdots\cdots\cdots\cdots\cdots\cdots & \\
a_{n1}a_{12}^{-1} + a_{n2}a_{22}^{-1} + \cdots a_{nn}a_{n2}^{-1} &= 0
\end{aligned}$$

If elements a_{ij} are known, the elements a_{ij}^{-1} of the inverse can be found by solving these simultaneous equations. According to the so-called Cramer's rule, the result is

$$a_{ij}^{-1} = \frac{\text{cofactor of } a_{ji} \text{ in } |a_{ij}|}{|a_{ij}|} \tag{29}$$

where

$$|a_{ij}| = |\mathbf{A}| \neq 0$$

Although (29) is a concise definition for the elements of the inverse of a nonsingular square matrix, the formula is not used for numerical computation, except when the matrix has very few elements, such as a 3 × 3 matrix. This is because there are other schemes of numerical computation that are less laborious. For our purpose it is sufficient to know that a nonsingular square matrix has an inverse whose elements are uniquely determined.

---

[2] There is no reason to change i into δ in (28), except that Kronecker's delta is an established symbol.

From the definition of inverse matrix and identity matrix we have the following equations:

If

$$\mathbf{C} = \mathbf{A}\,\mathbf{B}$$
$$\mathbf{A}^{-1}\,\mathbf{C} = \mathbf{A}^{-1}\,\mathbf{A}\,\mathbf{B} = \mathbf{I}\,\mathbf{B} = \mathbf{B}$$
$$\mathbf{B}^{-1}\,\mathbf{A}^{-1}\,\mathbf{C} = \mathbf{B}^{-1}\,\mathbf{B} = \mathbf{I}$$
$$\mathbf{B}^{-1}\,\mathbf{A}^{-1}\,\mathbf{C}\,\mathbf{C}^{-1} = \mathbf{I}\,\mathbf{C}^{-1} = \mathbf{C}^{-1}$$

or

$$\mathbf{B}^{-1}\,\mathbf{A}^{-1} = \mathbf{C}^{-1}$$

In other words

$$(\mathbf{A}\,\mathbf{B})^{-1} = \mathbf{B}^{-1}\,\mathbf{A}^{-1} \tag{30}$$

Similarly,

$$(\mathbf{A}\,\mathbf{B}\,\mathbf{C})^{-1} = \mathbf{C}^{-1}\,(\mathbf{A}\,\mathbf{B})^{-1} = \mathbf{C}^{-1}\,\mathbf{B}^{-1}\,\mathbf{A}^{-1} \tag{31}$$

10. Scalar Products and Transposition

So far, the matrix products that have been defined are $\mathbf{A}\,\mathbf{x}$ and $\mathbf{A}\,\mathbf{B}$. Products such as $\mathbf{x}\,\mathbf{y}$ and $\mathbf{x}\,\mathbf{A}$ have yet no meaning. In this article we define the meaning of some new products.

(A) SCALAR PRODUCT IN CARTESIAN COORDINATES

In vector analysis two vectors can form a scalar product with certain physical or geometrical significance.

Let the following notations be adopted:

$|\mathbf{x}|$ and $|\mathbf{y}|$ = lengths of two vectors represented by $\mathbf{x}$ and $\mathbf{y}$

$\rho(\mathbf{x}, \mathbf{y})$ = scalar product of the two vectors

θ = the angle between the two vectors

The geometrical meaning of scalar product is then

$$\rho(\mathbf{x}, \mathbf{y}) = |\mathbf{x}|\,|\mathbf{y}|\cos\theta \tag{32}$$

If the elements of the matrices $\mathbf{x}$ and $\mathbf{y}$ stand for the components of the vectors in a Cartesian coordinate system with scale factor equal to unity, it is known that

$$\rho(\mathbf{x}, \mathbf{y}) = x_1y_1 + x_2y_2 + , \cdots , x_ny_n = x_iy_i$$

In matrix notation we write

$$\rho(\mathbf{x}, \mathbf{y}) = [x_1x_2 \cdots x_n]\begin{bmatrix} y_i \\ y_2 \\ \cdot \\ \cdot \\ \cdot \\ y_n \end{bmatrix} = \bar{\mathbf{x}}\,\mathbf{y} \tag{33}$$

The components of the first vector are now arranged as a row, instead of a column, to conform to the pattern of element-pairing procedure previously established in defining products $\mathbf{A}\,\mathbf{x}$ and $\mathbf{A}\,\mathbf{B}$. In these two cases we take a row of the first matrix and pair its elements with a column of the second matrix. The sum of the products of the pairs becomes an element of the product. The symbol $\bar{\mathbf{x}}$ denotes a row matrix that is obtained by making the elements in the column matrix $\mathbf{x}$ into a row.

Evidently,

$$\bar{\mathbf{x}}\,\mathbf{y} = \bar{\mathbf{y}}\,\mathbf{x}$$

(B) SCALAR PRODUCT IN GENERAL PARALLEL COORDINATES

If the elements of the matrices $\mathbf{x}$ and $\mathbf{y}$ are the components of two vectors referring to a general parallel coordinate system other than a rectangular Cartesian system, the matrix product $\bar{\mathbf{x}}\,\mathbf{y}$ or $\bar{\mathbf{y}}\,\mathbf{x}$ is *no longer the scalar product defined by* (32). To obtain $\rho(\mathbf{x}, \mathbf{y})$ in a general parallel coordinate system, we may first transform the given coordinate system into a Cartesian coordinate system. It must be realized that the scalar product $\rho(\mathbf{x}, \mathbf{y})$, which is a scalar quantity of definite geometrical meaning, *remains invariant under any transformation of coordinates*. In other words, it is a quantity of definite numerical value, no matter what kind of reference system is used for computation.

Let $\mathbf{x}$ and $\mathbf{y}$ be two column matrices whose elements represent the components of two vectors in some given parallel coordinate system. Let $\mathbf{A}$ be a square matrix representing *a* transformation that transforms the given coordinate system into *a* Cartesian coordinate system with unit scale factor. We use the article "a" in the foregoing sentence, instead of the article "the," because the transformation is not unique, for two coordinate systems may both be Cartesian but with differently oriented axes. The matrices $\mathbf{u}$ and $\mathbf{v}$ defined by

$$\mathbf{u} = \mathbf{A}\,\mathbf{x} \qquad \text{and} \qquad \mathbf{v} = \mathbf{A}\,\mathbf{y} \tag{34}$$

thus represent the components of the same two vectors referred to a Cartesian coordinate system. Because of the invariance of scalar product

$$\rho(\mathbf{x}, \mathbf{y}) = \rho(\mathbf{u}, \mathbf{v}) = \bar{\mathbf{u}}\,\mathbf{v}$$

the symbol $\bar{\mathbf{u}}$ stands for a row matrix obtained by rearranging the column matrix $\mathbf{u}$ into a row. To conform to the established pattern[3] of matrix multiplication, we may write

$$\bar{\mathbf{u}} = [u_1 u_2 \cdots u_n] = [x_1 x_2 \cdots x_n] \begin{bmatrix} a_{11} a_{21} \cdots a_{n1} \\ a_{12} a_{22} \cdots a_{n2} \\ a_{1n} a_{2n} \cdots a_{nn} \end{bmatrix}$$
$$= \bar{\mathbf{x}}\,\bar{\mathbf{A}}$$

[3] That is, by pairing the rows of the first matrix with the columns of the second matrix.

In longhand this equation is the same as the first one of (34), in which the symbol $\bar{\mathbf{A}}$ stands for a matrix that is obtained by rearranging the elements of the matrix $\mathbf{A}$ in such a way that the rows of $\mathbf{A}$ become the columns of $\bar{\mathbf{A}}$ and the columns of $\mathbf{A}$ become the rows of $\bar{\mathbf{A}}$ without otherwise disturbing the order of things. In other words, the elements in $\mathbf{A}$ and $\bar{\mathbf{A}}$ are related by

$$\bar{a}_{ij} = a_{ji} \qquad \text{or} \qquad a_{ij} = \bar{a}_{ji}$$

Thus

$$\rho(\mathbf{x}, \mathbf{y}) = \rho(\mathbf{u}, \mathbf{v}) = \bar{\mathbf{u}}\,\mathbf{v} = \bar{\mathbf{x}}\,\bar{\mathbf{A}}\,\mathbf{A}\,\mathbf{y}$$

Let

$$\bar{\mathbf{A}}\,\mathbf{A} = \mathbf{M} \tag{35}$$

$$\rho(\mathbf{x}, \mathbf{y}) = \bar{\mathbf{x}}\,\mathbf{M}\,\mathbf{y} \tag{36}$$

(C) TRANSPOSITION

The operation of converting the columns of a matrix into a row, and vice versa, is called a *transposition.* The result of the transposition is called the *transpose* and is denoted by a bar over the letter representing the matrix transposed. Thus $\bar{\mathbf{A}}$ is called the transpose of $\mathbf{A}$ and $\bar{\mathbf{x}}$ is the transpose of $\mathbf{x}$. The following simple formulas pertaining to transposition can easily be proved.

(i) If $\mathbf{A} = \bar{\mathbf{B}}$, then

$$\mathbf{B} = \bar{\mathbf{A}} \qquad \text{or} \qquad \overline{(\bar{\mathbf{A}})} = \mathbf{A}$$

(ii) If $\mathbf{A}\,\mathbf{B} = \mathbf{C}$,

$$\bar{\mathbf{B}}\,\bar{\mathbf{A}} = \bar{\mathbf{C}} \qquad \text{or} \qquad \overline{(\mathbf{A}\,\mathbf{B})} = \bar{\mathbf{B}}\,\bar{\mathbf{A}} \tag{37}$$

Similarly

$$\overline{(\mathbf{A}\,\mathbf{x})} = \bar{\mathbf{x}}\,\bar{\mathbf{A}}$$

$$\overline{(\mathbf{A}\,\mathbf{B}\,\mathbf{C})} = \bar{\mathbf{C}}\,\bar{\mathbf{B}}\,\bar{\mathbf{A}} \tag{38}$$

(D) METRIC MATRIX OF A PARALLEL COORDINATE SYSTEM

If $|\mathbf{x}|$ represents the length of the vector $\mathbf{x}$, according to (32),

$$|\mathbf{x}|^2 = \rho(\mathbf{x}, \mathbf{x}) = \bar{\mathbf{x}}\,\mathbf{M}\,\mathbf{x} \tag{39}$$

The matrix $\mathbf{M}$ is consequently called the *metric matrix* of the coordinate system. For a given parallel coordinate system $\mathbf{M}$ is uniquely determined, even though the matrix $\mathbf{A}$ in (34) is not. To prove this statement, let us assume that there is another matrix, say $\mathbf{N}$, that will yield the length of a vector through (39); then

$$\bar{\mathbf{x}}\,\mathbf{N}\,\mathbf{x} = \bar{\mathbf{x}}\,\mathbf{M}\,\mathbf{x}$$

or

$$n_{ij}x_ix_j = m_{ij}x_ix_j$$

Since $\mathbf{x}$ is arbitrary, the two sides can be equal only if the coefficients are identical:

$$n_{11} = m_{11} \qquad (n_{12} + n_{21}) = (m_{12} + m_{21}) \qquad n_{22} = m_{22}, \cdots$$

or, in general,

$$(n_{ij} + n_{ji}) = (m_{ij} + m_{ji})$$
$$\mathbf{N} + \bar{\mathbf{N}} = \bar{\mathbf{M}} + \mathbf{M} \tag{40}$$

But, according to (35) and (37), a metric matrix is always symmetrical in the sense that $\mathbf{M} = \bar{\mathbf{M}}$ because

$$\mathbf{M} = \bar{\mathbf{A}}\,\mathbf{A} \qquad \bar{\mathbf{M}} = \overline{(\bar{\mathbf{A}}\,\mathbf{A})} = \bar{\mathbf{A}}\,\mathbf{A} = \mathbf{M}$$

So must

$$\mathbf{N} = \bar{\mathbf{N}}$$

Thus (40) reduces to

$$\mathbf{N} = \mathbf{M}$$

(E) ORTHOGONALITY RELATION BETWEEN TWO VECTORS

Two vectors are said to be orthogonal to each other if their scalar product is zero. Geometrically, we see that

$$\rho(\mathbf{x}\,\mathbf{y}) = |\mathbf{x}|\,|\mathbf{y}| \cos\theta = 0$$

implies that $\theta = \pm\pi/2$. For two vectors $\mathbf{x}$ and $\mathbf{y}$ to be orthogonal in a general parallel coordinate system the condition is

$$\bar{\mathbf{x}}\,\mathbf{M}\,\mathbf{y} = \bar{\mathbf{y}}\,\mathbf{M}\,\mathbf{x} = 0$$

In a Cartesian coordinate system,

$$\mathbf{M} = \mathbf{I}$$

the orthogonality relation is expressed simply as

$$\bar{\mathbf{x}}\,\mathbf{I}\,\mathbf{y} = \bar{\mathbf{x}}\,\mathbf{y} = 0$$

Index